NULL MODELS
IN ECOLOGY

To Dan, Don, Fran, Joe, Larry, and Van

NULL MODELS
IN ECOLOGY

NICHOLAS J. GOTELLI
GARY R. GRAVES

SMITHSONIAN INSTITUTION PRESS

WASHINGTON AND LONDON

Edited and typeset by Princeton Editorial Associates
Designed by Kathleen Sims

Library of Congress Cataloging-in-Publication Data
Gotelli, Nicholas J., 1959–
    Null models in ecology / Nicholas J. Gotelli, Gary R. Graves.
        p.   cm.
    Includes bibliographical references and index.
    ISBN 1-56098-657-3 (alk. paper).—ISBN 1-56098-645-X (pbk.: alk. paper)
    1. Null models (Ecology).   2. Biotic communities—Statistical methods.
    3. Monte Carlo method.   I. Graves, Gary R.   II. Title.
    QH541.15.N84G67   1996
    574.5'01'5195—dc20   95-26734
                                                                                              CIP

British Library Cataloguing-in-Publication Data is available.

Manufactured in the United States of America
02 01 00 99 98 97 96   5 4 3 2 1

∞ The paper used in this publication meets the minimum requirements of the
American National Standard for Permanence of Paper for Printed Library Materials
Z39.48-1984.

CONTENTS

PREFACE

Writing this book was an enormous task. The literature on null models encompasses many subdisciplines in ecology, some of which are characterized by ambiguity and controversy. Some of the controversies are long-standing, and the biological issues have sometimes been lost in the cross fire of statistical criticisms. Perhaps for this reason, some ecologists have rejected the entire null model approach, arguing that it fails to give us useful answers in ecology. We disagree. We see null models as basic tools for community ecologists, especially useful in areas where experiments are impossible and standard analyses fail us. Null models represent statistical tests that are tailored to a particular ecological question. Ideally, they incorporate many important aspects of the biology of the component species.

What should a book on null models cover? A broad coverage might include any statistical test designed to distinguish pattern from randomness, whereas a very narrow definition might cover only randomization tests for competitive patterns in island faunas (usually avifaunas). We aimed for the middle ground. In this book, we review the use of Monte Carlo methods and certain statistical tests that have been important in the intellectual history of community ecology.

In many cases, null models have addressed the most important questions in the discipline. How do species partition resources? What controls species diversity and how do we measure it? How are communities organized at different trophic levels? Historically, questions such as these were often based on fuzzy definitions, clouded by vague terminology, and burdened with excessively complex mathematical models. One of the important contributions of null models has been to force community ecologists to state precisely what they mean and what their models predict.

Because null model tests have frequently contradicted conventional wisdom in ecology, they have often been controversial. During the 1970s and 1980s, the debate over null models and competition theory generated something akin to religious fervor on both sides of the issues (Figure P.1). We have done our best

Figure P.1. This drawing reflects the early criticism that competition theory constituted a "religion" for ecology. The ecologist G. Evelyn Hutchinson is depicted noting that two corixids have a size ratio of 1.30, shown by holding up one finger on one hand and one and three fingers on the other hand (much the same way in Christian iconography three upheld fingers symbolize the Trinity). As he was inspired by the corixids found in the pool marked in honor of the patron saint Santa Rosalia, the saint appears behind Hutchinson. However, the bones of Santa Rosalia have been scientifically determined to be the bones of a goat, so Santa Rosalia is portrayed as a goat. The Galápagos finches are depicted in the background because they appear to show Hutchinsonian ratios in bill dimensions. The lemur on Hutchinson's shoulder with "FSU" on its sweatshirt symbolizes Florida State University's challenge to the paradigm that would arise many years later. From a 1991 Christmas card by Shahid Naeem.

to give an even-handed account of these controversies, although our bias in favor of the use of null models cannot be eliminated.

WHAT THIS BOOK IS NOT ABOUT

We chose to limit our discussion of null models to community-level processes. Consequently, we have not discussed null models of population dynamics, animal behavior, landscape ecology, ecosystem modeling, or phylogeny. We have also omitted purely statistical issues such as bootstrapping and jackknifing. Although we occasionally illustrate the probability equations used in these analyses, this is not a cookbook or workbook of null models; we don't present any computer programs for readers to use.

A second null model book needs to be written, one that contains null model software that would allow researchers to analyze data more easily using these tests. For the time being, null model analyses are accessible only to those with some programming expertise, although advances in software design are lowering this threshold. This book describes the application (and misapplication) of available null models and which sorts of tests are appropriate for different problems.

Although we attempted to be comprehensive, the field is active and the literature base is constantly expanding. Our coverage extends approximately through the end of 1993, with some later citations provided by enthusiastic colleagues. Articles that we would like to have discussed but could not include Dayan and Simberloff (1994), Lafferty et al. (1994), Naeem and Hawkins (1994), Pleasants (1994), Silvertown and Wilson (1994), Williams (1995), and Wilson (1995). No doubt this list will have grown further by the time this book is in print.

ORGANIZATION OF THE BOOK

Each chapter in this book discusses an area of research in community ecology that has been the subject of null model analysis. We have tried to review both the specific null model tests and the general questions associated with each research front. Throughout the book, we have used figures taken from original publications whenever possible. Although the book may lack the visual conformity and appeal of redrawn figures, we feel the original illustrations best depict the data as the authors intended. Each chapter concludes with a brief list of recommended tests for a particular question. We included this list of recommendations because many colleagues have requested guidance in choosing among null models. None of the tests is perfect, but we prefer them over the available alternatives. Because this is a dynamic field, some of our recommendations undoubtedly will be supplanted by future developments in null model analysis.

THEMES OF THE BOOK

There is some inevitable redundancy among the chapters, because certain broad themes recur in different contexts. These include the following:

1. What is the distinction between nonrandom patterns and the mechanisms that produce them? Null models can reveal unusual patterns but cannot, by themselves, elucidate a particular mechanism. Additional data are usually necessary to distinguish among competing hypotheses that can explain a pattern detected by a null model analysis. For example, although a null model can be used to establish that the difference in species richness between two assemblages is unlikely to reflect sampling error (Chapter 2), it cannot reveal why they differ.

2. What are the relative merits of conventional statistical tests versus Monte Carlo simulations? Conventional statistical tests may not always be appropriate for questions in community ecology because of nonnormality and nonindependence of data. Monte Carlo simulations are often preferable, although in some cases they generate similar results (e.g., Bowers and Brown 1982). Statistical tests such as rarefaction (Hurlbert 1971) and the variance ratio (Schluter 1984) are useful as null models, but they can be cumbersome to calculate by hand and are unfamiliar to many ecologists.

3. How can problems of redundancy and statistical independence be resolved? In other words, what are the independent units that represent the sampling universe for randomizations? If the same combinations of species recur in different assemblages, it is unclear whether these assemblages represent independent "samples," particularly if they have been collected at a small spatial scale. Similarly, it may not be legitimate to treat individual species as independent replicates if they are closely related and possess many traits that reflect their common ancestry.

4. How much biology should be included in the null model? A null model of "no structure" is easily rejected for most assemblages but does not provide a very powerful test of the predictions of ecological theory. When we incorporate more structure into the model, the simulation becomes more realistic and may provide a better test of model predictions. However, if too much structure is incorporated, the simulations may so closely reflect the observed data that the null hypothesis can never be rejected. This trade-off between generality and realism is common to all model-building strategies (Levins 1966).

5. *What is the relative importance of Type I and Type II errors in null model tests?* Because null model tests are based on techniques of randomization, they control for Type I error (incorrectly rejecting the null hypothesis) by requiring that observed patterns fall in the extreme tail of a distribution of simulated values. However, the possibility of Type II error (incorrectly accepting the null hypothesis) has only recently been explored by evaluating the power of null models to detect pattern when a particular mechanism is in operation. An assessment of Type II error is critical if investigators are going to use the results of a null model to claim that a particular mechanism is not important in producing a pattern (Toft and Shea 1983).

6. *How should appropriate source pools be constructed?* Establishing the source pool of species is a critical step in constructing a null model. Historically, the total species list for an archipelago or set of assemblages has been used, but there are other, more powerful approaches, which we discuss in the Epilogue and elsewhere in the book.

CONTENT OF THE BOOK

Chapter 1 is a review of the history of null models and the philosophical issues surrounding the approach. The literature on hypothesis testing in the philosophy of science is extensive, as is the rhetoric on both sides of the null models issue. We have tried to emphasize the important points of controversy and suggest some possible solutions to the criticisms that have been leveled against null models. We also review the literature on the species/genus (S/G) ratio, one of ecology's earliest null model controversies, and summarize other historical null model studies that have not been so well appreciated.

Chapter 2 discusses species diversity indices and the use of rarefaction as a distribution-free sampling model for comparing species richness of different samples. Because the concept of species diversity is intimately linked to the relative abundance of species in an assemblage, Chapter 3 reviews null models of species abundance distributions, including Caswell's (1976) innovative "neutral models" and MacArthur's (1957) celebrated broken-stick model.

In Chapters 4 and 5, we address null model studies of niche overlap. Chapter 4 describes how complex mathematical models of niche overlap have been translated into simple null models that can be applied to field observations of resource utilization. These null models have been applied to estimates of dietary components or use of small-scale microhabitats. Chapter 5 focuses on time as a niche axis. In animal communities, temporal partitioning may be expressed as differences in the diet of predators that forage synchronously versus asynchronously. In plant communities, temporal partitioning may be expressed as staggered sequences of flowering phenology, which reduce overlap for shared pollinators.

Chapters 6 and 7 are the longest in the book, because they detail the heart of the null model controversies: analyses of size ratios (Chapter 6) and co-occurrence patterns (Chapter 7). Size ratio analyses include tests of character displacement and Hutchinson's 1.3 rule, as well as analyses of more subtle divergence and convergence in ecomorphology.

Chapter 7 addresses community assembly and the lengthy controversy over checkerboard distributions and island co-occurrence patterns. Also included are null model tests for nestedness, incidence functions, minimum patch sizes, guild structure, and functional groups.

Chapter 8 examines the species-area relationship. The passive sampling model is used as a null model for the correlation between area and species richness, and a simple Markov model is used to predict variability in species richness and turnover in species composition. The chapter also suggests ways in which alternative hypotheses, such as habitat diversity, can be critically tested in species-area studies.

We return to co-occurrence patterns in Chapter 9, but in this case, species occurrences are continuous and are not restricted to islands or discrete habitat patches. Examples include small-scale quadrat or line-transect data, and large-scale maps of biogeographic ranges. Such data may be analyzed in one dimension, such as the occurrence of species along environmental gradients, or in two dimensions, such as the overlap of species geographic ranges. This chapter also addresses null model tests of distribution-abundance relationships, bimodality, Pleistocene refugia, taxon cycles, and Rapoport's rule.

Chapter 10 reviews the use of null models in the analysis of food web structure. Beginning with early simulation studies of stability and complexity, null models of food webs have developed somewhat independently of the rest of the community ecology literature, even though similar tests are used in co-occurrence and niche overlap studies. This chapter describes null model tests of food chain length, connectance, guild structure, and the relationship between complexity and stability. The temporal constancy of species rank abundances is also compared to null models as a test of community stability.

Finally, the Epilogue considers more general issues, such as data quality and source pool construction, and gives our perspective on trends in null model studies. Here, as elsewhere in the book, we are unlikely to persuade those readers who have already made up their minds about null models. For example, one anonymous reviewer of the proposal for this book wrote:

Since I am not a fan of the null model approach, it would not disappoint me if they fail in their enterprise. However, I'd be interested to see how they put it all together and I think many others would also, for I feel we are doomed to have these ideas with us for a long time.

Whatever the reader's persuasion, we hope this book will at least provide grist for discussion and serve as a stimulus for further research with null models.

ACKNOWLEDGMENTS

When we first contemplated this book, we contacted a number of colleagues and asked them to send us reprints and give us their perspective on null models in ecology. Many provided reprints, preprints, unpublished manuscripts, extensive commentary, personal anecdotes, and historical reflections on null models. We thank the following for their thoughtful responses to our initial query: Jim Brown, Ted Case, Hal Caswell, Rob Colwell, Ed Connor, Arthur Ghent, Mike Gilpin, Jim Haefner, Fran James, Craig Loehle, Brian Maurer, Bob May, Earl McCoy, Eric Pianka, Stuart Pimm, Beverly Rathcke, Bob Ricklefs, Peter Sale, Dolph Schluter, Tom Schoener, Jonathan Silvertown, J. Bastow Wilson, and S. Joseph Wright.

Once chapter drafts were ready, the following colleagues provided us with a thorough reading of particular chapters: Scott Armbruster (5), Bill Boecklen (8), Alison Brody (5), Jim Brown (1,6), Ed Connor (1), Mark Lomolino (1,7), Bob May (1), Dolph Schluter (1,6,7), Dan Simberloff (1,2,6,7), and Lewi Stone (7). Jim Brown read the entire manuscript, provided detailed comments throughout, and developed the list of "recurrent themes" that we describe in the preface. Neil Buckley read and edited every single chapter, tracked down literature citations, cleaned up our prose, and suffered through galley proofs as well. We couldn't have completed this book without his help and advice.

Peter Cannell and the staff at Smithsonian Press transformed our manuscript into an actual book. We are grateful to Shahid Naeem for allowing us to publish one of the panels from his ecological triptych. N.J.G. acknowledges the support of the National Science Foundation and the Fulbright Foundation while this book was prepared. He thanks Maryanne for tolerating him while he wrote. G.R.G. thanks the Smithsonian Institution for support, and Sonya and Hillary as reasons to live.

1
PHILOSOPHY, HISTORY

Does competition lead to "forbidden combinations" of species that never coexist? Are species extinctions selective with respect to body size, geographic range, or trophic status? Has natural selection modified the body sizes of sympatric species? What factors are responsible for the relative abundance of species in an assemblage? These are the types of questions in community ecology that can be explored with null models.

Among ecologists, null models have gained popularity only in the last 20 years. The phrase "null models" was apparently coined by Robert K. Colwell and David W. Winkler at a 1981 conference at Wakulla Springs, Florida, devoted largely to the topic (Strong et al. 1984). Null models have been applied to a diverse set of questions and have yielded new insights into pattern and mechanism in community ecology. In this book, we survey both the theoretical framework and the empirical findings of null models in several disciplines of community ecology.

We restrict our focus to the community level of analysis, although we note that null models have also gained popularity in other areas of evolutionary biology (Nitecki and Hoffman 1987), including animal behavior (Aronson and Givnish 1983), population regulation (Crowley 1992), paleobiology (Raup et al. 1973; Gould et al. 1977), and phylogenetic reconstruction (Archie 1989). Our emphasis is not simply on randomization or Monte Carlo methods (Manly 1991), but on null models that have been tailored to address specific mechanisms and patterns in community ecology. Null models have been controversial in this context, and critics have raised important technical and philosophical objections (Harvey et al. 1983). In this chapter, we review the origins of these controversies and describe the earliest uses of null models in community ecology.

1

METHODS IN COMMUNITY ECOLOGY

Three empirical tools in ecology are laboratory, field, and "natural" experiments (Connell 1975). Diamond (1986) and Wiens (1989) have presented in-depth reviews of the strengths and weaknesses of these approaches. Laboratory experiments allow an investigator the greatest amount of control over independent variables, so that hypotheses can be rigorously tested (Mertz and McCauley 1980). Laboratory experiments have yielded data that have proved very difficult to gather in the field, such as parameter estimates for population growth models (Gause 1934; but see Feller 1940; Haefner 1980). In a simplified environment, laboratory experiments may be viewed as "simulations" that use real animals rather than a computer. The chief weakness of laboratory experiments is that biological realism is usually sacrificed for precision, so it is difficult to apply the experimental results to real communities.

By contrast, field experiments are widely regarded as the sine qua non for understanding nature (Underwood 1985)—the investigator manipulates variables in the field and then directly measures their effects. If the experiment is to be meaningful, the "signal" of manipulation must be detectable above the background "noise" of uncontrolled factors. The strength of this method is the realistic environment in which the experiment is embedded. In some systems, a long tradition of field experimentation has led to a detailed understanding of community structure (Paine 1977; Brown and Heske 1990).

Despite their importance, field experiments have several limitations. First, constraints of time, money, and resources severely limit replication and spatial dimensions of field experiments. Consequently, approximately 80% of all field manipulations have employed quadrats of only 1 m^2 (Kareiva and Anderson 1988). It is difficult to generalize the results of such small-scale experiments to larger spatial scales (Wiens et al. 1986). Second, it is often impossible to manipulate one, and only one, factor in a field experiment, and therefore it is difficult to establish appropriate controls (Hairston 1989). Third, the number of treatments necessary to reveal interactions at the community level may be prohibitive. For example, a minimum of five replicated treatment combinations is necessary to control for intraspecific effects in a two-species competition experiment (Underwood 1986). If there are age- or size-structured interactions among species (Polis et al. 1989), this number will increase severalfold. Finally, most field experiments have been conducted with small, relatively short-lived animals and plants and may have little relevance to the ecology of long-lived organisms. Some of the most important questions in ecology, such as the origin of latitudinal gradients in species diversity, may never be answered with field experiments. Another approach is needed.

The "natural experiment" (Cody 1974) overcomes some of the limitations of field and laboratory experiments, although it is not a true experiment because no variables are manipulated. Instead, an investigator compares two or more communities that are thought to differ mainly in the factor of interest. For example, to understand the effect of predators on prey abundance, one could compare prey distributions on islands with and without predators (e.g., Schoener and Toft 1983). Natural experiments form the basis of many studies in community ecology; their use is limited only by the imagination of the investigator, not by the constraints of experimental design.

The problem with natural experiments is not the discovery of pattern, but the inference of mechanism (James and McCulloch 1985; McGuinness 1988). Both predator and prey abundances may depend on the level of a third, unmeasured variable, such as the frequency of disturbance. Even when confounding variables are controlled statistically, the direction of cause and effect may not be obvious. Do predators control prey community structure, or do prey assemblages dictate predator community structure? Finally, the natural experiment begs the critical question: what predator and prey assemblages would exist in the absence of any trophic interactions?

Null models can address this last question through a statistical analysis of ecological pattern. A typical null model generates communities expected to occur in the absence of a particular mechanism. Patterns in these "pseudo-communities" (Pianka 1986) are then compared statistically to patterns in the real community. Finally, deviations from the null model can be compared to the predictions of ecological theory.

DEFINING THE NULL MODEL

The null model formalizes a particular null hypothesis in ecology: "Null hypotheses entertain the possibility that nothing has happened, that a process has not occurred, or that change has not been produced by a cause of interest. Null hypotheses are reference points against which alternatives should be contrasted" (Strong 1980). Although Strong's (1980) description of the null hypothesis captures its important features, we propose a more detailed working definition of an ecological null model:

A null model is a pattern-generating model that is based on randomization of ecological data or random sampling from a known or imagined distribution. The null model is designed with respect to some ecological or evolutionary process of interest. Certain elements of the data are held constant, and others are allowed to vary

stochastically to create new assemblage patterns. The randomization is designed to
produce a pattern that would be expected in the absence of a particular ecological
mechanism.

The null model is not a true experiment. Instead, it is a thought experiment that allows us to explore the range of possible worlds and patterns were certain ecological mechanisms not in operation. It is superior to the natural experiment because it incorporates stochastic effects and allows for a variety of possible outcomes, including that of "no effect."

There are at least two different interpretations of ecological null models. Simberloff (1983a) considered the null model as a complex form of statistical randomization. This interpretation places null models within the framework of statistical hypothesis testing. The statistical null hypothesis allows for simple pattern tests that may not require direct consideration of mechanisms. The second interpretation, epitomized by the simulations of Colwell and Winkler (1984), is that null models are explicit colonization scenarios used to test effects of biotic interactions in natural communities. Taken to their extreme, these scenarios do not qualify as null models because they are too complex and may incorporate effects of interest. We favor a more balanced view that null models describe the assembly of communities, but do not specify all the details of the colonization process. The analyses reveal community patterns that are relevant to tests of ecological theory.

NULL MODELS AND MATHEMATICAL MODELS

Although null models have a firm empirical base, there are many similarities between the construction of null models and mathematical models in ecology. Above all, they both benefit from simplicity and generality. Simplicity is important because it allows the investigator to highlight a few mechanisms without becoming entangled in complex interactions of many variables (Caswell 1988). For example, a mathematical model of predator-prey interaction may ignore the age structure of populations, whereas a null model of species co-occurrence may ignore habitat variation. Both factors can be, and have been, incorporated into more complex models. However, mathematical models become insoluble with too many parameters, and null models become difficult to generate and interpret with too many background factors. Thus, it would be a mistake to assume that a model is superior because it is more "realistic." The more detailed a model becomes, the more idiosyncratic its behavior, and the less applicable its results are to other systems (Levins 1966). Simple, well-formulated models should be the goal of both mathematical ecology and null model testing.

Mathematical models and null models both emphasize a plurality of approaches to solving problems in community ecology. For example, a problem such as population growth in a resource-limited environment can be addressed with a variety of analytical tools, none of which provides a single "right" answer to the question (Woolhouse 1988). Similarly, many different null models can be constructed to generate community patterns in the absence of interspecific competition (Schluter and Grant 1984; Graves and Gotelli 1993). As Pianka (1994) notes, "The pseudocommunity approach is pregnant with potential and would seem to be limited only by our own ingenuity." The diversity of null models has not always been appreciated. Some critics have dismissed null models entirely without acknowledging that their criticisms are applicable to only one type of randomization algorithm.

The differences between null models and mathematical models are as important as the similarities. Mathematical models do not require empirical data for analyses, whereas null models are framed with reference to a real data set. Mathematical models highlight certain mechanisms by explicitly incorporating them (Caswell 1988). In contrast, null models deliberately *exclude* a mechanism in order to gauge its effect. Finally, null models are designed to test patterns in real data sets, whereas some mathematical models are constructed for heuristic purposes or for comparison with other models (Roughgarden 1983).

FEATURES OF NULL MODELS

Ecological null models have several important attributes:

1. Null models precipitate a sharp distinction between pattern and process. This dichotomy requires ecologists to distinguish between the patterns they observe and the different mechanisms that can produce them (Rathcke 1984). Null models force ecological theory to generate simple predictions of how nature is structured, and allow empiricists to test those predictions with real data. Much of the confusion and controversy in community ecology today can be traced to the complex predictions generated by much of theoretical ecology, and by the failure of ecologists to clearly distinguish pattern from process (Peters 1991).

2. Null models allow for the possibility of no effect. In an experimental study, one possible outcome is that the statistical null hypothesis of no difference among treatment means cannot be rejected. Similarly, one possible out-come of a null model analysis is that observed community patterns cannot be distinguished from those generated by the null model. If the null model has been *properly* constructed, we can conclude that the mechanism is not operat-ing, or that the theory does not generate unique predictions. If the null model is flawed, it may not be rejected because it incorporates some of the processes it was designed to reveal, or because it simply has weak statistical power.

Alternatively, if the null model is rejected, and the pattern is consistent with predictions of theory, this provides some positive evidence in favor of the mechanism. However, positive evidence should not be construed as a definitive test (Brady 1979), because different mechanisms can generate similar ecologi-cal patterns. As before, the null model may also be rejected improperly if it is flawed. In particular, if the model is "too null" and does not incorporate realistic biological constraints, it may generate predictions that are very differ-ent from patterns seen in real communities. The controversy over null models is reflected in these alternative interpretations of the acceptance or rejection of a null model.

The strict falsificationist protocol embodied in null models is in contrast to a more inductive approach that was popularized in ecology by Robert H. MacAr-thur—ecologists searched for community patterns to corroborate a mechanism, but usually did not ask what the patterns would look like in the absence of the mechanism. Although MacArthur (1957, 1960) pioneered the "broken stick" as a null model for species abundance patterns (see Chapter 3), he also wrote that the group of researchers interested in making ecology a science "arranges ecological data as examples testing the proposed theories and spends most of its time patching up the theories to account for as many of the data as possible" (MacArthur 1962). The use of an explicit hypothesis test of expected patterns in the absence of a mechanism is what distinguishes the null model approach from other comparisons of model predictions with real data.

3. Null models rely on the principle of parsimony. Parsimony suggests that we favor simple explanations over complex ones (Brown 1950). Thus, if a null model that excludes predators successfully predicts prey community structure, parsimony dictates that we abandon the predation hypothesis—it adds unnecessary complexity. However, there is no guarantee that simple explana-tions are correct; parsimony is an empirical or aesthetic principle, not a logical one.

Either implicitly or explicitly, parsimony guides many of our attempts to explain patterns in nature. In evolutionary biology, for example, parsimony has guided systematists to search for the smallest amount of character change necessary to reconstruct a phylogeny (Hennig 1966; Wiley 1981). The parsimony principle is unlikely to lead to the emergence of new hypotheses in science (Dunbar 1980; Loehle 1990a), but it is invaluable for testing and choosing among existing alternatives (Platt 1964; Loehle 1987).

4. Null models rely on the principle of falsification. Proponents of null models draw their inspiration from statistical hypothesis-testing and from the writings of Karl R. Popper (1959, 1965, 1972), who emphasized the importance of falsification of hypotheses and the asymmetry of scientific data: negative evidence can be used to refute an hypothesis, but confirmatory evidence cannot be viewed as a "test" of an hypothesis (Brady 1979).

Not all ecologists (or philosophers) agree with this view (itself unfalsifiable!). Some have pointed out that falsification is not the only way to make progress in evaluating ecological models (James and McCulloch 1985). Others have accepted the logic of comparing model predictions to data in order to detect anomalies, but not to reject hypotheses (Southwood 1980). Finally, some critics (e.g., Toft and Shea 1983) have suggested that incorrect acceptance of a null hypothesis (Type II error) is just as serious a mistake as incorrect rejection (Type I error). Conventional statistical tests emphasize the latter over the former (Shrader-Frechette and McCoy 1992), on the grounds that falsity (Type I error) is a more serious mistake than ignorance (Type II error).

Although null models rely on falsification, they do not conform precisely to the "strong inference" protocol of defining a set of mutually exclusive alternative outcomes (Platt 1964). Instead, the null hypothesis can be an aggregate of several possible mechanisms that is pitted against the predictions of a single alternative hypothesis. However, multiple alternatives can be tested with multiple null models (Schluter and Grant 1984; Graves and Gotelli 1993).

5. Null models emphasize the potential importance of stochastic mechanisms in producing natural patterns. Although much early ecological theory was based on deterministic mathematics, many patterns in nature have a stochastic component that reflects underlying environmental variability (Wiens 1977; den Boer 1981; Schmitt and Holbrook 1986). Because of this, ecologists have emphasized replication and repeatability of natural patterns (Strong et al. 1984). Null models reflect this natural variability in community structure and require that the "signal" of mechanism be stronger than the "noise" of natural variation (May 1974).

However, the inclusion of stochastic forces in null models does not imply that patterns in nature are random (Connor and Simberloff 1986). Some factors that determine community structure are so variable in time and space that it is simpler to represent them as stochastic elements than to model them explicitly. As a familiar example, the trajectory of falling rain is determined by a complex interaction of wind speed, air temperature, and other factors. Nevertheless, the spatial pattern of drops is "random" (Simberloff 1980a) and can be described by a Poisson distribution. Simple community patterns, such as the canonical log normal distribution of species abundances, may also arise from complex interactions among factors (May 1975a).

THE CONTROVERSY SURROUNDING NULL MODELS

The use of null models in ecology has been highly contentious. Some proponents of null models (Connor and Simberloff 1979; Strong et al. 1979) have used this tool in a vigorous assault on the framework of competition theory, claiming, in essence, that "the emperor has no clothes." Defenders of competition theory have countered that null models are fatally flawed and inherently biased against detecting biotic interactions (Grant and Abbott 1980; Diamond and Gilpin 1982). Thus, the null model debate is embedded in two different controversies: (1) the importance of interspecific competition to community structure (Schoener 1982); (2) the way to go about testing theory in community ecology (Strong et al. 1984).

The controversy over competition theory calls for an historical perspective (see also Schoener 1982; Simberloff 1982; Wiens 1989). Ecology has always had an uneasy relationship with theoretical developments. McIntosh (1980) documents the change from the 1930s, when ecology had little theoretical framework, to the 1980s, when models had proliferated to the point where they could predict any possible ecological pattern (Pielou 1981a). Mathematical ecology flourished in the intervening years, owing, in part, to the influence of G. Evelyn Hutchinson and his student Robert H. MacArthur.

MacArthur synthesized the Hutchinsonian niche (Hutchinson 1957) with the competitive exclusion principle (Gause 1934; Hardin 1960). His models predicted a limit to the similarity of coexisting species, and a community packed like molecules of a crystal, with each species neatly fitting into the community niche space. In *Geographical Ecology* (1972), MacArthur extended these ideas to large geographic scales and suggested that the effects of competitive exclusion would be strong enough to control species coexistence on islands and entire continents. MacArthur's inductive approach of simple models supported by a few well-chosen empirical examples was rapidly incorporated into textbooks (Hall 1988). In a modified form, his ideas on species coexistence and ecological niches continue to define much of the current research program for academic ecology.

PARADIGMS IN COMMUNITY ECOLOGY

In retrospect, MacArthur's approach constituted an important ecological paradigm (sensu Kuhn 1970), in which the primary focus was the coexistence of competing species in a community (Wiens 1989). A good indicator of paradigm status is that alternative viewpoints, and even conflicting data, are swept aside in favor of the reigning theory. Thus, in 1978, Diamond was able to advise ecologists to be suspicious of results suggesting that species were not directly or even currently competing with one another (Strong 1980)!

By the early 1980s, several important challenges to the MacArthurian paradigm had emerged (Schoener 1982): (1) Null model analyses indicated that some of the patterns ascribed to interspecific competition could arise from models that were competition-free; (2) mathematical analyses suggested that simple limits to similarity or exclusion of competitors were sensitive to model formulation (Abrams 1975; Turelli 1978a; Armstrong and McGhee 1980); (3) the "variable environments" hypothesis predicted that animal populations are rarely at carrying capacity (Andrewartha and Birch 1954; Wiens 1977; den Boer 1981), suggesting that competitive effects are important only during occasional "resource crunches" (Wiens 1977; but see Gotelli and Bossert 1991); (4) empirical and theoretical studies indicated that predation was often a stronger biotic interaction than competition (Connell 1975), particularly at lower trophic levels (Hairston et al. 1960). Although Schoener (1982) argued that MacArthurian competition was not a failed paradigm, competition theory is no longer accepted uncritically, as it often was before these challenges.

Not all ecologists accept the view of the dominance of a MacArthurian paradigm. Plant ecologists focused on studies of competition and the niche well before MacArthur's work became influential (Jackson 1981), and the Mac-Arthurian approach may have been more of a preoccupation with American ecologists than with Europeans (May and Seger 1986). Wiens's (1989) analysis of literature citations over several decades also suggests that competitive explanations for avian community patterns were about as popular before MacArthur as during his reign. Nevertheless, MacArthur's blend of mathematical competition models and nonexperimental supporting data had a long-lasting influence on community ecology.

In a roundtable issue of *Synthese,* Simberloff (1980a) argued that ecology has passed through not one, but three successive paradigms. The first was one of essentialism, in which populations and communities achieved an ideal, deterministic form. In community ecology, essentialism is embodied in Clements's (1904) idea of the community as a superorganism of tightly integrated species. The second paradigm was one of materialism, in which communities were not forced into a few monoclimax types; rather, the focus of study was the variation in composition and organization of communities, and the processes that lead to these differences. The MacArthurian approach, with its emphasis on geographic variation in community structure and complex interactions among species, seems to embody elements of both of these paradigms. Simberloff's (1980a) third paradigm was one of probabilism, in which variation in community structure is viewed as the outcome of a small set of probabilistic pathways. Although Simberloff (1980a) did not explicitly develop this point, it is clear that null models are central to testing mechanisms of community structure in a probabilistic framework.

In response to his essay, Levins and Lewontin (1980) argued that Simberloff (1980a) had mistaken the stochastic for the statistical and had confused the ideas of reductionism with materialism and idealism with abstraction. Levins and Lewontin's (1980) ecological criticism was that, in rejecting the Clementsian superorganism, Simberloff (1980a) "falls into the pit of obscurantist stochasticity and indeterminism." Levins and Lewontin (1980) believed the community to be a meaningful whole, with dynamics that are distinct from those levels below (populations) and above (ecosystems). In contrast, Simberloff (1980b) argued that community organization was a hypothesis to be tested. Simberloff's (1980b) null hypothesis was that emergent community properties are epiphenomena caused by patterns at the species level. That is, the synecological "whole" is primarily the sum of its autecological "parts."

CRITICISMS OF NULL MODELS

Roughgarden (1983) espoused a very different view of community structure, sparking another roundtable of essays in *American Naturalist* concerning competition, community structure, and null models in ecology. Prompted by challenges to competition theory (Connor and Simberloff 1979; Strong et al. 1979; Connell 1980), Roughgarden's (1983) essay was a defense of mathematical competition theory as well as a salient critique of null models. Roughgarden (1983) argued against null models and hypothesis testing. Instead, he suggested that we use common sense to establish facts in ecology and evaluate mechanisms on the basis of our ability to "build a convincing case. A convincing case should include on-site experiments together with biogeographic and distributional data, and data addressing viable alternative hypotheses."

Roughgarden (1983) felt that null hypotheses were "empirically empty," because biological processes such as stochastic dispersal and population extinction were not incorporated in the randomization procedures (but see Caswell 1976). He argued that null models (as they had been developed by 1983) were not ecological analogs of the neutrality hypothesis in population genetics, because the underlying mechanisms had not been demonstrated. Even if the mechanisms could be established, null models would have no "logical primacy" over other types of models, in contrast to the claims of Strong et al. (1979). Whereas Strong et al. (1979) implied that pattern must be established before processes can be investigated, Roughgarden (1983) maintained that processes such as interspecific competition could be studied productively before establishment of pattern: "Sometimes it is obvious that a process is occurring. Knowledge of that process may aid in discovering its consequences." Finally, Roughgarden (1983) did not think that ecological null models were analogous to statistical null hypotheses: "A null hypothesis in statistics is a justified model of sampling procedure. It is not a hypothesis that the world has no structure."

In the same roundtable issue, Quinn and Dunham (1983) voiced similar concerns and raised three philosophical objections to the null model approach:

1. *Formal hypotheses about mechanisms cannot be stated in such a way as to allow meaningful disproof.* In other words, mechanisms in community ecology cannot generate simple predictions about patterns that can then be subject to a "litmus test" (Roughgarden 1983) for proof or disproof.

2. *Testing mechanisms as distinguishable hypotheses leads to univariate critical tests.* These tests are invalid if there are strong interactions among the mechanisms.

3. *In hypothetico-deductive formalism, understanding is only increased when a hypothesis is rejected.* Reliable null hypotheses may be impossible to construct, because we cannot generally deduce the nature of expected patterns that would emerge in the absence of any given biological process.

REPLIES TO THE CRITICS

These roundtable essays demonstrated that much of the debate involved personal styles of research and philosophy that could not be classified as "right" or "wrong" (Salt 1983). Simberloff (1983a) was sympathetic to Roughgarden's (1983) common-sense approach, but considered it overly simplistic and therefore likely to lead us astray. Strong (1983) wrote, "Yes, common sense sometimes leads to sound judgment, but it is also ordinary, free from intellectual subtlety, not dependent on special or technical knowledge, and it is unreflective opinion." Strong (1983) also pointed out that a common-sense approach lacks two critical elements, imagination and testing, that feature prominently in the construction and interpretation of null models.

Our own opinion is that null models have been useful in ecology and that many of the flaws pointed to by critics can be addressed. Roughgarden's (1983) complaint that null models do not explicitly describe colonization processes is not necessarily damning if the randomization reflects the major patterns produced during colonization. Whether or not null models have "logical primacy" (Strong et al. 1979), they should be investigated first, so that stochastic and sampling effects can be distinguished from biologically meaningful patterns (Järvinen 1982). As a practical matter, null models should be tested first because they may save a huge amount of time that could be frittered away in search of a nonexistent process or phenomenon.

Null models do not portray the world as "having no structure" or even as being random. Rather, the null hypothesis (for community-wide competition) is that species occurrences are random *with respect to one another.* Moreover, randomization procedures are a well-established protocol in statistics for constructing null hypotheses; all of the conventional statistical tests, such as the F-ratio and the chi-squared distribution, have analogs based on a randomization test (Manly 1991). Indeed, some statisticians feel that randomization tests are actually preferable, because they are burdened by fewer assumptions (Edgington 1987).

Finally, we must take issue with Quinn and Dunham's (1983) argument that null models are not appropriate for ecology because ecological theory makes ambiguous predictions. This seems a damning criticism of theory rather than of null models! If we are to bridge the wide gulf between theoretical and empirical ecology, we must force ecological theory to give us simple predictions that we can test with data (Pielou 1981a; Simberloff 1982). This real-world portability, rather than the realism of underlying assumptions, may be the most useful criterion for judging the fitness of a model (Brown 1981). In its original, unadulterated form, MacArthurian competition theory and other simple ecological models do make predictions about species richness, co-occurrence, and niche overlap that can be tested with appropriate null models. We survey these tests in later chapters.

In summary, null models have been controversial in ecology for three reasons: (1) the null model principles of parsimony and falsification are not accepted by some ecologists; (2) the findings of some null models directly contradicted predictions of orthodox competition theory; (3) the rhetoric of some of the early papers was contentious and often extreme, ensuring that a lively exchange on the issues would follow. In particular, the "assembly rules" debate has involved many players and has spanned over two decades, with no clear resolution in sight (Diamond 1975; Connor and Simberloff 1979; Alatalo 1982; Diamond and Gilpin 1982; Gilpin and Diamond 1982; Connor and Simberloff 1983, 1984; Gilpin and Diamond 1984; Gilpin et al. 1984; Gilpin and Diamond 1987; Wilson 1987; Roberts and Stone 1990; Stone and Roberts 1990, 1992).

If these exchanges were the sole impact of null models, they would remain only an interesting footnote in the history of ecology. But the influence of null models has been pervasive in ecology, and has spread far beyond the original focus on interspecific competition and species associations. Food web structure (Pimm 1980a,b; 1984), island extinction patterns (Gotelli and Graves 1990), and vertical (Underwood 1978a) and horizontal (Pielou 1977, 1978) zonation of intertidal communities represent just a few examples of problems that have been addressed with null models. Even landscape ecology, one of the more holistic subdisciplines of the field, has adopted null models of minimalist assumptions that describe random movement of individuals through a hetero-geneous landscape (Milne 1992). Null models have also had a positive influ-ence on experimental ecology, forcing investigators to articulate alternative mechanisms and make a priori predictions about pattern. Finally, the construc-tion of an appropriate null model and evaluation of its underlying assumptions is an important step toward rigor and clear thinking in community ecology (Platt 1964; Rathcke 1984; Peters 1991).

S/G RATIOS AND THE HISTORY OF NULL MODELS

Null models in ecology were first used in the analysis of species/genus (S/G) ratios. These ratios may reflect the intensity of competition, which Darwin (1859) and many others suggested was greatest within a genus: "As species of the same genus have usually, though by no means invariably, some similarity in habits and constitution, and always in structure, the struggle will generally be more severe between species of the same genus, when they come into competi-tion with each other, than between species of distinct genera."

Elton (1946) addressed the hypothesis with data on the number of species per genus, or the average S/G ratio, in a variety of animal and plant communities. He was impressed by the fact that most genera in insular or local assemblages were represented by only a single species, with an average S/G ratio of 1.38 for animal communities and 1.22 for plant communities. In contrast, the S/G ratio was considerably larger for regional floras and faunas. For example, the average S/G ratio for British insects was 4.38, a value never reached in any of the local surveys.

What was the explanation for this pattern? Elton (1946) briefly considered the "null hypothesis" that S/G ratios represented sampling artifacts in small communities: "One possible explanation of the statistical relationships described above would be that the frequencies of species in genera simply reflect those of the fauna as a whole. For if, say 86% of species in the British Isles belonged to genera of which only one species was present in their region, the figures . . . would be the record of a faunistic distribution, rather than any peculiarity of homogeneous communities taken separately."

Elton (1946) rejected this null hypothesis and reasoned, incorrectly as it turned out, that disparity between regional and local S/G implied that competition within communities limited the coexistence of congeners. Citing Darwin's (1859) writings and Gause's (1934) laboratory studies, Elton (1946) argued that S/G ratios were lower for local communities because interspecific competition for limited resources precluded the coexistence of several species in the same genus.

Williams (1947a) took a very different approach and gave ecology one of its earliest null models. He asked what the S/G ratios of local communities would look like in the absence of competition. He emphasized that real communities must be compared to this null expectation in order to evaluate the role of competition: "It is, however, most important to consider in detail what exactly happens when a selection of a relatively small number of species is made from a larger fauna or flora, without reference to their generic relations . . . as a true interpretation can only be made by comparing the observed data with the results of a selection of the same size made at random."

Williams (1947a) assumed that the relative abundance of species followed a log series, based on his previous work on this problem (Fisher et al. 1943). From the log series, the expected S/G ratio in a random sample of species can be predicted. Williams (1947a) reanalyzed Elton's (1946) data, and found that in every case, the expected S/G ratio decreased as fewer species were sampled. Consequently, the match between expected and observed S/G ratios was quite good. When deviations did occur, S/G ratios were typically *larger* than expected by chance (Figure 1.1). Williams (1947a) argued that S/G ratios were influenced by two factors: (1) competition, which would be most severe among congeners and reduce the ratio, and (2) environmental suitability, which would be most similar among congeners and increase the ratio because similar species

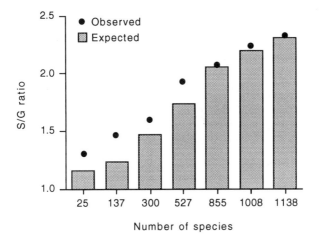

Figure 1.1. Expected and observed species/genus (*S/G*) ratios for vascular plants of the British Isles. Each point represents a single island. Expected values are determined by random sampling from the presumed source pool, the vascular plants of Britain (1,666 species; *S/G* ratio = 2.727). Elton (1946) believed that small *S/G* ratios on islands reflected strong competition between congeners and a limit to coexistence of closely related species. However, the expected *S/G* ratio is also small in randomly sampled communities that are not structured by competition. Observed *S/G* ratios are usually quite close to this expectation. Competition should depress the ratio below the expectation, but most communities show deviations in the positive direction. Data from Simberloff (1970).

would occur in the same habitat. Williams (1947a) argued that if competition was influencing *S/G* ratios in Elton's (1946) local communities, its effect was overshadowed by other factors operating in a reverse direction. In any case, no special significance could be attached to small *S/G* ratios per se.

Bagenal (1951) criticized Williams's (1947a) analysis and pointed out that some of Elton's (1946) local assemblages incorporated different habitats or were sampled at different times. Consequently, they could not be used to assess Gause's (1934) hypothesis of competitive exclusion, which Bagenal (1951) interpreted as applying only to species co-occurring in similar habitats. Moreau (1948) also noted this problem with Elton's (1946) analyses and offered more appropriate data for examining *S/G* ratios: detailed records on the occurrence and habitat associations of 172 species of African birds. Within the 92 genera represented, only 16% (excluding the Ploceidae) of the possible cases of habitat overlap among congeneric pairs were observed, and only a third of these apparently overlapped in diet. Moreau (1948) concluded that when habitat affinities were properly defined, competitive exclusion was important in limiting coexistence of congeners and more distantly related species pairs as well.

Moreau (1948) assumed that 16% overlap was "low," but he did not consider sample size effects in his analysis. Williams (1951) reanalyzed Moreau's (1948) data, again using the log series to estimate the expected S/G ratios in small communities. As in some of Elton's (1946) assemblages, congeneric co-occurrence among Moreau's (1948) birds was many times greater than expected by chance, suggesting that competitive effects on the S/G ratio were swamped by similar habitat affinities of congeners. Williams (1951) also explored the statistical power of his test: if there were fewer than nine species in the assemblage, the expected S/G ratio was so low that competitive effects could never be detected. Finally, in *Patterns in the Balance of Nature* (1964), Williams again analyzed S/G ratios of British birds and plants, and Moreau's (1948) African bird communities. To relax the assumption of a log series distribution, Williams used numbered discs to represent species in different genera. He then took random samples to confirm that the S/G ratio declines with decreasing S, regardless of the underlying species abundance distribution.

In spite of Williams's (1947a, 1951, 1964) thorough treatment of this topic, S/G ratios and other taxonomic indices continued to be used as an index of competition without reference to an appropriate null hypothesis (Grant 1966; Moreau 1966; MacArthur and Wilson 1967; Cook 1969). However, Hairston (1964) did heed Williams's (1964) results and pointed out three biological assumptions implicit in his analyses:

1. The number of different habitats occupied by a species is unrelated to the size of the genus of that species.
2. The presence of a species in one habitat can be interpreted without reference to its presence or abundance in other types of habitat.
3. The human observer divides the total area into habitats in the same manner as do the species being studied.

Hairston (1964) felt Williams's (1947a) first assumption was violated and suggested that species belonging to species-rich genera usually occupied more habitats than species from monotypic genera. This sort of distribution would lead to lower S/G ratios within a single habitat type. Hairston (1964) also rejected assumptions (2) and (3), based on his own detailed studies of salamander ecology. He wrote that "it is not possible to draw valid conclusions about interspecific competition from an analysis of generic relations of species in a series of communities or habitats . . . it can be concluded that this approach is not a satisfactory substitute for more detailed studies."

Simberloff (1970) reviewed the controversy and analyzed *S/G* ratios for a number of data sets. Using computer simulations, he generated the expected *S/G* ratio for small communities by drawing from appropriate source pools. As Williams (1964) had shown earlier, the expected *S/G* ratio varied from a minimum of 1.0 (for a community of one species) to a maximum equal to that of the source pool. Between these limits, the expected curve was slightly convex; its shape depended on the underlying species abundance distribution in the source pool. The procedure is a computer simulation of rarefaction (Chapter 2) in which the expected species richness and its variance (Heck et al. 1975) can be calculated for a random sample of individuals from a collection.

Simberloff (1970) found that the expected *S/G* ratio was relatively insensitive to alterations in the source pool composition. For 180 island floras and faunas, 70% of the *S/G* ratios were larger than expected, contrary to the predictions of the competitive exclusion hypothesis (see McFarlane 1991 for a noteworthy exception). Three hypotheses might account for large *S/G* ratios:

1. Similar habitat affinities of congeneric species (Williams 1947a).
2. Restricted habitat affinities of monotypic genera (Hairston 1964).
3. A positive correlation between dispersal ability and taxonomic affinity. In other words, if species of certain genera are especially good at dispersal, they will tend to be overrepresented in island avifaunas.

Simberloff (1970) noted that it is not possible to distinguish among these hypotheses on the basis of species lists, although he did point to examples of widely distributed species of monotypic genera, which argues against hypothesis (2).

Several important points emerge from the history of *S/G* ratios. First, failure to consider an appropriate null hypothesis can lead investigators astray, causing them to attribute biological mechanisms to patterns that may represent sampling artifact. Second, when the null hypothesis is explicitly cast, it forms a reference point for examining patterns. In the case of the *S/G* ratio, observed ratios were frequently higher, not lower, than expected. Third, a good deal of controversy surrounds the construction of any null model. Important questions of source pool designation, taxonomic effects, and dispersal abilities were debated in this early literature, and ecologists continue to lock horns over these same issues today.

Finally, it is fascinating to see history repeat itself. Järvinen (1982) describes a controversy over *S/G* ratios among European plant ecologists in the 1920s, which predated the Eltonian controversy among English and American animal

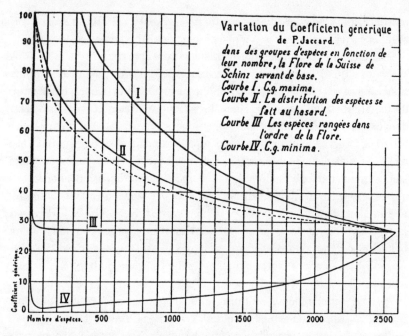

Figure 1.2. An early null model of taxonomic ratios for vascular plants of Switzerland by Maillefer (1929). The y axis is the genus/species ratio multiplied by 100, and the x axis is the number of species in the sample. Curves I and IV show the maximum and minimum values possible for the ratio, while Curve III is the expected value, based on random draws from a deck of marked cards. The dashed line is the standard deviation. Curve II is the expected value when species are sampled in systematic order. The controversy among European plant ecologists near the turn of the century was identical to the more familiar debate among animal ecologists over *S/G* ratios in the 1940s. Both groups used null models to understand the sampling properties of taxonomic ratios. From Järvinen (1982), with permission.

ecologists. The biogeographer Jaccard (1901) introduced the "generic coefficient" (*G/S* ratios, expressed as percentages) and argued that it reflected gradients of ecological diversity. Palmgren (1925) believed that the generic coefficient merely reflected the species richness of a region and said nothing about ecological diversity. Palmgren (1925) reasoned that if the number of species colonizing an area is small, chances are good that only a few genera will be represented. Maillefer (1929) discussed the statistical limitations of the generic coefficient and, like Williams (1964), used randomly shuffled cards to represent the Swiss flora and to derive expected generic coefficients (Figure 1.2). He also found that congeneric coexistence was higher than expected. Finally, the mathematician Pólya (1930) derived the expectation of the *G/S* ratio, predating the work of Simberloff (1970), Hurlbert (1971), and Heck et al. (1975) by 40 years.

Why did most ecologists ignore or dismiss the works of Palmgren (1925) and Williams (1964)? Most likely, because probabilistic tests and notions of stochastic sampling effects simply did not fit the reigning ecological paradigms of the time (Simberloff 1970; Järvinen 1982). For similar reasons, most ecologists overlooked Munroe's (1948) independent discovery of the equilibrium theory of island biogeography (Brown and Lomolino 1989). Järvinen (1982) also noted the unfortunate tendency of (American) ecologists to ignore important literature not published in English. Finally, the lack of computers made it impractical to conduct randomization tests prior to the 1970s.

OTHER APPROACHES

After the S/G ratio debates, null model controversy arose again in the late 1970s over provocative papers from the ecology group at Florida State University (the so-called "Tallahassee Mafia"; Donald R. Strong, Jr., quoted in Lewin 1983). In the intervening years, null models were by no means ignored in the ecological literature. Like Elton (1946), some authors stated a null hypothesis but failed to test it. For example, in a review of competition and niche studies, Schoener (1974a) argued that observed utilization niches overlapped less than would be expected in the absence of interspecific competition. Other authors attempted to use conventional statistical tests to evaluate null hypotheses. Brown (1973), for example, used a chi-squared distribution to test the null hypothesis that coexistence is just as likely for species pairs with body size ratios greater or less than 1.5. The nonindependence of species pairs invalidates the chi-squared test (Kramer and Schmidhammer 1992), although in practice, results were identical to those generated by an appropriate null model analysis (Bowers and Brown 1982).

Some studies in this period made explicit use of null hypotheses. Sale (1974) and Inger and Colwell (1977) randomized resource utilization data to evaluate niche overlap in the absence of competition (see Chapters 4 and 5), providing a direct test of Schoener's (1974a) stated null hypothesis. Using a very different sort of null model, Caswell (1976) analyzed species abundance distributions (Chapter 3) and introduced the term "neutral model" into the ecological literature. In the study of species co-occurrence (Chapter 7), E. Chris Pielou developed elegant null models (Pielou and Pielou 1968; Pielou 1972a), but her work was virtually ignored for more than a decade (Simberloff and Connor 1981). Cohen (1978) proposed randomization algorithms for food web matrices, some of which are identical to procedures used in competition analyses of presence-absence matrices (Simberloff 1978a). Finally, computer simulations of randomly connected food webs (Gardner and Ashby 1970; May 1972) produced surprising results (Chapter 10) and were in the spirit of later null models, although patterns were not compared with real data. Perhaps because some of these studies did not challenge the MacArthurian paradigm, they did not gain the notoriety of later null model papers, although in many cases the results were equally provocative.

RECOMMENDATIONS

Whether or not one accepts a strict falsificationist protocol, we recommend the use of null models for the analysis of nonexperimental data. Null models are particularly valuable for testing unique predictions of community theory, and for testing patterns when the assumptions of conventional statistical tests are violated. Chapters 2–10 illustrate the utility of null models for a variety of specific ecological questions.

2
SPECIES DIVERSITY

Studies of species diversity are a major component of community ecology and biogeography. Patterns of species diversity in time and space form the basis of many important ecological models, including mechanisms of succession (Connell and Slatyer 1977), explanations for latitudinal diversity gradients (Pianka 1966; Stevens 1989), hypotheses of mass extinction in the fossil record (Raup et al. 1973), and relationships between diversity and stability (May 1973; Goodman 1975). Measures of species diversity are often used to evaluate the success of nature reserves in preventing extinction (Soulé and Wilcox 1980), and to assay the effects of environmental pollution on the "well-being" of natural ecosystems (Tomascik and Sander 1987).

SPECIES DIVERSITY

Unfortunately, "species diversity" has taken on a variety of confusing meanings (Hurlbert 1971). Here, we define diversity as a measure of both the number of species in the community and their relative abundances (Margalef 1968; Washington 1984). Diverse communities are characterized by a large number of species and/or a relatively even distribution of species abundances (Lambshead et al. 1983). Considerable effort has been expended to devise a single numerical index that measures these two properties (see reviews by Peet 1974; Washington 1984; Magurran 1988). Regardless of the mathematics of the index, all diversity indices incorporate three important assumptions (Peet 1974):

> 1. *All individuals assigned to a specific class are assumed to be*
> *equal.* Most diversity indices do not recognize intraspecific differences among individuals, even though age- and size-structured populations may have important community-level effects (Polis et al. 1989). In theory, ages, sexes, or size classes could be

treated as different "species" (Hendrickson and Ehrlich 1971), but their numerical dependence on one another is different from their dependence on other species.

2. *All species or classes are assumed to be equally different from one another.* Thus, diversity indices will not permit us to directly identify keystone species (Paine 1966), which have an inordinate influence on local community structure. If communities are organized into guilds of species that share similar resources (Root 1967), removal of species within a guild will have different effects on diversity than removal of species not in a guild.

3. *Community structure is assumed to be measured in appropriate units.* For most animal communities, individuals are assigned to species or "operational taxonomic units" (OTUs; Sneath and Sokal 1973) and counted. For assemblages of plants or sessile invertebrates, measures of biomass or percent cover may be more appropriate. The "correct" units are important in interpreting diversity measures (Dickman 1968). For example, many ecologists have interpreted the relative abundance of a species in a community as a reflection of its relative use of ecological resources (MacArthur 1960; Sugihara 1980). Thus, in plant communities, numerically dominant species sequester more water, light, and nutrients than relatively rare species (Greig-Smith 1964; but see Rabinowitz et al. 1984). In animal communities, however, resource use may be more or less even than suggested by relative abundance distributions, because rare species tend to be large-bodied and comprise more biomass than their numbers would suggest (Harvey and Godfray 1987; Pagel et al. 1991).

PROBLEMS WITH DIVERSITY INDICES

Rather than addressing these important assumptions, most descriptions of diversity indices focus on the algebra of the index and the theoretical value of the index in measuring diversity. Washington (1984) reviewed a plethora of diversity, similarity, and biotic indices used in both theoretical and applied contexts. Most of these indices are highly correlated with one another (Ghent 1991), and many families of indices can be derived from a single algebraic expression (Hill 1973).

Perhaps the most celebrated index is the Shannon-Wiener diversity index: $H' = -\Sigma p_i \ln(p_i)$, where p_i is the relative abundance of the ith species ($\Sigma p_i = 1.0$).

The index has been used since the 1950s (Good 1953; MacArthur 1955) and became a "magic bullet" among ecologists (Washington 1984). The tenuous theoretical justification for H' came from information theory (Margalef 1958), but the idea that H' is a measure of entropy (reviewed by Goodman 1975) is no longer warranted (Hurlbert 1971). Nevertheless, the Shannon-Wiener index continues to be used and until recently, was thoroughly entrenched in the ecological literature. With the exception of metrics such as Hurlbert's (1971) PIE (probability of an interspecific encounter), most diversity indices cannot be interpreted in biologically meaningful ways.

Another problem with diversity indices is that they lack a probabilistic basis. Because the indices are not sampled from a known distribution, it is impossible to assign a probability value to them (Ghent 1991). Consequently, there is no way to evaluate the statistical and biological differences between two communities with H' values of, say, 1.7 and 2.0. Some ecologists have repeatedly sampled communities to estimate the mean and variance of a diversity index, or have used a jackknife of an individual sample to obtain confidence limits about a diversity index (Adams and McCune 1979). However, these approaches are unsatisfactory because all diversity indices are highly sensitive to both the number of species and the number of individuals in the collection; repeated sampling does not eliminate those biases. Another solution is to rescale the index algebraically so that it is bounded between 0.0 and 1.0. However, scaling procedures do not remove the sampling bias caused by differences in the size of two samples (Peet 1975).

In spite of these serious conceptual and statistical problems, there is a continued interest in measures of species diversity (Magurran 1988), and a need to quantify patterns statistically in natural communities. We offer two suggestions. The first is to abandon the idea of incorporating both evenness and species richness into a single index. Although there is obviously a relationship between species richness and relative abundance, the two components of diversity are distinct and should be analyzed separately (James and Rathbun 1981). The second suggestion is to use explicit null models to estimate the nonbiological effects of sample size on species richness and species evenness. Null models for species richness have been well developed, but relatively little work has been done with the evenness problem.

SPECIES RICHNESS

Species richness, as measured by a direct count of species, is the simplest and easiest diversity index to interpret (Peet 1974). However, species counts are influenced not only by the species richness of the surrounding community, but also by the number of individuals counted and the amount of area sampled (Williams 1964). The areas sampled might represent natural, insular communities, such as oceanic islands, or arbitrary sampling units, such as vegetation quadrats. In either case, the more area sampled, the more species will be detected (e.g., Connor and McCoy 1979; Anderson and Marcus 1993). For insular communities, island area typically accounts for 50% of the variation in species number (Boecklen and Gotelli 1984). Even within a well-defined area, the number of species recorded depends on the thoroughness of sampling. For example, the number of botanical collecting trips to the Galápagos Islands was a better predictor of plant species number than area, elevation, or isolation (Connor and Simberloff 1978).

Consequently, unless two communities are censused exhaustively and identically, it is inappropriate to compare simple species counts. The problem is illustrated in Table 2.1, which shows the number of individuals of different carabid beetle species collected from pitfall traps in young (<20 years old) and old (20–60 years old) pine plantations in northern Europe (Niemelä et al. 1988). A total of 243 individuals of 31 species was collected from the young plantations, compared to 63 individuals of 9 species collected from the old plantations.

Which community exhibits greater species richness? We cannot automatically assume that richness was greater for the young plantations. Almost four times as many individuals were collected in the young plantations, so it is not surprising that more species accumulated. Nor can we simply rescale the smaller collection by a constant multiplier, because the relationship between the number of individuals in the collection and the number of species is seldom linear.

RAREFACTION

Sanders (1968) addressed the problem of comparing the species richness of different habitats in a study of marine benthic communities. He devised an algorithm for "rarefying" the large samples, that is, calculating the expected species richness based on random subsamples of individuals. This rarefied sample can then be compared directly with the smaller collection, because the species richness of both collections is now based on an identical number of individuals.

If the rarefaction procedure is carried out for a number of different abundances, a rarefaction curve can be plotted on a graph that has the number of

Table 2.1
Pitfall trap collections of carabid beetles from young and old pine plantations in
northern Europe

Species	No. individuals collected	
	Young plantations	Old plantations
Calathus micropterus	48	29
Pterostichus oblongopunctatus	23	9
Notiophilus biguttatus	3	1
Carabus hortensis	2	0
Carabus glabratus	15	1
Cychrus caraboides	6	1
Amara brunnea	2	0
Trechus secalis	30	15
Leistus terminatus	3	1
Amara familiaris	1	0
Amara lunicollis	7	0
Bembidion gilvipes	2	0
Bradycellus caucasicus	1	0
Calathus melanocephalus	3	0
Carabus nitens	1	0
Carabus violaceus	1	0
Cicindela sylvatica	10	0
Cymindis vaporariorum	3	0
Harpalus quadripunctatus	7	0
Harpalus sp.	1	0
Leistus ferrugineus	1	0
Miscodera arctica	13	0
Notiophilus aestuans	2	0
Notiophilus germinyi	9	0
Notiophilus palustris	9	0
Pterostichus adstrictus	23	0
Pterostichus cupreus	1	0
Pterostichus diligens	1	2
Pterostichus niger	7	0
Pterostrichus strenuus	4	4
Synuchus vivalis	4	0
Total abundance	243	63
Total species richness	31	9

From Niemelä et al. (1988).

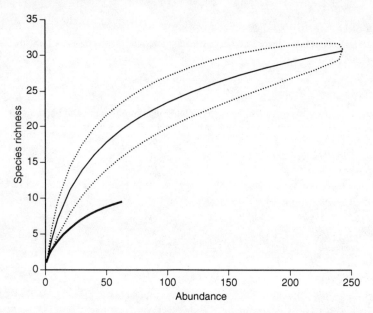

Figure 2.1. Rarefaction curves for carabid beetle assemblages in old and young pine plantations. The dotted line represents the 95% confidence interval for the young plantation curve and the thick line represents the old plantation curve. Data from Table 2.1.

individuals on the abscissa and the number of species on the ordinate. The rarefaction curve increases monotonically from a minimum point at $(1,1)$ (a random sample of one individual will always contain exactly one species) to a maximum at (N,S), where N and S are the number of individuals and species, respectively, in the original sample. Figure 2.1 shows the two rarefaction curves (and their 95% confidence limits) for the data in Table 2.1. The rarefaction curve for the old pine plantations lies significantly below that of the young pine plantations. Thus, the higher species richness of the young pine plantations was not simply an artifact of the greater number of individuals collected. For example, 63 individuals of 9 species were collected from the old pine plantations, whereas a random sample of 63 individuals from the young pine plantations would be expected to contain approximately 20 species.

Sanders's (1968) rarefaction was correct in principle, but his algorithm overestimated the expected number of species for a random subsample (Hurlbert 1971; Fager 1972; Simberloff 1972). The only case in which Sanders's (1968) formula is correct is when the individuals in the collection are uniformly distributed in space (Kobayashi 1982). Although competition in some communities may generate a uniform spatial distribution (e.g., Ryti and Case 1986; Chapin et al. 1989), random or clumped spatial patterns are much more typical. Thus, Sanders's (1968) algorithm should not be used as a general null model.

The correct rarefaction model is based on the hypergeometric distribution, sampling without replacement from some parent distribution (Feller 1968), which in this case is the observed collection. Although rarefaction usually is applied to collections of individuals classified as species, the technique is appropriate for any hierarchical classification, such as species/genus (S/G) ratios, discussed in Chapter 1.

When individuals are sampled equiprobably and independently of one another, the expected species richness ($E(S_n)$) in a small sample is

$$E(S_n) = \sum_{i=1}^{S}\left[1-\binom{N-m_i}{n}\Big/\binom{N}{n}\right] \tag{2.1}$$

where N is the total number of individuals in the collection, S is the total number of species in the collection, m_i is the number of individuals of species i in the collection, and n is the number of individuals in the subsample (Hurlbert 1971). The term inside the summation sign is the probability that a sample of n individuals will contain species i. Summing over all the species in the collection gives the expected species richness. The variance is

$$\sigma^2(S_n) = \binom{N}{n}^{-1}\left[\sum_{i=1}^{S}\binom{N-m_i}{n}\left(1-\frac{\binom{N-m_i}{n}}{\binom{N}{n}}\right)\right.$$

$$\left. + 2\sum_{\substack{j=2\\i<j}}^{S}\left(\binom{N-m_i-m_j}{n}-\frac{\binom{N-m_i}{n}\binom{N-m_j}{n}}{\binom{N}{n}}\right)\right] \tag{2.2}$$

(Heck et al. 1975). Both equations are formidable to calculate by hand, but fortunately, published computer algorithms (Simberloff 1978b) and ecological software packages (Ludwig and Reynolds 1988) are available. In spite of the repeated publication of Equations 2.1 and 2.2, Sanders's (1968) original algorithm continues to be incorrectly used, particularly by marine ecologists (e.g., Beukema 1991). We suspect this error persists because of the important influence of Sanders's (1968) paper, and because his equation can be solved on a hand calculator.

ASSUMPTIONS OF THE RAREFACTION MODEL

The rarefaction model entails a number of assumptions and restrictions:

1. *Sampling has been sufficient to guarantee an adequate characterization of the parent distribution* (Tipper 1979). If the samples are too small, rarefaction curves will always appear similar, because all rarefaction curves converge at the (1,1) coordinate.
2. *The spatial distribution of individuals is random.* If the distribution is not random, Equation 2.1 will give a biased estimate of the expected species richness. Specifically, the more spatially clumped individuals are, the more the rarefaction curve will overestimate the expected species richness (Simberloff 1986). Different rarefaction algorithms are available for different spatial distributions (Kobayashi 1982, 1983; Smith et al. 1985), but unless a great deal of information is available on the spatial organization of the assemblage, Equation 2.1 should be used.
3. *The samples to be compared are taxonomically "similar" and are drawn from the "same" community type.* For example, two collections of lepidoptera might exhibit similar rarefaction curves, but if one collection contains only moths and the other only butterflies, it would be incorrect to conclude they were drawn from the same distribution (Simberloff 1978b). Likewise, assemblages should be sampled from similar habitats, although this is often a matter of judgment (Raup 1975); many studies use rarefaction for the purpose of comparing species richness in different habitats (e.g., James and Warner 1982; Mehlhop and Lynch 1986). What is important is that the sampling efficiency not change in different habitats. For example, a comparison between samples of birds mist-netted in a prairie and in a forest might be invalid if some species avoided the net disproportionately in the open prairie.
4. *Standardized sampling techniques are used for all collections.* Different sampling methods have different biases, so collections should not be compared by rarefaction (or any other technique) unless they were gathered with similar methods. For example, marine benthic collections gathered with cores and dredges should not be compared by rarefaction (Abele and Walters 1979a), because these two methods have very different sampling properties. Similarly, it would not be appropriate to use rarefac-

tion to compare the diversity of extant and fossil echinoderms, because the fossil record is biased toward taxa with skeletonized hard parts (Raup 1975). Even subtle differences in sampling area (Engstrom and James 1981) and trap design (Butman 1989) can affect the size and diversity of the collection. A standardized method must be used for meaningful comparisons.

5. *Rarefaction can be used for interpolation to a smaller sample size, but not for extrapolation to a larger sample size.* Because the rarefaction curve makes no assumptions about the shape of the underlying parent distribution, it cannot be properly extrapolated to larger sample sizes (e.g., Calef and Hancock 1974). If one is willing to assume, a priori, a particular species abundance distribution, such as the log normal (Preston 1962), then it is possible to derive the expected species richness for samples of any size (e.g., Kempton and Taylor 1974). As described later in this chapter, there are several estimators of total species richness based on species accumulation curves that are more appropriate for extrapolation (Colwell and Coddington 1994).

STATISTICAL ISSUES IN RAREFACTION

Rarefaction can be used to ask two slightly different questions (Simberloff 1978b): (1) For a collection of N individuals of S species, what is the expected number of species in a small sample of n individuals ($n < N$)? (2) What is the likelihood that two collections of sizes N and n were both drawn from the same parent distribution (Figure 2.2)? Equations 2.1 and 2.2 are appropriate for answering the first question. However, ecologists are usually more interested in answering the second question, and in this case, Equation 2.2 is a biased estimator of the variance. Smith and Grassle (1977) gave approximate confidence intervals for the expected variance in this case, but the calculation is complex.

However, Equation 2.2 is a minimum variance estimator, so if two samples do not differ in expected species richness based on this variance, they certainly will not by other measures. For several large collections of diatoms (Patrick 1968), Equation 2.2 gave similar results to other variance estimators (Simberloff 1979a); thus it seems a reasonable choice for most studies. The important point is to use *some* estimator of variance so that the null hypothesis that two collections were drawn from the same parent distribution can be tested.

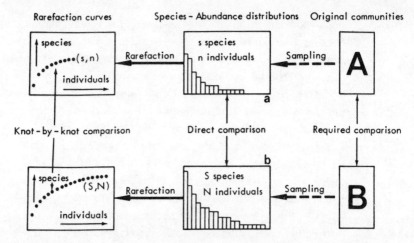

Figure 2.2. Samples from two communities are compared by rarefaction curves to generate expected species richness. From Tipper (1979), with permission.

It is also important to calculate rarefaction curves along their full length, that is, for several different values of n. If two rarefaction curves should cross, then the difference in expected species richness of the two collections will depend on the abundance being compared (Simberloff 1979a). However, most groups of published curves do not cross (Simberloff 1978b). Another reason for calculating curves along their full length is that they are based on discrete "knots" of abundance. If too few knots are used for comparison, pairs of rarefaction curves can appear more or less similar, depending on the placement of the knots. For a collection of S species and N individuals, a minimum of $S + 1$ subsamples of n, evenly spaced along the x axis, should be used to construct the curve (Tipper 1979). Once the curves have been constructed, conventional statistical tests can be used to compare expected species richness at different knots. In many cases, simply plotting rarefaction curves and their 95% confidence intervals is sufficient to reveal differences in expected species richness.

One final issue is how to deal with multiple collections from the same habitat or location. Tipper (1979) recommended calculating separate rarefaction curves for each, then using means and variances of the expected species richness to estimate the composite rarefaction curve. However, if the individual samples are small, the composite curve will be too short to allow for a powerful test. In such cases, pooling samples will provide a more accurate estimate of the relative abundances of rare species in the collection. In a winter bird-population study (Engstrom and James 1981), a pooled rarefaction curve accurately predicted observed species richness in nine 6.5-ha subplots, even though the subplots varied somewhat in habitat structure.

SPECIES RICHNESS VERSUS SPECIES DENSITY

Rarefaction allows for a comparison of the number of species in samples that have been standardized for abundance. A closely related measure of diversity is species density (Simpson 1964), which is the expected number of species per unit area. Species density allows for comparison of the number of species in samples that have been standardized for the area censused. Species density depends on the species abundance relationship, the density of individuals, and, to a lesser extent, their spatial distribution (James and Wamer 1982). The spatial scale and the boundaries of the community from which the sample was drawn influence both species richness and species density. The two measures need not give similar results.

A study of North American breeding birds (James and Wamer 1982) illustrates the distinction between species richness and species density. Using census data from a variety of forest habitats, James and Wamer (1982) compared species number for samples with an equal number of individuals (species richness) and for samples with an equal area (species density). Rarefaction curves generated for each forest type did not cross, indicating that differences among habitats were consistent. The rate of species accumulation also differed among habitats. For example, at an abundance of 50 territorial pairs, the accumulation curve for the wax myrtle forest was leveling off, whereas the curve for second-growth forest was still rising rapidly.

Determining species density on equal-sized areas requires an estimate of the density of territorial pairs. James and Wamer (1982) used point estimates of density in each habitat, and then extrapolated these estimates to larger and smaller areas. Their analysis assumed that density was constant across all areas, yielding a set of linear abundance curves (Figure 2.3b). These curves did not fall out in exactly the same order as the original rarefaction curves. For a plot of a given size, James and Wamer (1982) used these density curves to estimate the number of territorial pairs, and then used the rarefaction curves to get the expected species richness (Figure 2.3a). The interaction between density and expected species richness determined species density in different habitats. The resulting species density (Figure 2.3c) was highest in the tulip tree-maple-oak forest, in part because this habitat supported the greatest density of individual territories.

James and Wamer's (1982) study nicely illustrates the interplay of area, density, and species abundance in producing patterns of species richness. Their

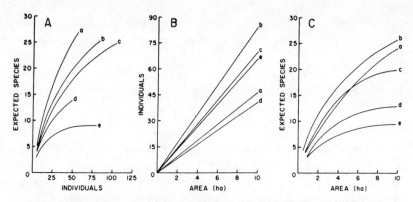

Figure 2.3. Avian species richness in five forest habitats. (A) Rarefaction curves, which give the expected species richness for a sample of individuals. (B) Density relationships for each habitat, which were assumed to be linear across a range of plot sizes. (C) Species density relationships, which incorporate both species richness and density relationships. Note the different orderings of the habitats based on these measures. (a) Maple-pine-oak second-growth forest; (b) tulip tree-maple-oak forest; (c) cottonwood floodplain forest; (d) mature jack pine with birch forest; (e) wax myrtle forest. From James and Warner (1982), with permission.

method should be used whenever sampling is based on plots or quadrats of known area. However, not all sampling methods are area-based. Point counts, baits, or stationary traps may sample individuals from an unknown area. For these sampling schemes, species richness can still be compared by plotting the expected abundance per sample on the x axis of the rarefaction curve (Engstrom et al. 1984).

Figure 2.4 illustrates two rarefaction curves based on pitfall trap samples of ants in an Oklahoma grassland (Gotelli in press). Each curve is a pooled sample of the contents of six pitfall traps. The "ant lion zone" traps were placed beneath a cliff ledge in a dense aggregation of ant lion larvae, whereas the other traps were placed approximately 1 m beyond the ant lion zone in a "predator-free zone" (Gotelli 1993). The two rarefaction curves were very similar to one another: the ant lion zone curve fell completely within the 95% confidence interval for the predator-free zone curve, a pattern that was consistent across three different sites and five consecutive years (Gotelli in press).

Although rarefaction curves were similar in the two habitats, abundance per trap was not. Ant abundance was significantly greater in the predator-free zone, and this translated into a greater species number on the rarefaction curve. In James and Warner's (1982) analysis, differences in bird species density were caused by differences in abundance and expected species richness. In the

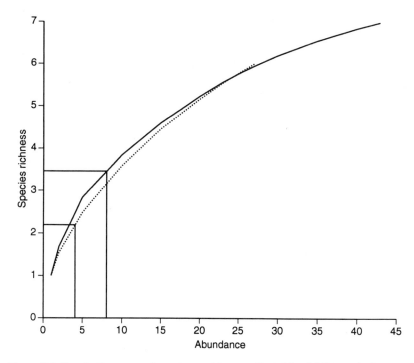

Figure 2.4. Rarefaction curves for ant assemblages collected in pitfall traps in the presence (dotted curve) and absence (solid curve) of ant lion predators. The two rarefaction curves are indistinguishable, but abundance per trap (which affects species richness) is greater in the absence of predators. Vertical lines indicate average abundance in the two microhabitats. See Gotelli (in press).

Oklahoma ant assemblage, differences in species density were primarily due to differences in abundance. Indicating the expected or average sampling abundance on a rarefaction curve (e.g., Engstrom et al. 1984) gives important information about both species richness and species density of a sample.

USES OF RAREFACTION

In this section, we review some of the diverse applications of rarefaction to problems in ecology and evolutionary biology.

Deep-Sea Diversity

Sanders's (1968) paper was noteworthy not only for introducing rarefaction, but for popularizing the "stability-time" hypothesis in the ecological literature.

Sanders (1968) compared rarefaction curves for marine invertebrates (polychaetes and bivalves) in different benthic habitats and found the highest species richness for shallow tropical reefs and the deep ocean floor. Sanders (1968; Sanders and Hessler 1969) argued that these habitats were relatively constant and experienced little abiotic fluctuation through time. Under these circumstances, biotic interactions were thought to promote species coexistence and lead to complex, stable assemblages with high species richness. In contrast, habitats with low species richness, such as estuaries, were subject to variable abiotic conditions. Physiological stress controls the assemblage and low species richness results, because few species can tolerate highly variable conditions. The relatively high deep-sea diversity was a surprising finding, and Sanders's (1968) explanation reflected conventional wisdom that species-rich, biologically complex communities such as tropical rain forests evolved over long periods of physical stability (Fischer 1960).

Abele and Walters (1979a,b) pointed out the potential circularity in this argument—stressful environments are often defined or recognized as those with low species richness (Peters 1976)—and also attacked Sanders's (1968) methods. They noted that in some cases Sanders (1968) compared dredge and core samples and that the original rarefaction algorithm was biased. Abele and Walters (1979a,b) calculated corrected rarefaction curves (and their 95% confidence intervals) and found that most did not differ significantly from one another. Although estuaries were relatively depauperate, deep-sea samples did not appear to be unusually species-rich.

Abele and Walters (1979a) suggested that deep-sea diversity could be effectively explained by the large area of the habitat and by small-scale variation in habitat quality. Recent intensive sampling of the continental slope has again generated high estimates of species richness (Grassle and Maciolek 1992), and these have been attributed to microhabitat heterogeneity and small-scale biogenic disturbances. Whatever the "correct" explanation for deep-sea diversity, rarefaction was an important tool for revealing the basic patterns of diversity that precipitated this debate.

Evolutionary Ecology

As discussed in Chapter 1, the rarefaction methodology was developed independently by A. Maillefer (1929), C. B. Williams (1947a), and others to examine species/genus (S/G) ratios and other indices of taxonomic diversity. Whether one is examining species richness in a benthic core sample, or the number of coexisting congeneric species on an island, rarefaction is the appropriate method for studying the diversity of a hierarchically classified sample.

Although the questions were very different from those addressed by Sanders (1968), the statistics of rarefaction are identical for comparisons of taxonomic diversity. The result from many independent studies is that taxonomic diversity indices rarely deviate significantly from an appropriate rarefaction curve (Simberloff 1970; Harvey et al. 1983). The confidence bands for most rarefaction curves are broad, so that small assemblages would have to be most unusual taxonomically to generate a statistically significant result.

However, this does not mean that taxonomic diversity indices have no value. Although individual communities may not deviate significantly, samples of multiple communities may reveal nonrandom patterns. For example, Simberloff (1970) found that approximately 70% of the examples of S/G ratios deviated in a positive direction: in most genera, there were slightly more coexisting species in a genus than expected by chance. Gotelli and Abele (1982) found that the number of bird families represented on islands of the West Indies did not differ statistically from the rarefaction curve of the pooled species list. However, deviations from the rarefaction curve were positively correlated with island area, perhaps reflecting increased habitat diversity on large islands. Similarly, Järvinen and Sammalisto (1976) discovered a latitudinal gradient in S/G ratios of breeding birds on Finnish peatlands. After correction for the number of species in each sample, the S/G ratio still increased with latitude. These results suggest that the (standardized) residual from a rarefaction curve is a useful diversity index that controls for differences in the size of the assemblage. For multiple samples, this residual can then be correlated with other physical or biological attributes of the community.

Sampling Efficiency

Because most communities cannot be fully enumerated, their properties will always have to be inferred from those of a sample. Common species will usually be encountered first when sampling, and there will be diminishing returns on effort as the rare species in an assemblage are captured only with more intensive effort. What is the correct stopping point? If the individuals are sampled randomly, the rarefaction curve shows the expected accumulation of species and can be used to plan effective sampling strategies.

For breeding birds of North American forests, some rarefaction curves did not begin to reach an asymptote until 75 pairs had been censused, corresponding to a minimum plot area of approximately 10 ha (James and Wamer 1982). Using rarefaction, Haila and Kuusela (1982) determined that single-census visits to small Baltic islands would reveal 70% or more of the resident bird species. Heck et al. (1975) rarefied a large collection of benthic invertebrates and found that 90% of the species could be expected from a collection that was 70% as large as the original. In summary, rarefaction can be used to efficiently minimize the collection effort required for a single sample, allowing for more spatial or temporal replication of samples.

Paleobiology

Rarefaction is an ideal technique for comparing the diversity of fossil assemblages, because differences in the "abundance" of fossil collections are likely to reflect both taphonomic biases and collection effort. A simple "balls in buckets" null model illustrated such sampling effects in the measurement of higher levels of taxonomic diversity (Raup 1972). Raup (1975) discussed the biological considerations in using rarefaction in paleobiology, and Tipper (1979) reviewed the use (and abuse) of the technique in paleobiology.

Rarefaction was used to show that an apparent increase in echinoid families after the Paleozoic was real, whereas there has not been a significant increase in familial diversity since the mid-Cretaceous (Raup 1975). In paleontological studies, rarefaction is frequently carried out at high taxonomic levels (orders, families), because it is often difficult to reliably classify fossils at the generic and specific levels.

For example, Raup (1979) used rarefaction to estimate species losses at the Permo-Triassic boundary. He first constructed rarefaction curves for orders, families, and genera of living echinoid species as a reasonable estimate of a generalized rarefaction curve for a clade. In addition to the other restrictions imposed by rarefaction, Raup's (1979) analysis assumed that the rarefaction curve for living echinoids was comparable in shape to that of other fossil clades. Next, he estimated the percent extinction of orders, families, and genera of well-skeletonized marine organisms at the Permo-Triassic boundary. Finally, he back-calculated from these percentages on the living rarefaction curve to estimate extinction at the species level. The resulting estimate of 88 to 96% extinction at the species level agreed with rates estimated by other methods (Valentine et al. 1978).

Antia (1977) used rarefaction to explore the effects of taphonomic biases on the estimation of diversity and the characterization of fossil assemblages. He thoroughly sampled living mollusc assemblages and dead molluscan shell cumulates from seven marine habitats in southeastern England. Although rarefaction of the dead shell cumulates consistently over-estimated diversity compared to the living assemblages, expected species richness in different habitats was consistent for fossil and living assemblages. This fact suggests that rarefaction can be effectively used to compare the diversity of different fossil assemblages, even though they may be subject to preservational biases. Because rarefaction estimates diversity for an entire assemblage, it is relatively robust to preservational biases that may distort the abundances of individual species.

Pollution Studies

Pollution effects can be monitored by the performance of individual indicator species (Shubert 1984) and by changes in indices of community structure (Washington 1984). Rarefaction has been used in both field and laboratory studies as a simple index of community response to pollution. For example, Dean-Ross (1990) found that the expected number of bacterial strains in laboratory streams decreased in response to high (but not low) concentrations of zinc. Berger (1990) examined the recolonization by benthic macrofauna of oiled and unoiled sediment boxes in two Norwegian fjords. In a eutrophic fjord, oil had no effect on expected species richness as measured by rarefaction; abundance and species richness of both control and oiled sediments returned to ambient levels in 3 months. In contrast, oil significantly reduced expected species richness in a noneutrophic fjord: recovery time was approximately 9 months for the oiled treatment and 16 months for the control. In pollution studies, it is especially important to compare both expected species richness and species density. If a pollutant is equally toxic to all resident species, it will effectively "rarefy" an assemblage to a reduced abundance. The rarefaction curves for a control and treatment assemblage would be identical in this case, even though abundance and species density are reduced by the treatment.

Successional Gradients

Rarefaction of breeding bird assemblages in successional gradients has revealed temporal trends in species richness and/or species density. Using mist-net captures, Mehlhop and Lynch (1986) compared avian assemblages near Chesapeake Bay, in habitats ranging from recently abandoned pasture to mature hardwood forest. The highest expected species richness occurred in forests of intermediate age. However, capture rates increased with forest age, so patterns of species density may be different, as James and Warner (1982) found. In seral stages of beech forest in Hungary, expected bird species density increased with stand age (Moskat and Szekely 1989). For standardized plots of 28 ha, species density increased from a minimum of 12 species in 1- to 2-year-old clear-cuts to a maximum of 26 species in century-old beech forests.

Engstrom et al. (1984) is one of the few successional studies to track temporal changes in species richness directly. In the upland coastal plains of the southeastern United States, frequent lightning fires discourage hardwood growth and maintain a virtual monoculture of long-leaf pine. If fire is suppressed, a structurally complex beech-magnolia forest develops. The species density was 21 bird species per 8.6-ha plot for long-leaf pine forest compared to 16 species for beech-magnolia forest. Engstrom et al. (1984) generated rarefaction curves for census data collected during 15 successive years on a single plot of long-leaf pine from which fire had been excluded since 1967. Expected bird species density declined during the first 10 years of the study, then began increasing again in 1978. Changes in species density were accompanied by dramatic changes in species composition; open-habitat species dropped out during the first five years and were replaced by species associated with mesic vegetation.

RELATED QUESTIONS

Although rarefaction is used to study the total number of species in an assemblage, investigators frequently are curious about the abundance of a particular species (or higher taxon) in a sample. For example, in many tropical communities, certain bird families present on the mainland are consistently absent from nearby islands (MacArthur et al. 1972; Terborgh and Winter 1978). The apparent "disharmony" of island faunas (Carlquist 1974) has often been attributed to the effects of interspecific competition (Case et al. 1979) and reduced habitat availability on islands (D. L. Lack 1976). Before such explanations can be invoked, it is necessary to reject the null hypothesis that the groups are missing from islands by chance, and are not present simply because the total number of species on the island is small.

Haila and Järvinen (1983) studied missing species in the avifaunas of islands in the Baltic Sea. They compared the avifauna of the island of Ulversö (68 species) with the avifauna of Main Åland (121 species). Main Åland is the largest island in the archipelago, and the Ulversö fauna is a proper subset of the Main Åland fauna. Why were 53 species (121 − 68) absent from Ulversö? On Main Åland, 45 species occurred on fewer than six line transects and were defined as "rare." Only six of these rare species occurred on Ulversö, compared to the expected number of 5.2. Thus, 39 of the 53 absences (74%) could be accounted for on the basis of "rarity" on Main Åland. The remaining absences could attributed to habitat impoverishment of Ulversö (12%) or poor dispersal potential (3%). Rarefaction curves for assemblages censused in different island habitats on Main Åland were good predictors of species richness in those same habitats on Ulversö. The results suggest that the small area of Ulversö and differences in habitat availability were the most important determinants of the composition and size of insular avifaunas.

We can modify the rarefaction algorithm to evaluate the frequency of any particular species in a collection of individuals. From the hypergeometric distribution, the expected abundance of any particular species s_i in a small random sample is

$$E(s_i) = \frac{nm_i}{N} \qquad (2.3)$$

which is simply its proportional frequency in the parent distribution. The variance is

$$\sigma^2(s_i) = \left(\frac{m_i n}{N}\right)\left(1 - \frac{m_i}{N}\right)\left(\frac{N-n}{N-1}\right) \qquad (2.4)$$

and the probability of obtaining the observed number of occurrences or fewer is

$$P(x \le c) = \sum_{x=0}^{c} \frac{\binom{m_i}{x}\binom{N-m_i}{n-x}}{\binom{N}{n}} \qquad (2.5)$$

Gotelli and Abele (1982) used the hypergeometric model to examine the number of species in different bird families that occurred on islands of the West Indies. Although rarefaction showed that each island supported the expected number of families, there were some significant deviations: on most islands there were more species of Columbidae and Mimidae than expected by chance, whereas Psittacidae were weakly underrepresented. Graves and Gotelli (1983) also found little evidence for extinction-prone taxa on land-bridge islands off the coast of South America: only one family (Bucconidae) was significantly underrepresented, whereas three families (Columbidae, Tyrannidae, and Parulidae) were overrepresented. However, species with small mainland geographic ranges were consistently underrepresented on land-bridge islands (Figure 2.5). The results of these null model studies contrast with earlier regression analyses (Faaborg 1979), which suggested that species in certain Neotropical bird families were unusually extinction-prone on islands.

Equation 2.5 also can be used to design effective sampling strategies. When the focus of a study is a particular species, rather than the entire community, an important question is how many individuals must be sampled to ensure capture of the target species. Returning to the carabid beetle data of Niemelä et al.

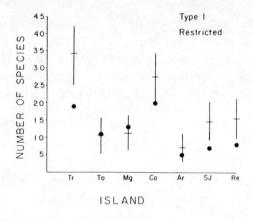

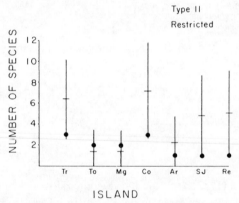

Figure 2.5. Observed and expected avian species richness on Neotropical land-bridge islands. The horizontal bar represents the expected number of species with restricted (=small) mainland geographic ranges, and the vertical line indicates two standard deviations. Expectation and variance were calculated from Equations 2.3 and 2.4. The observed number is shown by a filled circle. "Type I restricted" are species whose mainland ranges total less than 100 1° × 1° blocks. "Type II restricted" are species whose entire range fits within a contiguous 10° x 10° block. For both measures, species with restricted mainland geographic ranges were underrepresented on land-bridge islands, compared to the null model of random sampling from adjacent mainland source pools. Island codes: Tr = Trinidad; To = Tobago; Mg = Margarita; Co = Coiba; Ar = Aruba; SJ = San José; Re = Rey. San José and Rey are oceanic islands. From Graves and Gotelli (1983), with permission.

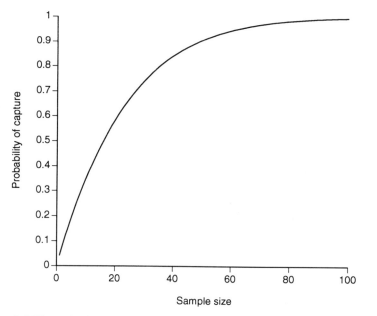

Figure 2.6. The probability of finding at least one individual of the carabid *Cicindela sylvatica* in pitfall samples from young pine plantations. Data from Table 2.1. Probabilities calculated using Equation 2.5.

(1988), Figure 2.6 illustrates the probability of capturing at least one individual of *Cicindela sylvatica* for a given sample size. A minimum of 31 individuals is needed in a sample to ensure with a 75% probability that *C. sylvatica* will be represented. Twice this number is needed to ensure a 95% probability.

CRITICISMS OF RAREFACTION

Rarefaction has been criticized for a number of reasons: it assumes a random spatial distribution of individuals (Kobayashi 1982, 1983), it loses information about species identity and relative abundance (Williamson 1973), and it is difficult to calculate by hand (Magurran 1988). However, all but the last criticism apply to other diversity indices as well. The potential disadvantages of rarefaction are outweighed by the facts that species richness is easy to interpret and that the rarefaction curve is based on an appropriate statistical model.

Furthermore, the shape of the rarefaction curve does reflect the shape of the relative abundance distribution, albeit indirectly. If the relative abundances in

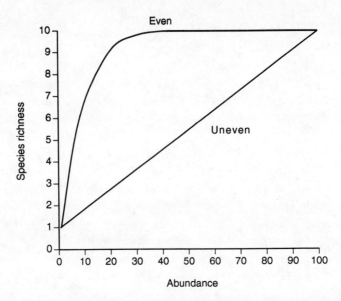

Figure 2.7. Rarefaction curves reflect the shape of the underlying species abundance distribution. Both rarefaction curves were drawn from samples of 100 individuals of 10 species. In the "even" sample, each species is represented by 10 individuals. In the "uneven" sample, 9 species are represented by 1 individual, and 1 species is represented by 91 individuals.

the collection are at maximum evenness (all species have equal abundance), then the rarefaction curve rises rapidly to an asymptote, because few samples are required to accumulate quickly all of the species. In contrast, if the relative abundances are maximally uneven (all species except the dominant represented by a single individual), then the rarefaction curve will increase in a slow linear fashion, because it takes many samples to accumulate additional species, all of which are rare (Figure 2.7). If density is constant with respect to island area or sample quadrat size, then similar comments apply to the shape of the species-area relationship under a null model of passive sampling (see Chapter 8).

Lambshead et al. (1983) noted that the rarefaction curve is related to the k-dominance plot, which graphs percentage cumulative abundance against species rank. They recommended using k-dominance plots, because they are easier to calculate and to interpret than rarefaction curves. However, k-dominance plots are based on percentages, so they are distorted by small sample sizes. The rarefaction curve is the only diversity measure that is sensitive to rare species and is unbiased by sample size (Smith and Grassle 1977).

EXTRAPOLATION AND ESTIMATION
OF TOTAL SPECIES RICHNESS

What is the asymptotic species number in an assemblage? Although rarefaction is used to interpolate species richness, extrapolation would be necessary to determine the total number of species present in an assemblage (Bunge and Fitzpatrick 1993). Species accumulation curves (Palmer 1990) can be used to estimate the asymptote of species richness as sample size increases. Colwell and Coddington (1994) summarized the diverse literature on this problem and compared many of the proposed theoretical solutions to a large data set on plant species richness. They found that the most promising nonparametric estimators have been adapted from mark-and-recapture statistics. For a single collection of species, the best estimator of total species richness was (Chao 1984)

$$S_{tot} = S_{obs} + (a^2 / 2b) \qquad (2.6)$$

S_{tot} is the estimate of the total number of species, S_{obs} is the observed number of species, a is the number of species represented by only a single individual ("singletons"), and b is the number of species in the sample represented by exactly two individuals ("doubletons"). The variance for this estimate is

$$\sigma^2_{S_{tot}} = b\left[\left(\frac{a/b}{4}\right)^4 + (a/b)^3 + \left(\frac{a/b}{2}\right)^2\right] \qquad (2.7)$$

For the carabid beetle data in Table 2.1, a is 4 and b is 8. The estimated total species richness for the young plantations is 39 species, with a variance of 40.0. Extrapolation is obviously much riskier than interpolation. Nevertheless, Equations 2.6 and 2.7 performed well in an empirical test. Further tests are needed against other data sets, but these equations seem especially promising for estimating total species richness in applied conservation problems (Colwell and Coddington 1994).

SPECIES EVENNESS

In spite of the extensive literature on evenness indices, there have been few null model studies of evenness. The essential problem is that rare species are missed disproportionately in small collections, so that any measure of evenness will decrease with sample size. The most extreme case is a collection of one individual, which represents minimum evenness for any index. For this reason, evenness cannot be evaluated by visual inspection of species abundance distributions (James and Rathbun 1981). Differences in the appearance of species abundance distributions may reflect differences in abundance or species richness, rather than differences in evenness. Even if total abundance and species richness are identical (which they never are), species abundance distributions may differ by chance.

Ghent (1991) used an explicit null model to examine the behavior of a number of diversity and niche breadth indices. His null model was that individuals are assigned to species equiprobably. He then used a multinomial exact test to assess the probability of finding the observed distribution by chance. An important result of his analysis was that nearly all the common diversity indices (e.g., Shannon's H', Brillouin's H, and Simpson's C') yielded similar rank orderings of probabilities based on the equiprobable model. Consequently, the choice of the particular index to use is much less important than is the comparison with an appropriate null model. Ghent (1991) also argued that use of any of these indices implied an underlying null model of an equiprobable distribution of individuals. He recommended using Simpson's C' as an index, because its rank orderings were identical to those based on the variance of species counts.

Ghent's (1991) approach is promising for studies of niche breadth (see Chapter 4) but seems less suitable for diversity indices. Rather than assigning individuals equiprobably to different species, we prefer a null model that is based on rarefaction—a random sample of individuals is drawn from a given species abundance distribution to estimate sampling effects for the index. For such an analysis, we suggest Hurlbert's (1971) probability of an interspecific encounter (PIE), which measures the chance that two individuals drawn randomly from the collection represent different species:

$$\text{PIE} = \left(\frac{N}{N-1}\right)\left(1 - \sum_{i=1}^{S}\left(\frac{m_i}{N}\right)^2\right) \tag{2.8}$$

This index is closely related to Simpson's (1949) "measure of concentration." Hurlbert's (1971) PIE also has an important analog in population genetics. It is equivalent to the calculation of heterozygosity (H), the probability that two alleles are not identical by descent (Charles J. Goodnight, personal communication).

Returning again to the beetle data in Table 2.1, we used a Monte Carlo simulation to draw, without replacement, samples of individuals from the two assemblages. For each subsample, we calculated PIE, and repeated the procedure 100 times to estimate the variance and the 95% confidence interval at several abundance levels (Figure 2.8). Although the variance decreased with

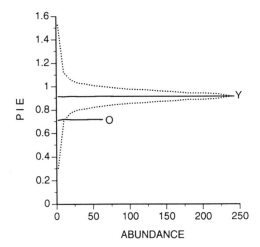

Figure 2.8. An unbiased evenness index. Hurlbert's (1971) PIE (Probability of an Inter-specific Encounter) is graphed as a function of abundance in the sample. Samples were drawn randomly from the young (Y) and old (O) plantation data in Table 2.1. The curves and 95% confidence interval for the young plantation data (dotted line) were constructed from 100 random samples at each level of abundance. Note that the index remains unbiased, even at small sample sizes.

increasing sample size, PIE was correctly estimated even for small samples. Because PIE is an unbiased estimator and has a straightforward statistical interpretation, we prefer it as a simple diversity index.

The same restrictions and assumptions for the rarefaction model also apply to the analysis of species diversity. However, there is an important conceptual difference between the rarefaction curve and the sampling curves for diversity indices. In the rarefaction curve, the response variable is the number of species. In the diversity curves, the response variable is a metric that depends on both species richness and the number of individuals. Consequently, the variance in Figure 2.8 has two components: (1) variation due to the number of species in the sample, and (2) variation due to the evenness of the sample for a given number of species. Thus, the evenness curve still depends on species richness for a given level of abundance. The problem is that there is no way to control species number and abundance simultaneously in a nonarbitrary fashion. Nevertheless, the simulations at least control for the gross effects of abundance differences.

Finally, we note an interesting diversity index that is based directly on rarefaction. Siegel and German (1982) constructed a scaled index that measures the position of the observed rarefaction curve relative to boundaries set by curves of maximum evenness and maximum unevenness for the collection. The drawback to their approach is that no probability value can be assigned to the index. Tagatz et al. (1983) used the index in a study of benthic colonization of creosote-contaminated sediment. Among a set of eight experimental treatments, the index ranged only from 0.42 to 0.52, and there is currently no way to assess the significance of this variation. Nevertheless, the approach of using bounded rarefaction curves is promising and deserves further study with null models.

RECOMMENDATIONS

We recommend the rarefaction curve (and its variance) as a useful measure of species richness. If collections are based on standardized sampling effort, then it will be possible to measure density, species density, and species richness with rarefaction. The rarefaction curve can also be used to estimate sampling efficiency, and the associated hypergeometric model can be used to measure the expected abundance of a particular species. For questions of species evenness, we recommend a Monte Carlo simulation of Hurlbert's (1971) PIE. This diversity index is unbiased at small sample sizes and has a simple interpretation as the probability that two individuals drawn randomly from an assemblage represent different species. Finally, to extrapolate from a sample and estimate total species richness, Colwell and Coddington (1994) should be consulted.

3
RELATIVE ABUNDANCE

In Chapter 2, we examined several sampling models for species diversity indices. These models began with an observed collection of individuals and species, and then sampled randomly to predict the diversity of smaller collections. These models accounted for differences in diversity between communities as sampling properties, so they were neutral with respect to species interactions. But what determines the species abundance distribution in the first place? A null model for species diversity must address the population processes that determine abundance, rather than just the sampling processes that might account for differences between collections.

A NULL MODEL FOR SPECIES DIVERSITY INDICES

Drawing inspiration from models of population genetics (Ewens 1972), Caswell (1976) pioneered an important approach to null models of species diversity. In models of population genetics, random extinction and mutation determine allelic frequencies in populations, and serve as benchmarks for gauging the effects of natural selection. In models of community assembly, random births and deaths within populations might determine relative abundances, and serve as benchmarks for gauging the effects of species interactions.

Caswell (1976) developed three such "neutral models," all of which gave qualitatively similarly results. In Model 1, there was no limit to population size. Species entered the community at a colonization rate v, and thereafter populations grew according to a stochastic model of exponential growth in which average birth and death rates were equal. In Models 2 and 3, total population size was bounded. In Model 2, a randomly chosen individual died at each time step and was replaced by a new individual, either of the same species or a "mutant" (i.e., a new species invading the community). Model 3 was similar. Each generation, a random sample of individuals was removed from the population and replaced with individuals from the previous generation, each of which could mutate to a new species. Although Models 2 and 3 were somewhat constrained by the cap on total population size (Ugland and Gray 1982a), changes in population size of species were independent (Caswell 1983). Model 1 was computationally simpler, and was used in comparison with several empirical data sets.

Caswell (1976) first compared the shape of the species abundance curve produced by Model 1 to the log series, log normal, and broken-stick distributions. The curve for the neutral model followed a log series distribution, although its shape was determined somewhat by v, the rate at which new species entered the community. At large values of v, the neutral model curve tapered off and began to resemble a log normal curve, at least up to the mode of the distribution. Because it generated plausible species abundance curves, Model 1 was a reasonable null model for species diversity indices.

Caswell (1976) modified formulae in Ewens (1972) to generate the expected species diversity (H') and its variance for communities with a given number of individuals and species. A standardized deviate, V, quantified the extent to which observed diversity was above or below the predictions of the neutral model. Because the neutral model was predicated on the number of species in the collection, variation in V reflected changes in relative abundance that were not confounded with changes in species richness. V showed only modest dependence on sample size, probably because abundance and species richness were underlying components of the model. Calculation of expected diversity in the neutral model is cumbersome, but Goldman and Lambshead (1989) presented a modified algorithm that is suitable for personal computers.

Caswell (1976) used the neutral model to compare observed and expected diversity levels for published data sets that included complete counts of individuals (or pairs of breeding birds) in well-sampled communities. His purpose was to test whether species diversity differed systematically between simple and complex communities. If communities were self-regulated by internal dynamics, diversity should have been highest in stable, late successional, and undisturbed systems (Margalef 1968). For each assemblage, V was plotted against successional stage (or an ordinated continuum index) for different communities.

Caswell's (1976) results refuted conventional wisdom about the diversity of complex, species-rich communities. For the successional data, V fluctuated between positive and negative values. There was no tendency for diversity to increase with successional stage, and in many cases diversity was substantially reduced in "climax" communities (Figure 3.1). For temperate bird and tree communities, diversity was usually greater than that predicted by the neutral model ($V > 0$), whereas for tropical communities, diversity was less than

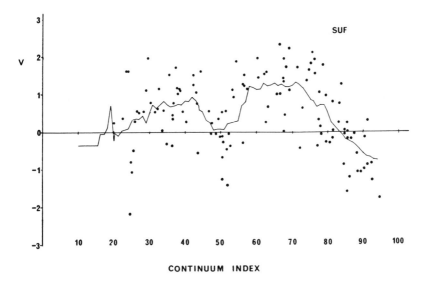

Figure 3.1. Expected and observed species diversity as a function of successional development in upland forests of southern Wisconsin (data from Auclaire and Goff 1971). Each point is a different site, and the line is a 10-point running average. The expected diversity from the neutral model is $V = 0$. Note the downward trend for diversity of late-successional sites. From Caswell (1976), with permission.

expected ($V < 0$). For stream fish assemblages, diversity was lowest in stable, high-order streams.

It is important to note that these patterns were not detected in the original diversity indices—H' values were typically higher for late successional, tropical, and high-order stream assemblages. The large H' values reflected the greater species richness in these assemblages, but Caswell's (1976) analysis revealed that relative abundances were actually less even than expected. If a general inference can be drawn from these results, it is that species interactions tended to reduce diversity; species diversity may be highest in nonequilibrial assemblages that are frequently disturbed (Sousa 1984).

In other studies, Caswell's (1976) neutral model accurately described species diversity. For example, the diversity and species abundance curves for bactivorous ciliates were similar to the neutral model predictions (Taylor 1979), suggesting that populations grew stochastically, exponentially, and independently of one another. For a community of tropical beetles sampled on an elevational gradient, Hanski (1983) found that evenness increased with species richness, and that relative abundances of some genera were more even than predicted by the log series and hence the neutral model. He claimed that interspecific competition was important in this assemblage, and that species were "tightly packed" along an elevational gradient.

A more typical pattern is for diversity to fall short of the neutral model predictions, as exemplified by Platt and Lambshead's (1985) analysis of 98 data sets for marine benthic assemblages. Diversity was usually higher in disturbed than undisturbed assemblages. Within an assemblage, diversity was usually higher after a disturbance than before. Other analyses of marine communities sampled along disturbance gradients also reveal higher diversity in more disturbed environments (Rainer 1981; Warwick and Gee 1984; Lambshead and Gooday 1990; Absalao 1991). These results suggest that it may be difficult to maintain high evenness in the absence of disturbance, and underscore the importance of analyzing abundance data with an appropriate null model.

SPECIES ABUNDANCE MODELS

If individuals in a community are randomly sampled, we usually find that most species are rare and a few species are common. What causes this pattern? That is, what forces determine the shape of the species abundance curve? MacArthur (1957, 1960) suggested the simplest null hypothesis: species abundances are entirely independent of one another and hence are sampled randomly from a uniform distribution (Pielou and Arnason 1966). Most real communities are not this even, but it has been difficult to understand why.

The study of species abundance distributions began as a statistical characterization of large samples of individuals. Fisher et al. (1943) successfully fit a log series distribution to collections of moths sampled at light traps. Preston (1948) found that a log normal distribution characterized large samples of bird and plant communities. The canonical log normal is a special form of this distribution in which the mean and variance are related to one another (Preston 1962); the canonical log normal distribution of species abundances forms the basis for quantitative predictions of the slope of species-area relationships (Preston 1948; MacArthur and Wilson 1967; see Chapter 8).

Neither the study of Fisher et al. (1943) nor that of Preston (1948) initially attached theoretical significance to these distributions; instead, they were simply used to characterize and describe species abundance patterns. Although the log series and the log normal distribution are common models of species abundance data (Figure 3.2), neither provides a perfect fit to data sets. For the log series, Fisher et al. (1943) did not count all individuals of the most common species, so the distribution was characteristic mostly of the rare species in the

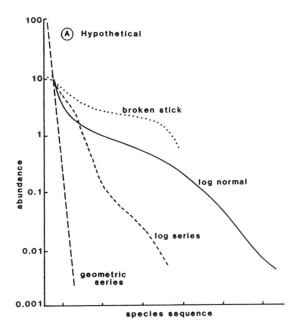

Figure 3.2. Hypothetical rank abundance plots for common species abundance models. From Magurran, A. E. *Ecological Diversity and Its Measurement.* Copyright © 1988 by Princeton University Press. Reprinted by permission of Princeton University Press.

assemblage (Hughes 1986). For the log normal, the fit is often biased in the tail of the distribution (Preston 1981).

In theory, it should not be difficult to distinguish between these distributions. The log series predicts that the rarest species should occur most frequently in a sample, whereas the log normal predicts that species of intermediate abundance should be most common. However, small samples from a log normal that fall to the right of Preston's (1948) "veil line" may be indistinguishable from the log series (Figure 3.3). The log normal is also difficult to distinguish from MacArthur's (1957) broken-stick distribution when sample sizes are small (Wilson 1993).

What factors might account for a log series or log normal distribution? If species are responding independently to different factors and their responses are expressed as differences in exponential growth, a log normal distribution will result (MacArthur 1957; May 1975a). For this same reason, the log normal distribution characterizes many nonbiological systems, such as the distribution of gross national products of different countries (May 1975a; Preston 1981). If

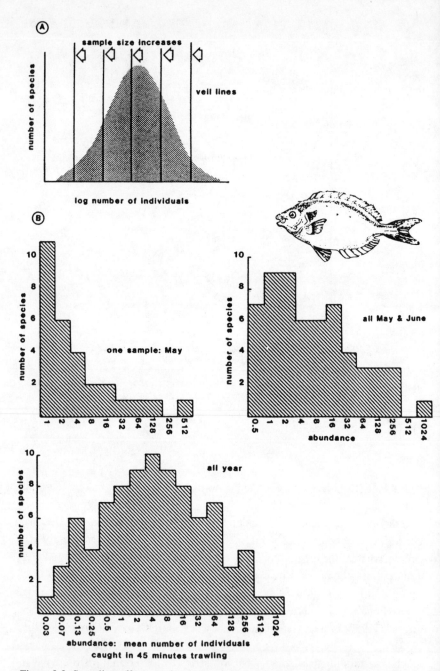

Figure 3.3. Sampling effects on the shape of the species abundance distribution. For the single (May) sample of fish diversity in the Arabian Gulf, the curve resembles a logarithmic series or a geometric series, but as more samples are added, the mode of the log normal distribution is revealed. From Magurran, A. E. *Ecological Diversity and Its Measurement.* Copyright © 1988 by Princeton University Press. Reprinted by permission of Princeton University Press.

species populations are at an equilibrium in small patches, the aggregate of their distribution may also follow a log normal (Ugland and Gray 1982b).

In contrast to these "statistical" explanations, Sugihara (1980) argued that the log normal distribution reflected hierarchical niche partitioning in natural assemblages. However, there are logical difficulties with this argument (Kolasa and Strayer 1988), and a set of species independently selecting hierarchical elements of habitat may lead to the same pattern (Kolasa and Biesiadka 1984). Similarly, Hughes's (1984) "dynamics model" is based on stochastic processes of survivorship, recruitment, and species interaction, and seems to explain the concavity of some species abundance curves better than either the log normal or the log series (Hughes 1986). However, the parameters in the dynamics model have never been confirmed empirically, and the same distributions can be explained by sampling effects (Barangé and Campos 1991).

THE BROKEN STICK

MacArthur (1957, 1960) pioneered a novel approach to species abundance distributions. As a simple null model of species abundance, he imagined a one-dimensional resource distribution that was simultaneously fragmented at randomly located points. The length of each resulting piece was proportional to the abundance of a species. When the species were ranked from most common to least common, they formed the "broken-stick" distribution (Figure 3.4). Biologically, the broken stick corresponds to a community in which all species colonize simultaneously and partition a single resource axis randomly.

The broken stick can also be interpreted as a model of sequential colonization, with each species randomly invading some proportion of the niche of established species. For the resident species, the probability of invasion by a colonizer is proportional to the fraction of niche space the resident has sequestered. Any species can have its abundance reduced by an invader, but common species are more susceptible to invasion than rare species (Tokeshi 1990). Barton and David (1956) described the statistics used to calculate the expected segment lengths, and the broken-stick model has been used as the basis for statistical tests of overlap of species niches (Chapters 4 and 5), geographic ranges (Chapter 9), and body sizes (Chapter 6).

The broken stick incorporates competitive effects but is null with respect to how resources are partitioned. However, the same distribution can result from a model of incomplete niche partitioning or a model in which individuals are assigned randomly and equiprobably to different species (Cohen 1968). This

(a) A stick, here 100 units long, represent a resource gradient .

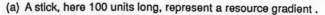

0   100

(b) For a 6-species (*n*) community, 5 (*n* -1) random throws are made at the stick .

0   100

(c) The stick is broken at each point that a throw landed. The 6 segments of stick represent the 6 species, the length of each segment represents the fraction of the resource used by that species, and hence its abundance.

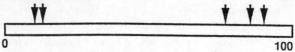

11.0   2.6   63.4   8.6   4.5   10.0

(d) In a ranked-abundance plot, the 6 species are arranged in sequence of decreasing order of abundance, and the abundances plotted on a log scale.

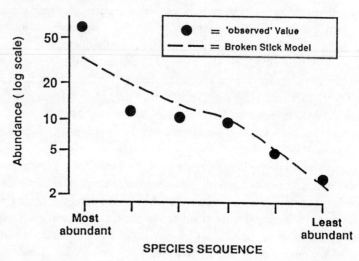

Figure 3.4. Simulation of MacArthur's (1957) broken-stick model. From Wilson (1993), with permission.

problem characterizes not just the broken stick but all the other models that have been fit to species abundance data. For each model in which biological effects can generate the pattern, there is a corresponding statistical or non-interactive interpretation (Table 3.1).

Table 3.1
Biological and statistical interpretations of common species abundance distributions

Distribution	Biological interpretation	Statistical interpretation
Broken stick	A one-dimensional resource axis is simultaneously and randomly broken (MacArthur 1957), or the breaks are sequential and proportional to segment length (Caswell 1976; Tokeshi 1990).	Individuals are randomly assigned to species (Cohen 1968).
Uniform	Species use resources independently of one another (MacArthur 1957).	Individuals of each species are sampled from an equiprobable, underlying distribution (Pielou and Arnason 1966).
Log series	Each species arrives at random time intervals and preempts a constant fraction of the remaining resources (May 1975a). Characterizes samples from small, stressed, or pioneer communities (Whittaker 1972; May 1975a).	Sampling or stochastic effects (Boswell and Patil 1971), small samples from a log normal community (Preston 1948), or a noninteractive community with independent birth and death rates and a high rate of species immigration (Caswell 1976).
Geometric series	Each species arrives at regular time intervals and preempts a constant fraction of the remaining resources (Motomura 1932; May 1975a).	Same as for log series. Also, species abundances are sequentially ordered and each is a random fraction of the previous species (Tokeshi 1990).
Log normal	Hierarchical niche subdivision, in which the probability of breakage is independent of segment length (Sugihara 1980), or an assemblage of species that specialize on different elements of habitat, which is subdivided hierarchically (Kolasa and Biesiadka 1984; Kolasa and Strayer 1988). Characterizes large, stable assemblages at equilibrium (Whittaker 1972; May 1975a).	Species populations grow exponentially and respond independently to different factors (MacArthur 1960; May 1975a), or an aggregate of species populations that are at equilibrium in small patches (Ugland and Gray 1982b).
Dynamics	A dynamic model that incorporates parameters for survivorship, recruitment potential, and gregariousness (Hughes 1984).	Sampling effects and aggregation of heterogeneous samples (Barangé and Campos 1991).

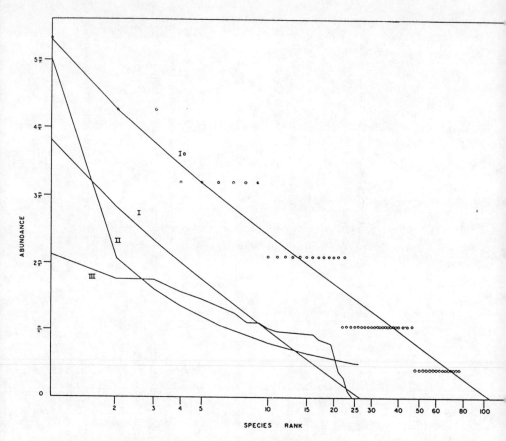

Figure 3.5. MacArthur's (1957) analysis of bird census data (106 species; open circles) from Pennsylvania. Curve Ia = broken stick expectation for an assemblage of 106 species. Curve I = broken stick (25 species). Curve II = expectation for a random uniform distribution (overlapping niches). Curve III = Monte Carlo simulation of random assignment of individuals to species (particulate niches). From MacArthur (1957).

MacArthur (1957) originally applied the broken-stick model to a census of temperate forest birds (Figure 3.5). The broken stick provided a better fit to the data than either a uniform distribution or a Monte Carlo simulation in which individuals were randomly apportioned to species (but see Cohen 1968). Subsequently, contradictory evidence for and against the broken stick accumulated (King 1964), and by 1966, MacArthur expressed a wish for the model to "die a natural death."

A major stumbling block to adequately testing the broken stick is that the model specifies that all possible partitionings of relative abundance are equally likely (Pielou 1975). Consequently, it is not appropriate to test the species abundance curve of a single assemblage against the predictions of the broken-stick model (Smart 1976; Pielou 1981). However, it is possible to measure the relative fit of a single data set to several species abundance models (Wilson 1991b), as MacArthur (1957) did. If the log series or log normal is among the alternative models, it may not be possible to recognize the broken stick unless there are many species in the sample (Wilson 1993).

THE RELATIONSHIP BETWEEN RESOURCE USE AND RELATIVE ABUNDANCE

The broken stick is only one of several models of one-dimensional resource partitioning (Sugihara 1980; Tokeshi 1990). All such models make the critical assumption that resource consumption is proportional to relative abundance. However, because large-bodied animals are usually rare (Damuth 1981, 1987) and have high per capita resource requirements (Elgar and Harvey 1987), resource use may not be proportional to abundance. In particular, a log normal distribution of abundances need not reflect a log normal distribution of resource use (Harvey and Godfray 1987).

Sugihara (1989) showed for a few data sets that variances in biomass and abundance were approximately interchangeable. However, a more detailed allometric analysis revealed that variances in biomass were usually greater than variances in abundance, so that resource use may be even more inequitable than suggested by relative abundances (Pagel et al. 1991a). Size distributions in assemblages or guilds of related species are often complex and polymodal (Warwick 1984; Griffiths 1986), which may contribute to high variance. Null model analyses also confirm that results are often sensitive to whether biomass or abundance data are used (Rainer 1981; Tokeshi 1990). Consequently, explanations for species abundance data that are based on resource partitioning must be evaluated carefully, and supported by data that establish the relationships between relative abundance and resource use.

NULL MODELS FOR RESOURCE PARTITIONING

Given all these difficulties, what is the best strategy for analyzing resource-partitioning models such as the broken stick? We suggest three guidelines for analysis. First, analyses should be restricted to small guilds of common, potentially interacting species. Although the log normal and log series distributions may characterize large samples that include many rare species, it seems unlikely to us that rare species are often important in resource partitioning. Restricting the analysis to guilds may also ensure that the species are not grossly different in body mass and per capita resource consumption. Second, analyses should be based on replicated samples of an assemblage. These can be averaged so that variability in relative abundances can be estimated and sampling effects minimized. For the broken stick, in particular, it is important to compare the model with the average species abundance curve of several assemblages. Third, Wilson's (1991b) procedures for measuring relative fit of the data to several alternative models should be used.

An exemplary study by Tokeshi (1990) followed all three of these guidelines. Tokeshi (1990) examined the relative abundance patterns for six common, closely related species of epiphytic chironomids that comprised 95% of the individuals and the biomass in a typical sample. The study site was a small English river that was sampled repeatedly through the year. Tokeshi (1990) compared average abundance and biomass distributions with the predictions of seven resource-partitioning models:

1. *Geometric series*. This was the only strictly deterministic model in Tokeshi's (1990) analysis. The model assumes that species arrived at regular time intervals and sequestered a constant fraction *k* of the remaining resources. To fit the geometric series, Tokeshi (1990) chose values of *k* that minimized the squared deviations between observed and expected relative abundances.

2. *Dominance preemption*. This is a more general form of the geometric series. Each species entered the assemblage and took some random fraction of the remaining resources. Because species sequestered only unused resources, each invader was competitively inferior to all previous invaders. The fraction of resources used was a random proportion drawn from the interval 0.5 to 1.0, so the expected distribution converged on a geometric series with *k* = 0.75.

3. *Random fraction*. This model envisions a completely random partitioning of niche space. The line segment was randomly broken

and one of the two segments was chosen (with equal probability) for a second break. One of the three resulting segments was again chosen randomly and equiprobably for breakage, and so on. This model yields an approximate log normal distribution for large sample sizes (Pielou 1975), and corresponds to Sugihara's (1980) description of a community with hierarchical niche partitioning. Note that the dominance preemption represents a special case of this model in which the largest segment was always chosen for subdivision.

4. *Broken stick*. Each species that entered the assemblage took a random fraction of the resources of the previous invaders. The probability that the niche of a resident species was invaded was proportional to its resource utilization.

5. *Dominance decay*. Another special case of the random fraction model, the dominance decay model is the exact opposite of the dominance preemption model. In the dominance decay model, the largest existing segment was always chosen for random breakage. Ecologically, this means the most abundant species in the assemblage always had its niche invaded. In the broken-stick model, the most abundant species was more likely to be chosen, but this was not a fixed rule. As a consequence, the distribution of relative abundances under the dominance decay model is more equitable than under the broken-stick model.

6. *Random assortment*. Tokeshi (1990) envisioned random assortment as a null model for niche partitioning, because the abundances of the component species were unrelated to one another. This scenario might occur if resources were nonlimiting, or if resources were limiting but the assemblage was subject to frequent random disturbances so that it never reached an equilibrium. Tokeshi (1990) reasoned that if the species were ranked from most to least abundant, then the abundance of each species would be some arbitrary fraction of the abundance of the species that preceded it. Hence, the random assortment model is a stochastic analog of the geometric series with $k = 0.5$.

7. *Composite*. In this model, the first two species competitively divided the resources (dominance preemption), whereas the abundances of the remaining species were determined by random assortment.

These seven models generated a family of species abundance curves that differed in their equitabilities (Figure 3.6). The dominance decay and broken-

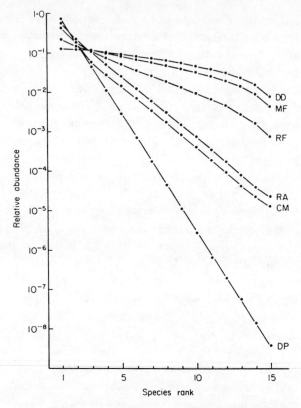

Figure 3.6. Expected rank abundance patterns for different models of resource parti-tioning. DD = Dominance Decay; MF = MacArthur Fraction (= Broken Stick); RF = Random Fraction; RA = Random Assortment; CM = Composite Model; DP = Domi-nance Preemption. Each point is the average from 1000 simulated distributions. From Tokeshi (1990), with permission.

stick models gave the most even distribution of expected abundances, whereas the dominance preemption model generated the steepest curve. With the excep-tion of the geometric series, Tokeshi's (1990) models all included stochastic elements, so the expected abundances and confidence intervals were estimated with one thousand simulations.

Relative abundances of chironomids were more equitable than predicted by the dominance preemption model (2), but less equitable than predicted by the broken-stick model (4). Only the random fraction (3) and random assortment (6) models fit the data well, with the observed relative abundances falling within the 95% confidence interval for all six species (Figure 3.7). In contrast, the biomass data matched the predictions of only the random assortment model (6).

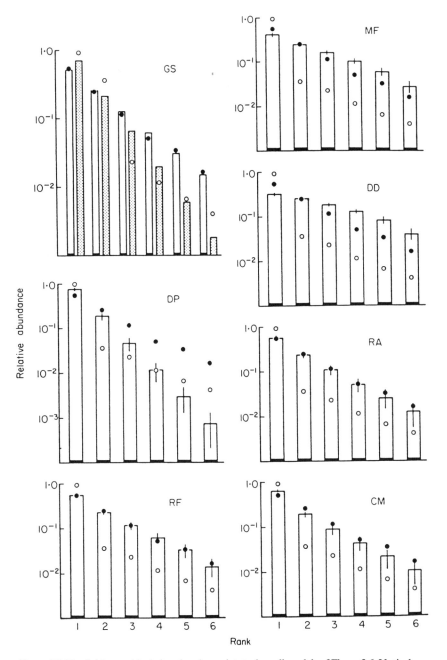

Figure 3.7. Fit of chironomid relative abundance data to the null models of Figure 3.6. Vertical bars = expected values; circles = observed values, averaged over several samples. ● = homogeneous summer data; ○ = heterogeneous summer/winter data, which was poorly fit by all models. Abbreviations as in Figure 3.6. For the Geometric Series (GS), a separate distribution was fit for each data set. Note that only the Random Fraction (RF) and Random Assortment (RA) models provide an adequate fit to the summer data. From Tokeshi (1990), with permission.

Tokeshi (1990) discussed the difficulties and ambiguities of interpreting species abundance data. He tentatively concluded that niche apportionment models did not account for relative abundance patterns in this chironomid community, because the data were best fit by the random assortment model. This interpretation is consistent with the fact that the chironomid community was dynamic, with considerable turnover in composition and substantial overlap in temporal activity and resource use (Tokeshi 1986; see Table 4.4).

However, the interpretation of Tokeshi's (1990) random assortment model is somewhat problematic. Because the random assortment model is a special case of the geometric series, data that fit the random assortment model could be described by a geometric series that reflects resource partitioning. More important, one could argue that a truly null distribution for competitive interactions would be that the abundance of each species was determined by a random draw from a uniform distribution, as MacArthur (1957) first suggested. This null distribution would not fit the chironomid data, which were less equitable than even the broken stick. Thus, some resource partitioning may have been important in determining relative abundances of chironomids, although the patterns did not conform to any of the models Tokeshi (1990) tested for this purpose. Tokeshi's (1990) results emphasize the importance of repeated sampling of small guilds of species, and of testing data against several alternative models.

Finally, we note that the most interesting questions about species abundance data may not be what determines the shape of the distribution, but what factors allow certain species to be abundant and cause others to be rare. In dynamic communities such as Tokeshi's (1990) chironomids, turnover is frequent, so the question of species identity is less important. But in most assemblages certain species are consistently abundant and others are consistently rare (Lawton and Gaston 1989; Ebeling et al. 1990; see Chapter 10). The study of factors contributing to commonness and rarity (e.g., Rabinowitz et al. 1984) may ultimately be more enlightening than further analyses of the form of the species abundance distribution.

RECOMMENDATIONS

We recommend Goldman and Lambshead's (1989) implementation of Caswell's (1976) neutral model as a benchmark for assessing species diversity. Tokeshi's (1990) models are worthwhile tests of resource partitioning, and these can be compared using the procedures of Wilson (1991b). Analyses of species abundance patterns will be most informative when they are based on replicated samples of a small number of ecologically "similar" species. We suggest that further research on species abundance should focus on the relationship between abundance and resource consumption and the biological factors that allow some species to be persistently common and cause others to be persistently rare.

4
NICHE OVERLAP

NICHE OVERLAP AND LIMITING SIMILARITY

Historically, analyses of niche overlap were based on the theory of limiting similarity (MacArthur and Levins 1967). This model predicts the coexistence of species and the overlap in their utilization of resources along a single, ordered resource dimension. The overlap of species 2 on species 1 in resource use is calculated as

$$\alpha = \frac{\int U_1(R)U_2(R)dR}{\int [U_1(R)]^2 dR} \tag{4.1}$$

where $U_1(R)$ and $U_2(R)$ are the utilization functions for species 1 and 2, respectively. Overlaps calculated this way have been equated with the competition coefficients of the Lotka-Volterra equations (Levins 1968). In other words, the amount of overlap in resource utilization is assumed to be proportional to the intensity of competition between two species (Schoener 1974b).

Community change in the limiting similarity model comes about through repeated colonization and extinction of species with different utilization curves. If adjacent species are "too close" together, one of the pair will go extinct, depending on the overlap and the carrying capacity of the environment, as dictated by the Lotka-Volterra equations (Schoener 1986a). On the other hand, if two species are widely separated on the resource axis, a third species can be sandwiched between them. After repeated colonizations and extinctions, an equilibrium will be established, with a maximum number of coexisting species separated by a critical minimum spacing (Figure 4.1).

The prediction of a limit to similarity is sensitive to a number of assumptions, including: (1) the normality of the resource utilization curves (Roughgarden 1974); (2) the measurement of overlap by Equation 4.1 (Abrams 1975); (3) the linearity of the zero isoclines assumed by the Lotka-Volterra model

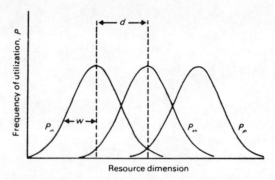

Figure 4.1. Resource utilization and limiting similarity in the MacArthur and Levins (1967) model. The model predicts a limit (d/w) to the similarity of competing species. This theory motivated a vast amount of ecological research into patterns of niche overlap, but relatively few studies have compared overlap patterns to an appropriate null model. From Schoener (1986a), with permission.

(Schoener 1976a); (4) the presence or absence of environmental stochasticity (May and MacArthur 1972; Turelli 1978a,b).

NICHE OVERLAP AND EVOLUTIONARY DISPLACEMENT

Limiting similarity models predict a reduction in niche overlap of competitors through ecological assortment of colonization and extinction. A second set of models also predicts a reduction in niche overlap through genetic change in competing populations that causes evolutionary shifts in niche position and/or niche width (Bulmer 1974). These models were inspired by the pattern of character displacement in allopatric versus sympatric populations (Brown and Wilson 1956) and by Hutchinson's (1959) suggestion that competing species might differ in body size by a constant ratio (see Chapter 6). These models are sensitive to the amount of within- and between-phenotype variance (Taper and Case 1992), whether or not resources are completely utilized (Milligan 1985), and the symmetry of resource use between species (Slatkin 1980). Depending on the underlying assumptions, some of these models predict a substantial displacement of competitors (Gotelli and Bossert 1991; Taper and Case 1992); others predict little displacement, or even convergence of utilization phenotypes (Slatkin 1980; Abrams 1986).

TESTING NICHE OVERLAP PATTERNS

The central prediction of both ecological and evolutionary models of displacement is that species should overlap less in resource use than they would in the absence of competition (Schoener 1974a). How has this body of ecological theory been treated in empirical analyses? First, empiricists have largely abandoned the idea of discovering a "magic number" for limiting similarity or body size differences (see Chapter 6). Instead, the qualitative prediction that competition should lead to reduced overlap has been investigated. Early analyses focused on the description and quantification of resource use (Schoener 1986a). If one had faith in the underlying theory of limiting similarity and character displacement, then utilization differences between species would reflect resource partitioning.

But this approach now seems naive. Even in the absence of competition, different species will utilize resources in different ways (Sale 1974). The mere demonstration of utilization differences is no longer accepted as sufficient evidence for competition (Connell 1980). Null models have been used to ask what niche overlap patterns would be expected in the absence of competition (Silvertown 1983). If competition influences resource utilization at the community level, niche overlap in nature should be significantly less than in an idealized competition-free community (Schoener 1974a).

Few studies of niche overlap are based on the direct measurement of resource utilization curves along an ordered niche axis, as diagrammed in Figure 4.1. Studies of dietary and habitat niches usually rely on discrete, unordered resource states, and studies of character displacement rely on measurements of body size or morphology, which are assumed to reflect resource utilization. Schluter and Grant's (1984) study of Galápagos finches is a notable exception, and their finding that utilization and availability curves are asymmetrical and polymodal contradicts one of the important underlying assumptions of niche theory (see Chapter 6).

Although null models can be used to establish whether observed niche overlap is more or less than expected by chance, it is still difficult to infer the mechanisms responsible for such patterns. For example, most null models do not distinguish between ecological niche shifts and evolutionary character displacement (Case and Sidell 1983). Interpreting patterns of high niche overlap can be equally problematic. High niche overlap may reflect intense competition for shared resources or, alternatively, a surplus of resources and the absence of competition (Glasser and Price 1988). Both scenarios have been revealed in experimental field studies of competition (Schoener 1983).

Interestingly, null model studies of niche overlap have not addressed these alternatives, and interpretations have been remarkably consistent: those authors who detected unusually low overlap have concluded that competition has been an important force, either currently or in the past (e.g., Pianka et al. 1979), whereas those who found unusually large niche overlap have concluded that competition is not currently important (e.g., Tokeshi 1986; Griffiths 1987). For any particular pair of species, the finding that niche overlap is statistically lower than expected is difficult to evaluate. Phylogenetic and historical effects may result in different utilization patterns for this pair that have nothing to do with competitive interactions. However, it is more difficult to explain strong low-overlap patterns for an assemblage of several coexisting species.

The Utilization Matrix

Construction of a utilization matrix is the starting point for a null model analysis of niche overlap. An investigator first defines a set of resource states, and then measures the utilization of these resources by each species in the assemblage. For example, if the states are microhabitats, then the number of individual occurrences of each species in the different microhabitats is recorded. Likewise, if dietary categories are of interest, the number or volume of prey items in each category is measured.

Utilization data often summarize extensive collecting efforts and natural history observations on undisturbed communities. Pianka's (1986) long-term studies are noteworthy in this regard. Twelve person-years of field work in Australia, North America, and South Africa yielded collections representing over 90 species and 15,000 individuals of desert lizards, with detailed observations on their microhabitat utilization and stomach contents. Table 4.1 illus-

Table 4.1

Frequency of microhabitat utilization by five species of North American lizards

| Species | Microhabitat | | | | |
	Open	Grass	Bush	Tree	Other
Cnemidophorus tigris	0.475	0.025	0.424	0.025	0.051
Uta stansburiana	0.279	0.046	0.473	0.046	0.156
Phrynosoma platyrhinos	0.950	0.000	0.050	0.000	0.000
Crotaphytus wislizeni	0.613	0.007	0.321	0.007	0.052

Adapted and simplified from Appendix C of Pianka (1986).

trates a utilization matrix with a small subset of Pianka's (1986) data. Species and resource states are represented by rows and columns, respectively. The entries in the matrix p_{ij} represent the fraction of total utilization by species i of resource state j. The matrix summarizes resource utilization along a single resource axis, which may be either ordered or unordered.

Overlap Indices

How can overlap between species be quantified with a utilization matrix? Many different indices have been proposed to measure the overlap between individual species pairs, and to quantify the overall "niche breadth" or degree of specialization of each species. Because these indices were first derived from the theory of limiting similarity, they emphasize pairwise comparisons of overlap along ordered resource axes, although the calculations work equally well with unordered resource states. For a pair of species, the overlap in resource use of species 2 on species 1 can be measured in terms of the frequency of utilization (p) of n different resource states. Some commonly used indices include

$$O_{21} = \frac{\sum_{i=1}^{n} p_{2i} p_{1i}}{\sum_{i=1}^{n} (p_{1i})^2} \qquad (4.2)$$

where p_{xi} is the frequency of utilization of resource state i by species x. This familiar index by MacArthur and Levins (1967) is the discrete version of Equation 4.1. Early studies equated this overlap with the Lotka-Volterra competition coefficient (Levins 1968), although this equivalence cannot be readily justified (Lawlor 1980a). Equation 4.2 is asymmetrical, in that the overlap of species 2 on species 1 does not equal the overlap of species 1 on species 2. Pianka (1973) proposed a modified symmetrical index:

$$O_{21} = O_{12} = \frac{\sum_{i=1}^{n} p_{2i} p_{1i}}{\sqrt{\sum_{i=1}^{n} p_{2i} \sum_{i=1}^{n} p_{1i}}} \qquad (4.3)$$

In this index, the denominator has been normalized, but the stability properties are the same as those of Equation 4.2 (May 1975b). The Czekanowski

Index (Feinsinger et al. 1981) has also been used as a simple measure of the area of intersection of two utilization histograms:

$$O_{12} = O_{21} = 1 - 0.5 \sum_{i=1}^{n} |p_{i1} - p_{i2}|$$ (4.4)

Finally, Colwell and Futuyma (1971) proposed an information theory index that quantifies the "uncertainty" in a utilization matrix. Similar equations have been used to quantify the niche breadth of a species, that is, the extent to which a species is specialized or generalized in its utilization of resources (Feinsinger et al. 1981).

As in the study of species diversity, there is a large, unsatisfying literature, mostly from the 1970s, that explores different algebraic measures of niche overlap (e.g., Colwell and Futuyma 1971; Pielou 1972b; Hurlbert 1978; Petraitis 1979). Niche overlap indices are invariably correlated with one another, sample-size dependent (Hanski 1978), and only tenuously linked to theories of competition (Lawlor 1980a). In the absence of an appropriate null model, it is impossible to evaluate or compare these indices, either among species or among communities. For example, under some circumstances, average overlap, as measured by Equation 4.4, can actually increase following species deletion from a community (Thomson and Rusterholz 1982). Even with an appropriate null model, different indices can generate different results. In a study of niche shifts in Greater Antillean *Anolis* communities, observed overlaps were usually less than expected, but the null hypothesis was rejected more often using Equation 4.2 than Equation 4.3 (Haefner 1988a).

Weighted versus Unweighted Indices

The most important assumption implicit in the use of overlap indices is that all resource states are equally available to all species. If resource states are not equally abundant, observed overlaps in utilization may not accurately reflect similarity in resource use. In particular, if some resource states are extremely common and others are extremely rare, species may appear very similar in their resource utilization (Lawlor 1980a).

How can resource indices be modified to account for resource availability? Colwell and Futuyma (1971) suggested expansion of the resource utilization matrix in proportion to the total utilization of each category. The resource categories in the expanded matrix are assumed to be equiprobable and thus to provide a better measure of species electivities. The Colwell and Futuyma (1971) technique has been applied to associations of drosophilid flies on different plant types (Sabath and Jones 1973) and anuran larvae in tropical ponds (Heyer 1974). However, the Colwell and Futuyma (1971) expansion is somewhat arbitrary and sample-size dependent (Hanski 1978) and still requires comparison with an appropriate null model (e.g., Sale 1974; Inger and Colwell 1977).

Schoener (1974b) and Lawlor (1980a) both suggested modifications of existing indices to account for the "electivity," the relative ability (or preference) of a consumer to catch and consume a particular prey type. In the simplest case, consumers will use resources in the proportions in which they are available in the environment (Holling Type I functional response). Thus

$$p_{ij} = a_{ij} R_j \qquad (4.5)$$

where Rj is the relative density of resource j and a_{ij} is the electivity of species i for resource j. Thus, the utilization (p_{ij}) of resource state j can be high either because the electivity for that resource is large, or because the resource is very common. Lawlor (1980a) argued that electivities are more relevant to theories of limiting similarity than direct utilizations, in part because electivities are a better measure of a consumer's phenotype. Incorporating resource availability may have a major effect on measures of overlap. Table 4.2 illustrates sample calculations for some of Pianka's (1986) data on microhabitat utilization by North American lizards. Calculated overlaps vary, depending on the availability of different resource states.

In theory, independent resource measurements could be incorporated with measures of utilization to estimate electivities, but in practice these data are rarely available. In addition, it may be impossible to realistically compare the densities of different resource categories. Consequently, the relative consump-

Table 4.2
Pairwise niche overlap of North American lizards

	Cnemidophorus tigris	*Uta stansburiana*	*Phrynosoma platyrhinos*	*Crotaphytus wislizeni*
Cnemidophorus tigris	—	0.934	0.776	0.969
Uta stansburiana	0.806	—	0.528	0.831
Phrynosoma platyrhinos	0.967	0.636	—	0.906
Crotaphytus wislizeni	0.991	0.751	0.986	—

Each entry is the overlap in utilization, calculated with Equation 4.3. Above the diagonal: overlap calculated assuming resource states are equally available. Below the diagonal: overlap calculated assuming that 95% of the available microhabitats are bushes. Based on the utilization data in Table 4.1.

tion of different prey items may serve as the most relevant "bioassay" of availability (Colwell and Futuyma 1971; but see Hanski 1978). If species are using resources randomly, then the summed resource use across species will reflect the relative availability of different resource states. Lawlor (1980a) advocated this approach for estimating electivities, and the Colwell and Futuyma (1971) matrix expansion produced a similar weighting.

If resource states are not equally abundant, observed utilizations will tend to overestimate the amount of ecological overlap. Electivities based on marginal resource totals remove some of this bias, and may be a more reliable measure of ecological overlap. For example, only two of 10 mean utilization overlaps for Pianka's (1967) North American lizard communities differed from null model expectations, whereas all 10 mean electivities differed significantly (Lawlor 1980b). For Greater Antillean *Anolis* communities, significant results were somewhat more common when comparing electivities versus utilization overlaps (Haefner 1988a). Some critics object to the use of marginal constraints in null model simulations (Case 1983a), on the grounds that these marginals may themselves be influenced by competition (Colwell and Winkler 1984). Analyses of niche overlap can be greatly affected by the methods used to estimate electivities (Lawlor 1980a; Haefner 1988a), but marginal constraints do not automatically bias the test towards accepting the null hypothesis.

We see two potential problems with electivity calculations. The first is that the electivities that are estimated from summed resource use will be influenced not only by the relative availability of different resource states, but also by overall productivity (Haefner 1988a). Second, Equation 4.5 may adequately describe the utilization of different microhabitats, but more complex functions may be necessary to characterize prey utilization, which can be affected by search images, handling times, and satiation levels.

Moreover, electivities may give large, counterintuitive weight to trace components in pooled diets (Winemiller and Pianka 1990). This will be especially true when electivities are estimated without reference to an appropriate sampling model (Ricklefs and Lau 1980). On the other hand, observed utilizations are biased towards the finding of large overlap when certain resource states are very common. To overcome these problems, Winemiller and Pianka (1990) proposed a hybrid index, the geometric mean of utilization and electivity:

$$g_{ij} = \sqrt{a_{ij}\, p_{ij}} \tag{4.6}$$

They suggested that g_{ij} should reduce the positive correlation of p_{ij} with resource availability and the negative correlation of a_{ij} with resource availability without entirely eliminating available resources from the analysis. However, electivity and utilization measure two different things, and it may not be wise to combine them in an aggregate index. One advantage of using observed utilizations (p_{ij}) to test niche overlap is that the tests will be conservative with respect to competition hypotheses. Because unequal resource availability will lead to large overlap, we can be sure that the reduction in overlap is strong when the null hypothesis is rejected. At least in comparison to idealized communities of known structure, results were quite similar for p_{ij}, a_{ij}, and g_{ij} (Winemiller and Pianka 1990).

Multidimensional Niche Metrics

Once an appropriate utilization measure and resource weighting have been selected, there is still the problem that the niche of a species is rarely represented along a single resource axis. Most authors have appreciated the multidimensional nature of the niche and have measured utilization along several resource axes. Most of these are subdivisions of the major niche axes of time, space, and food (Schoener 1974a). Multivariate approaches can be useful for reducing the number of correlated variables to a handful of independent resource axes (Green 1971). But even if individual utilization curves are properly evaluated, comparisons in multidimensional niche space are problematic. Specifically, the overlap among species in multidimensional space could be higher or lower than overlap along individual niche dimensions (Figure 4.2).

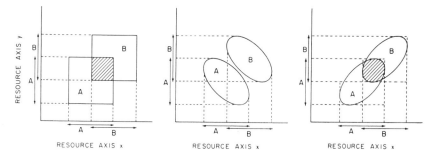

Figure 4.2. Multidimensional niche overlap is not always reflected in overlap along individual dimensions. In the left-hand plot, niche overlap of species A and B along two resource axes is independent, and the product accurately reflects total overlap. In the middle and right-hand plots, resource use is not independent, and the total overlap cannot be readily predicted from utilization of individual resources. From E. R. Pianka, R. B. Huey, and L. R. Lawlor. Niche segregation in desert lizards. In *Analysis of Ecological Systems*. D. J. Horn, R. D. Mitchell, and G. R. Stairs (eds). Copyright © 1979 by the Ohio State University Press. Reprinted by permission. All rights reserved.

There are two extreme cases. First, suppose that uniform resource utilization for a species is entirely independent along two orthogonal resource axes (x and y). Utilization of this rectangular niche space can be estimated as the simple product of overlap (xy). At the other extreme, utilization along two niche axes may be entirely correlated, so that knowing the utilization along one axis allows you to predict the other. In this case, the arithmetic average of the two axes $((x + y)/2)$ is the best estimate of multidimensional utilization. This "summation overlap" represents a maximum upper bound for overlap in a multidimensional niche space (May 1975b). Between these extremes, there is no way to predict from the unidimensional overlaps whether true overlap is large or small. The geometric mean overlap ($\sqrt{xy}$) may serve as a useful approximation of multidimensional overlap (Case 1983a), because it will always lie above the arithmetic mean and below the product mean.

Aggregate Statistics for Pairwise Overlaps

Even in proper multidimensional form, the overlaps calculated for each species pair do not convey a full picture of niche overlap at the community level. Several different statistics have been proposed for summarizing overlap for an entire assemblage. One obvious measure is the mean or median of all $\binom{n}{2}$ pairwise overlaps. The median may be preferable, because it will reflect the nonnormal distribution of pairwise overlaps. However, the expected median overlap quickly converges on the mean as species number increases (Case 1983a).

Mean or median overlap is a useful summary statistic for niche analyses, but, as a single number, it hides a good deal of pattern at the community level (Pianka 1980). Inger and Colwell (1977) recommended a more subtle measure. For each of the n species, order the remaining $n - 1$ neighbors on the basis of their overlap. If a single utilization measure is used, the ordering is based on the pairwise overlaps. If multiple niche axes are retained, the $n - 1$ neighbors can be ranked according to Euclidian distances. These orderings are then averaged to give the mean overlap of the first, second, . . . $n - 1$ neighbors in niche space. By definition, overlap is highest with the closest neighbor, then drops off as more dissimilar neighbors are compared (Figure 4.3). The plot of average overlap versus ranked neighbor distance can then be compared to the predictions of null models. Comparisons with all neighbors in niche space are of interest, because the hypothesis of diffuse competition predicts that utilization will be affected by many competing species (MacArthur 1972; Pianka 1974).

Figure 4.3. Nearest-neighbor plots in niche space for three assemblages of amphibians and reptiles in Thailand. Each point represents the average niche overlap of each species with its *n*th nearest neighbor. These curves can be compared with the predictions of null models and are more sensitive indicators of community structure than a simple median or mean of pairwise niche overlap. From Inger and Colwell (1977), with permission.

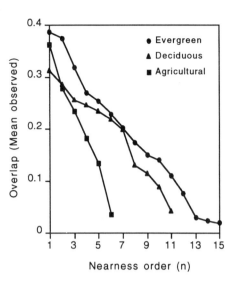

Still another approach is to compute the mean overlap for each species pair and compare it to the expected overlap for that pair in a null community. Particular pairs of species may exhibit nonrandom patterns of overlap that may not be apparent from the mean or median overlap of all possible pairs. However, assessing the statistical significance of many nonindependent pairs may be problematic (see Chapter 7). Haefner (1988a) compared all three measures with the same data set. He detected significant overlap more frequently with nearest neighbor and individual pairwise overlaps than with the mean overlap for an entire assemblage.

A NULL MODEL FOR THE HUTCHINSONIAN NICHE

How would niche overlap patterns appear in the complete absence of competition? If we could answer this question, we would have a reference for comparison with observed patterns of overlap. Innis and Haefner (1980) addressed the question with a detailed simulation of the Hutchinsonian niche that excluded competitive processes. The Innis and Haefner (1980) model began with random placement of rectangular niches of species in a two-dimensional niche space (Figure 4.4). Populations of each species were uniformly distributed throughout the niche space and were changed by two processes: (1) a random, uniform deviate was added at each time step, which could either increase or decrease population size; (2) populations were reduced in size through "perfect preda-

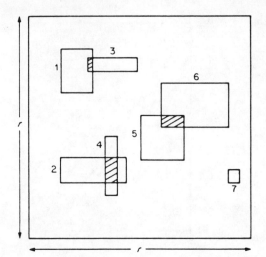

Figure 4.4. A null model of niche overlap. Seven hypothetical species are randomly placed in niche space, and niche overlap is calculated from the area of overlap. Niches change in size from stochastic growth and reduction from randomly occurring predators. From Innis and Haefner (1980), with permission.

tors." A predator niche was superimposed on the populations, and all individuals within that niche were removed. Niches of populations that declined to zero were removed from the simulation.

At each time step, the model generated the average niche size, average overlap between niches, species diversity, number of niches, average population size, and average number of neighbors. The model predicted that in the absence of competition, niche overlap would range from 25 to 100% for a community of specialists or generalists, respectively. The lower bound compared favorably with some estimates of minimal overlap from mammal (Brown 1975) and lizard (Pianka 1974) communities. The model also provided a baseline for comparisons with Pianka's (1972) niche overlap hypothesis: if competition were important, the number of species in a community would be negatively correlated with average niche overlap. However, if the niche breadth of colonizing species was variable, rather than constant, the Innis and Haefner (1980) model also predicted a negative correlation, even in the absence of competition.

The Innis and Haefner (1980) model is an important first step toward understanding niche dynamics in the absence of competition. However, it is a complex model, and much of the output is cast in terms of dimensionless parameters that are difficult to interpret. Most empirical null model studies have opted for a simpler approach through the randomization of utilization or species occurrence matrices. We outline these methods in the following sections.

SAMPLING ERROR IN NICHE INDICES

Two basic approaches have been used in null models of niche overlap: (1) randomization of utilization functions for dietary or activity data, and (2) randomization of species occurrences. Both approaches assume that utilization frequencies have been estimated accurately, which is probably true if many individuals or dietary items have been sampled. But at small sample sizes, estimates of utilization frequency may be biased and give inaccurate estimates of niche overlap. In the extreme case, if only one individual of a species is sampled, it will appear to be a "specialist" on whatever microhabitat it happens to be found in. These same problems arise in the study of diversity indices (Chapter 2) and relative abundance patterns (Chapter 3).

Ricklefs and Lau (1980) used Monte Carlo simulations to explore bias in several common niche overlap indices. Estimates of overlap were systematically biased downward when sample size was small and when expected overlap was high. Even with samples as large as 25 or 50, bias in some indices was substantial (Figure 4.5). To date, most null model analyses of niche overlap have not incorporated this sampling variability. Randomizing the raw utilization data (counts of individuals or dietary items) rather than the utilization frequencies would control for this source of bias.

Figure 4.5. Bias in niche overlap indices as a function of the true overlap value and the number of individuals sampled. The "coefficient of community" (S_{ij}) is equivalent to O_{12} in Equation 4.4. From Ricklefs and Lau (1980), with permission.

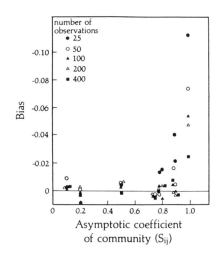

RANDOMIZATION OF SPECIES OCCURRENCES

Imagine a source pool of species, each with its own utilization function, that colonizes a small island. If competition limits niche overlap, then the particular combination of species that coexist on the island should have lower overlap than a randomly assembled set of species from the same source pool. A simulation of this scenario treats the utilization functions for each species (or population) as constants and randomizes the combination of species that co-occur. This analysis will be sensitive to the composition of the source pool fauna and whether species are sampled equiprobably.

Case (1983a) used this approach in a study of niche overlap of 18 species of lizards on 37 islands in the Sea of Cortez. Utilization along four niche axes (time of day, microhabitat, food size, and food type) was summarized as the product, summation, and geometric mean of overlap between each species pair. Using realistic criteria, Case (1983a) delineated a source pool of 18 mainland species that could potentially colonize each island. Observed island communities were a subset of these 18 species, and island species richness ranged from 1 to 13. For each island with i species, Case (1983a) enumerated all the unique combinations $\binom{18}{i}$ of exactly i species as null communities. For 30 of the 37 islands, the observed overlap was less than the median overlap for null communities of the same size (Figure 4.6). This result suggests that species combina-

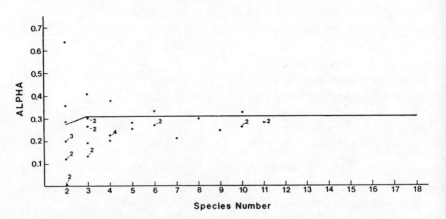

Figure 4.6. Niche overlap of insular lizard communities in the Sea of Cortez. The solid line is the median overlap for all possible combinations of a given number of species, assuming species colonize islands equiprobably. Most observed island assemblages fell below this expectation, suggesting that niche overlap was less than would be expected with random colonization. From Case (1983a), with permission.

tions that coexisted on islands had lower niche overlap than would be expected in the absence of competition.

An alternative to the competition hypothesis is that low overlap reflected nonrandom patterns of resource availability on islands. If the same nonoverlapping sets of resources were present on several islands, the same combinations of low-overlap species would tend to be found. For most island size classes, an improbably small number of species combinations was represented (Case 1983a), suggesting that the same low-overlap configurations tended to recur. This result argues against the competition hypothesis and in favor of the idea of nonrandom resource distributions.

Both of the preceding tests assumed that species colonized islands equiprobably. Case (1983a) relaxed this assumption with a simulation in which the probability of placement of each species in a random community was proportional to the number of island occurrences (Connor and Simberloff 1979). Compared to this model, only 23 of the 37 islands fell below the median, which is marginally nonsignificant ($0.05 < p < 0.10$), but still indicative of low niche overlap. Thus, differential dispersal ability of species may have contributed to the pattern of reduced niche overlap of insular lizards in the Gulf of Cortez. However, it is difficult to know whether the low overlap is a cause or a consequence of differential success of species on islands.

Schoener (1988a) also examined niche overlap of island lizard species sampled from a larger source pool. He analyzed utilization of seven microhabitat categories on satellite islands of the Greater Antilles, and found that coexisting species usually differed in the structural habitats they occupied. On two-species islands, each species occupied a different structural category. Coexistence in the same habitat was only found once on three-species islands, and never on four-species islands.

How likely were these patterns to have arisen by chance? Schoener (1988a) compared these habitat occupancy patterns to a null model based on four different source pool definitions: (1) all species from the appropriate "mainland" (one of the four Greater Antilles source islands); (2) the subset of mainland species whose structural-habitat categories were found on small islands; (3) only species present on two-, three-, or four-species islands (i.e., the archipelago method of using only species present on the islands); and (4) those species found on islands with equal or lesser species richness.

For each source pool, Schoener (1988a) assumed that all microhabitats were equally available and used a binomial expansion to calculate the tail probability of observing a given number of co-occurring species. About 15% of the tests were significant at the 0.05 level, and significant results were consistently obtained only for source pool (2), which Schoener (1988a) considered to be the most realistic of the four. Among the island sets, four-species islands and satellite islands of Cuba frequently showed nonrandom patterns.

These studies by Schoener (1988a) and Case (1983a) suggest that comparing overlap values of observed communities with those of null communities drawn from a larger source pool is an effective method for evaluating niche overlap. However, the results will be sensitive to sample size, methods used for designating source pools, and assumptions about the colonization potential of species.

RANDOMIZATION OF UTILIZATION MATRICES

Although comparisons of niche overlap in real communities with overlap in null communities derived from an appropriate source are worthwhile, no such "external reference" is available in many cases. Instead, the observed utilization matrix must be used to estimate overlap values in the absence of competition. The randomization algorithms (RAs) described below assume that interspecific variation in resource utilization provides information about expected niche overlap in the absence of competition. Lawlor (1980b) developed four algorithms that are listed in increasing order according to the amount of original utilization data retained in the null community:

1. RA1. For each species, utilization of each dietary category is replaced by a random uniform number [0,1]. After randomization, entries in the matrix are scaled so that the row sums for each species sum to 1.0.
2. RA2. Resource utilization is again replaced by a random uniform number [0,1], but only for those resource states in which utilization is greater than zero. Those resource states that were not used in nature by a species are left in the zero state. As in RA1, row sums are rescaled after randomization.
3. RA3. Resource utilization for each species is not replaced by a random number. Instead, the observed utilizations are randomly reassigned to different resource categories ("scrambled zeros"; Winemiller and Pianka 1990). Because the rows of the utilization matrix are simply reshuffled (Inger and Colwell 1977), RA3 effectively retains observed niche breadths for each species (Sale 1974).
4. RA4. Only the nonzero resource states in each row are reshuffled ("conserved zeros"; Winemiller and Pianka 1990). As in RA2,

the placement of the zeros is retained. Of the four algorithms, RA4 produces synthetic communities in which utilizations are most similar to the original communities.

The four randomization algorithms differ in whether utilizations are re-shuffled or replaced by a random number, and in whether the zeros in the matrix are retained or not (Table 4.3). Both decisions have implications for the structure of the null community, and affect the power of the test.

By replacing the observed utilizations with a uniform random variate (RA1), we assume that utilization of any resource state is possible and equiprobable. At the other extreme, reshuffling of nonzero utilizations (RA4) assumes that only permutations of nonzero utilizations are permissible. All these algorithms are reasonable methods for constructing random communities, although we still do not have a clear expectation of how utilization spectra should look in commu-nities that are unstructured by competition (Bradley and Bradley 1985).

This problem is highlighted in the treatment of the "zero" states. Assuming that sampling effort has been sufficient to ensure that the zeros are not due to inadequate censusing of individuals or dietary items, there are two principal interpretations of a zero in a utilization matrix. The first is that the observed utilization values are determined primarily by competition. In this case, compe-tition is so severe that some species are completely denied the use of certain resources by the presence of competitors. RA1 is consistent with this interpre-tation, because it allows a species in the null community to use a resource that it does not exploit in nature.

The other interpretation of zeros in the utilization matrix is that species are not able to use all resource states in a community because of constraints related to behavior, morphology, physiology, or phylogeny. These restrictions have

Table 4.3
Four null model randomization algorithms (RA)

	Zero states randomized	Zero states retained
Observed utilizations drawn from a uniform distribution	RA1	RA2
Observed utilizations reshuffled	RA3	RA4

The algorithms differ in whether unused resource states (zeros) are retained or randomized and in whether observed utilizations are reshuffled or replaced with a value drawn randomly from a uniform distribution. Adapted from Pianka (1986).

nothing to do with present or past competition, and should not be obscured in a null model test. Following this logic, RA2 and RA4 ensure that species which do not use certain resource states in nature never do so in a null community either. RA3 is a compromise. It retains the same *number* of zero states in the simulation, but does not constrain those zeros to their original placement.

PERFORMANCE OF RANDOMIZATION ALGORITHMS

What patterns result from these different simulations? RA1 destroys all structure in the matrix and usually results in null communities that exhibit a high mean and small variance in overlap. Figure 4.7 compares pairwise overlaps in microhabitat use of ground beetles collected in pitfall traps with simulated overlaps based on RA1 (Kobayashi 1991). Observed overlaps were much more variable than those predicted by RA1, and followed a nearly uniform distribution, compared to a peaked distribution of overlap values for the null commu-

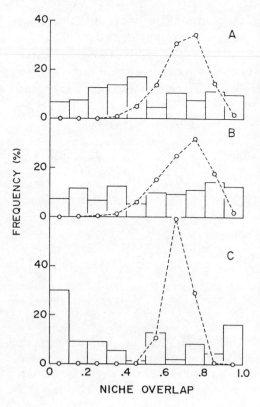

Figure 4.7. Observed and expected niche overlap of ground beetles collected from pitfall traps in Towada-Hachimantai National Park, Japan. Each histogram shows the distribution of species pairs with niche overlap calculated according to methods in Colwell and Futuyma (1971). The dashed line is the expected value generated by RA1. RA1 creates null assemblages with a high mean and low variance in niche overlap. From S. Kobayashi. 1991. Interspecific relations in forest floor coleopteran assemblages: niche overlap and guild structure. *Researches on Population Ecology* 33:345–360, Figure 2, page 352.

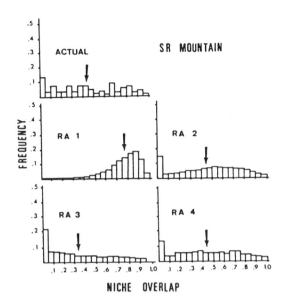

Figure 4.8. Observed niche overlap for a Texas grasshopper assemblage. Comparisons are shown with simulated data using RA1–RA4. Arrows indicate mean overlap. Note the low overlap of the observed data compared to RA1, and the similarity of the distributions for the more restrictive algorithms (RA2–RA4). From Joern and Lawlor (1981), with permission.

nities. High-overlap and low-overlap species pairs were more frequent than predicted by RA1, although there were more pairs below the expectation than above it. RA2 generated similar results, although simulated overlaps were more similar to observed overlaps because the zero structure of the utilization matrix was retained (Figure 4.8).

Winemiller and Pianka (1990) explored the performance of RA3 and RA4 in a series of detailed benchmark simulations that compared 100 randomized communities to idealized communities of known structure. Idealized communities consisted of 10 species with either "high," "medium," or "low" average overlap in their use of 10 resource states. Within each of these categories, four variants of assembly structure were established for a total of 12 trials: (1)–(3) "equal-sized guilds"—assemblages with two internal guilds of five species each (overlap in resource use occurred only among guild members); (4)–(6) "unequal-sized guilds" —assemblages with two internal guilds of three and seven species each; (7)–(9) "no guilds"—overlaps in resource use among all 10 species of the assemblage; (10)–(12) "core resources"—the 10 species shared four core resources with high (trial 10) or medium (trial 11) overlap, and did not overlap in use of the

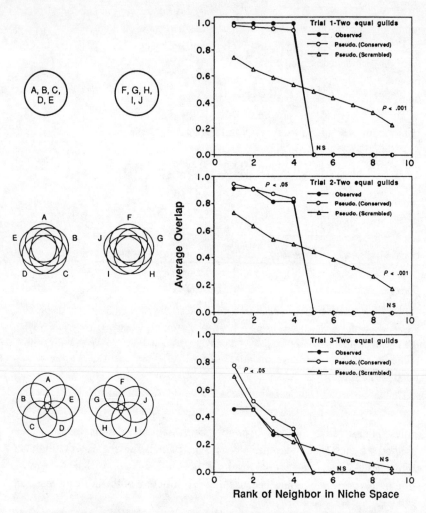

Figure 4.9. Benchmark performance of RA3 and RA4 compared to idealized communities. The three graphs correspond to patterns of high, medium, and low niche overlap of species organized into two internal guilds of five species each (A–E, F–J). For each assemblage, the observed average overlap is plotted as a function of the *n*th nearest neighbor. This curve drops off sharply beyond four nearest neighbors, which is the boundary for the internal guilds. Note that RA4 [Pseudo (Conserved)] closely mimics the observed overlap patterns, whereas RA3 [Pseudo (Scrambled)] produces a distinctive nearest-neighbor curve that reveals internal guild structure in the high- and medium-overlap trials. From Winemiller and Pianka (1990), with permission.

remaining six resources. Species in trial 12 had medium overlap for a core group of 40 shared resources and 60 nonoverlapping resources. All simulations were compared to observed communities using Inger and Colwell's (1977) nearest-neighbor distance. Statistical significance was assessed by the percentage of randomized mean overlaps that exceeded mean observed overlap.

These benchmark tests revealed that RA3 was superior to RA4 in detecting nonrandom overlap. For example, in trials (1)–(3) (two equal-sized guilds), the null hypothesis was never rejected for RA4 but was significant for RA3 under conditions of low and medium overlap. RA3 always generated a decreasing curve of average nearest-neighbor distances that did not change much as a function of resource overlap (Figure 4.9). In trials (1)–(6), RA3 accurately revealed the internal guild structure of the assemblages: overlap in RA3 correctly fell below the observed curve for the first four (or seven) nearest neighbors, which were in the same guild, and above the observed curve for the more distant neighbors, which were in different guilds. When no guild structure was present, simulated overlaps did not differ significantly from observed values. Thus, differences between observed overlaps and null communities can depend on internal guild structure as well as average overlap. For these reasons, nearest-neighbor plots may be superior to mean or average overlap values (Haefner 1988a). Finally, for shared resource scenarios, significant guild structure for RA3 was detected only when observed overlap was high. RA3, the original matrix shuffling used by Sale (1974) and by Inger and Colwell (1977), may be the best existing algorithm to use in resource overlap null models.

VARIANCE IN NICHE OVERLAP

Simulations can be used to study the variance as well as the mean of resource overlap. With RA3, variance in randomized communities generally decreased as neighbor distance increased (Winemiller and Pianka 1990). In contrast, observed variances in amphibian (Inger and Colwell 1977), lizard (Pianka 1986), and fish (Winemiller and Pianka 1990) communities exhibited a sharp peak at an intermediate neighbor distance (Figure 4.10). Both Inger and Colwell (1977) and Pianka (1986) interpreted this peak as evidence for the existence of internal guild structure. At low nearest-neighbor distances, variance in overlap is small, because all the species belong to the same guild. As nearest-neighbor distance increases, variance in overlap increases as some neighbors are sampled from other guilds. Finally, variance decreases at large neighbor distances because distant neighbors belong to different guilds. Null model comparisons with hypothetical communities that exhibit internal guild struc-

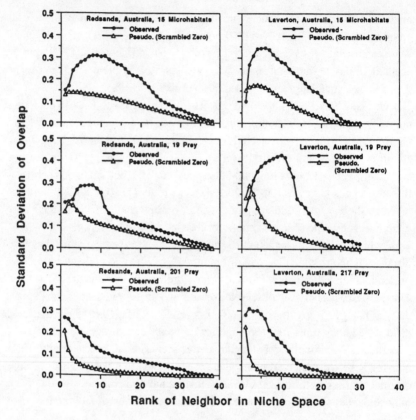

Figure 4.10. Comparisons of standard deviations of dietary and microhabitat niche overlap of Australian lizards with the predictions of RA3. Most assemblages exhibited a peak in variance at intermediate neighbor distance that was not present in the randomized communities. From Winemiller and Pianka (1990), with permission.

ture confirm this interpretation of the variance peak (Eric R. Pianka, personal communication). Whether cogent alternative explanations for the variance peak can be constructed remains to be seen.

Bradley and Bradley (1985) argued that nonrandom overlap patterns as revealed by RA1–RA4 need not imply competitive interactions. They pointed out that RA1–RA4 not only eliminate relationships among consumers, but also obscure the tendency for consumers to specialize on related types of resources. In RA1–RA4, the transition from one resource state to another is equiprobable ("random environment" model), whereas in nature, species will tend to forage on similar resources ("structured environment" model). Bradley and Bradley

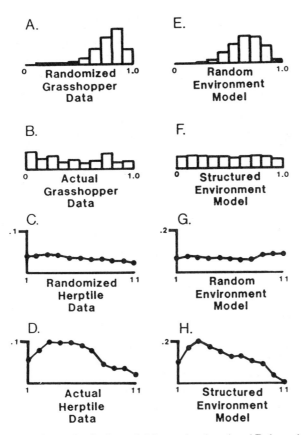

Figure 4.11. Alternative randomizations of niche overlap data. **A** and **B** show observed and randomized (RA1) niche overlap data of Joern and Lawlor (1981; see Figure 4.8). **C** and **D** show the standard deviation of niche overlap for the nth nearest neighbor from Inger and Colwell (1977; see Figure 4.3). **E–H** show two alternative null models that use Markov transitions to specify consumers that move randomly between different resource states ("random environment model") or that preferentially choose "similar" resources ("structured environment model"). Note the similarity of the observed data to the structured environment model. From Bradley and Bradley (1985), with permission.

(1985) used a Markovian model to simulate a consumer's transition between resource states under these two scenarios. The random environment model matched the predictions of Lawlor's (1980b) RA3 for pairwise overlaps and variances of overlap. In contrast, the structured environment model provided a good match with the observed data, including the variance peak at intermediate neighbor distances (Figure 4.11).

One could argue that Bradley and Bradley's (1985) model is too restrictive to test patterns of evolutionary divergence, because species would have more opportunity to specialize on different resources in the face of persistent competition. In any case, their results suggest that competitive interactions and internal guild structure are not the only possible explanations for nonrandom patterns of niche overlap.

RANDOMIZATION OF RESOURCE UTILIZATION PEAKS

Rather than analyze niche overlap per se, some authors have examined the spacing of utilization peaks on a single resource dimension. If species are competing for this resource, utilization peaks should be evenly spaced. The rationale and statistical analyses are identical to studies of flowering phenology of competing plants (Chapter 5) and body sizes of competing consumers (Chapter 6).

The null model in this case is MacArthur's (1957, 1960) broken stick—a number line is broken into random segments, and the length of each segment represents the spacing of resource peaks between two adjacent species (see Chapter 3). De Vita (1979) used the broken-stick model to compare measures of resource utilization peaks within assemblages of tropical hummingbirds (Snow and Snow 1972), herbivorous stem-boring insects (Rathcke 1976), and tropical intertidal snails (Kohn 1959). For each assemblage, De Vita (1979) compared segment lengths of individual species pairs with those predicted by the broken-stick model. The observed points all fell within two standard deviations of the predicted values, and De Vita (1979) concluded that the null hypothesis could not be rejected.

Three criticisms apply to De Vita's (1979) analysis. First, the distances between resource peaks are not independent points, so they should not be compared simultaneously to the null predictions (Pielou 1981). Second, De Vita (1979) did not provide an explicit test for evaluating the fit of the null model. The fact that all the points fell within two standard deviations was not a valid test (Shelly and Christensen 1982). Finally, distances measured for the "terminal" species are arbitrary and not equivalent to distances between adjacent species (De Vita 1979; Cole 1981).

Bush and Holmes (1983) offered a biological system and a new analysis that addressed all three criticisms. The spacing of helminth parasites along the small intestine of Lesser Scaup ducks (*Aythya affinis*) is well suited for tests of niche displacement. The vertebrate intestine is a complex linear gradient for parasites with biologically defined end points, the position of individuals

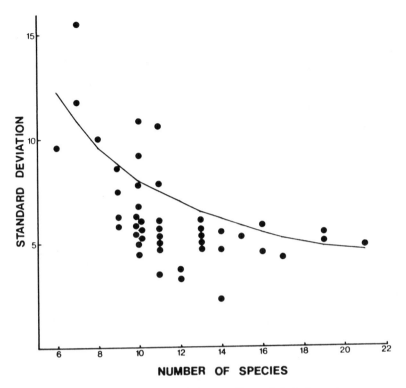

Figure 4.12. Variation of niche distances between adjacent helminth species co-occurring in the small intestine of lesser scaup (*Aythya affinis*). The solid line is the predicted value from the broken-stick model. Each point represents an independent assemblage. The results suggest that the spacing of the median individual of each parasite species is more regular than expected. From Bush, A. O., and J. C. Holmes. 1983. Niche separation and the broken stick model: use with multiple assemblages. *American Naturalist* 122:849–859. Copyright © 1983 by The University of Chicago. Reprinted by permission of the publisher.

within the gradient can be determined accurately, and many replicate communities can be sampled.

Bush and Holmes (1983) measured "location" as the placement of the median individual of a species. They summarized community dispersion patterns as a single number, the variance of segment lengths. This is the same approach used by Poole and Rathcke (1979) in their analyses of phenological overlap (Chapter 5). Whereas Poole and Rathcke (1979) derived the expected variance analytically, Bush and Holmes (1983) estimated it with a simulation of the broken stick. The observed variance was less than expected for most assemblages (Figure 4.12), suggesting that the spatial occurrence of species

Table 4.4

Summary of null model studies of resource utilization

Citation	Taxon	Samples	Overlap measurement	Resources	Multidimensional niche	Randomization	Overlap
Schoener (1988)	West Indian *Anolis* lizards (37)	24 island communities, compared to source pools from 4 Greater Antillean islands	Number of co-occurring species in each microhabitat	Structural microhabitat (8)	No	Binomial exact tests, assuming equi-probable species placement and equivalent resource availability	$O < E$, but only for appropriate source pools with habitat specialists eliminated.
Griffiths (1987)	Smooth and palmate newts (*Triturus*) (2)	Funnel-trap samples from a single pond in mid-Wales	Eq. 4.4	Pond location microhabitat (7) Time of year (22)	Product, average, individual	RA3	Microhabitat: $O > E$ Time: $O > E$
Case 1983	Sea of Cortez lizards (18)	37 island communities	Eq. 4.3	Food type (24) Food size (18) Microhabitat (16) Time of day–temperature (24)	Geometric mean	Utilization fixed; Species sampled equiprobably (or weighted by occurrence) from archipelago source pool	$O < E$
Pianka et al (1979)	Kalahari lacertid lizards (7)	Long-term censuses, diet analysis 10 sites	Eq. 4.3	Microhabitat (15) Time of day (24) Prey volume (19)	Multiplicative Summation means	RA2	Microhabitat: $O = E$ Food: $O < E$ Time: $O = E$
	Australian *Ctenotus* (7)	Long-term censuses, diet analysis 10 sites	Eq. 4.3	Microhabitat (15) Time of day (24) Prey volume (19)	Multiplicative Summation means	RA2	Microhabitat: $O = E$ Food: $O = E$ Time: $O = E$
	Australian geckos (9)	Long-term censuses, diet analysis 10 sites	Eq. 4.3	Microhabitat (15) Time of day (24) Prey volume (19)	Multiplicative Summation means	RA2	Microhabitat: $O < E$ Food: $O < E$ Time: $O > E$
	Australian *Varanus* (5)	Long-term censuses, diet analysis 10 sites	Eq. 4.3	Microhabitat (15) Time of day (24) Prey volume (19)	Multiplicative Summation means	RA2	Microhabitat: $O < E$ Food: $O = E$ Time: $O = E$

Source	Data	Index	Resources	Overlap measure	Null model	Results
Kalahari skinks (4)	Long-term censuses, diet analysis 10 sites	Eq. 4.3	Microhabitat (15) Time of day (24) Prey volume (19)	Multiplicative Summation means	RA2	Microhabitat: $O < E$ Food: $O = E$ Time: $O = E$
Kalahari geckos (6)	Long-term censuses, diet analysis 10 sites	Eq. 4.3	Microhabitat (15) Time of day (24) Prey volume (19)	Multiplicative Summation means	RA2	Microhabitat: $O < E$ Food: $O = E$ Time: $O > E$
Australian Amphibolurus (7)	Long-term censuses, diet analysis 10 sites	Eq. 4.3	Microhabitat (15) Time of day (24) Prey volume (19)	Multiplicative Summation means	RA2	Microhabitat: $O = E$ Food: $O < E$ Time: $O > E$
North American saurofauna (9)	Long-term censuses, diet analysis 10 sites	Eq. 4.3	Microhabitat (15) Time of day (24) Prey volume (19)	Multiplicative Summation means	RA2	Microhabitat: $O < E$ Food: $O < E$ Time: $O = E$
Kalahari saurofauna (17)	Long-term censuses, diet analysis 10 sites	Eq. 4.3	Microhabitat (15) Time of day (24) Prey volume (19)	Multiplicative Summation means	RA2	Microhabitat: $O < E$ Food: $O < E$ Time: $O > E$
Australian saurofauna (40)	Long-term censuses, diet analysis 10 sites	Eq. 4.3	Microhabitat (15) Time of day (24) Prey volume (19)	Multiplicative Summation means	RA2	Microhabitat: $O < E$ Food: $O < E$ Time: $O = E$
Tokeshi (1986) Chironomids of River Tud, eastern England (9)	Replicated vegetation samples. Gut contents of chironomids	Time: geometric mean proportion of the overlapping area under two resource utilization curves [0,1] Diet: Eq. 4.4	Time of year (365) Diet (3)	No	Time: (a) resource peaks placed randomly; (b) resource peaks limited to nonwinter months Diet: RA1	Time: $O > E$ Diet: $O >$ or $= E$ (in different months)
Sale (1974) MacArthur's (1958) warblers of New England (4)	Foraging time in different microhabitats	Eq. 4.4	Foraging zone (16)	No	RA3	$O < E$

(Table continues on next page)

Table 4.4

Summary of null model studies of resource utilization (*Continued*)

Citation	Taxon	Samples	Overlap measurement	Resources	Multidimensional niche	Randomization	Overlap
Sale (1974)	Ueckert and Hansen's (1972) grasshoppers of Colorado (14)	Stomach contents	Eq. 4.4	Dietary category (20)	No	RA3	$O > E$
Kobayashi (1991)	Forest-floor coleopterans of Toweda-Hachimantai National Park, Japan (18)	Pitfall traps	Colwell-Futuyma index	Habitat (6) Bait types (5)	Individual	RA1	Habitat: $O < E$ Bait type: $O < E$ Habitat × Bait type: $O < E$
Field (1992)	Spider-hunting pompilid wasps at a Breckland heath (24)	Water/pitfall traps	Eq. 4.3	Microhabitat (7) Time of year (9)	No	RA1, weighted by estimated areas of microhabitats and abundance of species	Microhabitat: $O < E$ Time of year: $O < E$
Haefner (1988a)	Greater Antillean *Anolis* lizard communities of Schoener and Schoener (1971a,b) (9)	First-sighting observations	Eq. 4.2, Eq. 4.3	Perch diameter Perch height	Product Summation Individual	Random selection of individuals and placement in sites; overlaps weighted by Lawlor's (1980b) electivities to account for unequal resource availability	Mixed. Eq. 4.2 gives less significant overlap than Eq. 4.3. Use of mean, median, or geometric mean gives weak or no support for niche shifts. Rank orders give better support.
Inger and Colwell (1977)	Herpetofauna of broadleaf evergreen forest, deciduous dipterocarp forest, and agricultural land in Thailand (105)	Quadrat, transect censuses	Colwell-Futuyma index, with weighting for resource availability	Microhabitat (26)	Principal components of niche axes	RA3	O (var) $< E$ for closest neighbors

Taxon	Data	Overlap index	Resources	Niche axis reduction	Null model	Result
Joern and Lawlor (1981) — Grasshoppers of 3 arid grassland communities in western Texas (35)	First sightings and gut content analyses	Eq. 4.3	Plant resource (56) Microhabitat (27)	No	RA1	Inger-Colwell comparison of neighbors. $O < E$ O (var) $> E$
MacNally and Doolan (1986) — Cicadas of eastern Australia (9)	First sightings	Average group centroid distances in multivariate niche space	Habitat (16) Morphology (10) Behavior (15)	Yes, factor analysis reducing to 3 niche axes	All possible n-species combinations were compared for a particular guild	$O = E$
Winemiller and Pianka (1990) — Freshwater fish assemblages of Cano Maraca, Venezuela (wet season) (59)	Gut content analyses	Eq. 4.3 with standardized electivity coefficients	Prey (94)	No	RA3 RA4	RA3: $O > E$ RA4: $O < E$
Freshwater fish assemblages of Cano Volcan, Venezuela (wet season) (19)	Gut content analyses	Eq. 4.3 with standardized electivity coefficients	Prey (68)	No	RA3 RA4	RA3: $O > E$ RA4: $O < E$
Freshwater fish assemblages of Cano Agua Fria, Venezuela (wet season) (50)	Gut content analyses	Eq. 4.3 with standardized electivity coefficients	Prey (82)	No	RA3 RA4	RA3: $O > E$ RA4: $O < E$
Freshwater fish assemblages of Quebrada, Venezuela (wet season) (23)	Gut content analyses	Eq. 4.3 with standardized electivity coefficients	Prey (67)	No	RA3 RA4	RA3: $O > E$ RA4: $O < E$

Taxon: number in parentheses is number of species compared. Resources: number in parentheses is number of resource states. Overlap: O = observed overlap, E = expected overlap based on the null model. Inequalities indicate statistically significant patterns ($p < 0.05$). O (var) = observed variances of overlap; otherwise, patterns refer to median or mean of pairwise niche overlaps.

was significantly regular. Note that a regular spacing does not preclude high overlap, because the analysis considers only the distribution of utilization peaks (Cole 1981).

SUMMARY OF FINDINGS

Table 4.4 describes some of the studies that have used null models to examine resource overlap. It is difficult to summarize the findings, because the methods vary widely from one study to the next. However, nearly all of these studies detected some nonrandomness in niche overlap, although not always in a negative direction. Most studies included more than one resource axis, summarized as a mean or aggregate overlap. Few studies explored the use of electivities versus utilizations, even though this may greatly affect the results. Finally, most studies randomized utilizations directly, even though these indices are sample-size dependent. In 1977, Inger and Colwell noted "there is no such thing as a standard protocol for community analysis." The same thing can be said with respect to overlap studies today. However, we now have a number of null models that can be used to assess the mean, variance, and nearest-neighbor distance of niche overlap in the absence of species interactions.

RECOMMENDATIONS

Several decisions need to be made in a null model analysis of niche overlap. Electivity measures are theoretically desirable, but utilization measures are usually more practical for analysis. Niche overlap analyses should ideally be based on 50 or more observations of use of food items or other resources by each species. If not, the indices may be biased, and the simulation procedures of Ricklefs and Lau (1980) should be followed. The choice of an overlap index is somewhat arbitrary; we suggest Pianka's (1973) index as symmetric measure of overlap between two species. To summarize overlap for an entire assemblage, we recommend using the median overlap and Inger and Colwell's (1977) nearest-neighbor plots of the mean and variance of overlap. If the source pool for an assemblage can be estimated independently, we recommend the procedures of Case (1983a) and Schoener (1988a) for determining whether overlap is unusually low for the particular combination of coexisting species. If there is no independent source pool, the observed utilization data will have to be randomized. Lawlor's (1980b) RA3 and RA2 seem to be the most desirable for this purpose.

5
THE TEMPORAL NICHE

Time represents an important resource axis that may be partitioned by an assemblage of competing species. Diel differences in activity times of vertebrate predators and seasonal differences in flowering times of animal-pollinated plants constitute the primary evidence for temporal partitioning. For example, owls and hawks that forage at different times of day may reduce competition for limited food resources (e.g., Craighead and Craighead 1956), and co-occurring plant species that flower at different times of the year may reduce competition for animal pollinators (e.g., Heinrich 1976; Stiles 1977).

Because it is both ordered and circular, the temporal niche axis has a unique geometric representation, with the two orthogonal components of season and time of day forming a three-dimensional ring (Figure 5.1). The temporal niche of a species represents a subset of the surface area of this ring. At the community level, we may ask if there are nonrandom patterns of overlap in the set of surfaces that represent a local assemblage. Because the temporal niche is both ordered and circular, it may need to be analyzed in null models differently than dietary or microhabitat data.

Temporal partitioning is also likely to reflect different selective forces in assemblages of animals and plants. For animals that can pick up and move, migration is always a potential response to local resource competition. In contrast, plants and sessile animals must cope with persistent competition from close neighbors. On the other hand, many vertebrates must forage more or less continuously, whereas most plants and invertebrates can afford to wait out periods of resource scarcity.

Under traditional models of exploitation competition (MacArthur and Levins 1967), time is not a truly independent (orthogonal) niche axis (Carothers and Jaksić 1984). However, differences in activity time may allow species to directly partition food resources in two ways. First, seasonal differences in activity may allow predators to coexist by exposing them to different prey

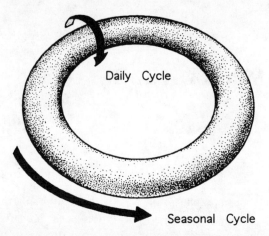

Daily Cycle

Seasonal Cycle

Figure 5.1. A three-dimensional representation of the temporal niche, showing both seasonal and diel axes. Temporal activity patterns can be represented as a subset of the surface of this ring. Null models predict overlap patterns on this surface in the absence of competitive interactions.

assemblages. Second, diel differences in activity may allow predators to partition a rapidly renewing resource. But in many animal communities, the second mechanism is unlikely, because a predator that consumes prey at night would still be competing with predators that hunt during the day. For vertebrate predators such as raptors or lizards, it seems especially unlikely that prey populations can renew fast enough to permit diel food partitioning (Schoener 1974c; Huey and Pianka 1983). A more reasonable scenario is that diel differences in activity evolved to minimize interference competition among foragers (Carothers and Jaksić 1984). For example, some ant assemblages are characterized by strong interference competition and dramatic diel shifts in the dominant foraging species (e.g., Klotz 1984; Hölldobler 1986). Diel foraging differences may also reduce overlap if prey activity schedules are nonoverlapping.

Nevertheless, temporal partitioning may be relatively uncommon in animal communities. Schoener (1974a) reviewed the early literature and concluded that animals often segregate food and habitat dimensions but rarely segregate along temporal niche axes. However, he did suggest that predators separated more often by diel activity time of day than did other trophic groups. Given this background, we now review null model studies of temporal partitioning in animal and plant communities.

TEMPORAL PARTITIONING IN ANIMAL COMMUNITIES

One way to analyze temporal partitioning is to treat activity time as any other niche axis. As described in Chapter 4, Lawlor's (1980b) randomization algorithms RA1 through RA4 could be used to reshuffle observed activity data, which could then be compared with conventional metrics for niche overlap. For example, Pianka et al. (1979) used RA2 to analyze extensive data on the seasonal and daily activity of desert lizards. In this algorithm, the percentage of time that an animal was active during a particular season (or time of day) was replaced by a random uniform number. The only restriction on this randomization is that "zeros" were retained. In other words, simulated activity could not occur at times of the year or day when an animal was inactive in nature. Temporal overlaps in lizard assemblages did not differ from the predictions of this null model, or they showed significant aggregation (high overlap). In contrast, overlap in measures of habitat and food was often less than that predicted by the null model (see Table 4.4).

Field (1992) used RA1 as a null model and found a significant reduction in seasonal overlap of spider-hunting pompilid wasps of Britain. However, RA1 does not retain the placement of zeros in the data and consistently produces a random community with a high mean and a low variance in overlap (Pianka et al. 1979; Winemiller and Pianka 1990). Consequently, Field's (1992) result does not necessarily suggest temporal resource partitioning.

Although RA1–RA4 are valid null models for looking at unordered dietary or microhabitat categories, we think they are usually inappropriate for the analysis of temporal overlap. On both daily and seasonal time scales, temporal activity patterns show strong modalities, with peak activity in certain months or hours of the day. Activity curves are often not simple bell-shaped distributions and may exhibit considerable skewness or multiple modes (e.g., Riechert and Tracy 1975). For ectotherms, in particular, these modes may reflect a temperature-humidity envelope that physiologically constrains animal activity (Tracy and Christian 1986). The RA1–RA4 algorithms destroy the shape of activity curves, so that patterns revealed by them do not necessarily reflect temporal resource partitioning.

A better approach is to retain the shape of the activity curve and randomize the placement of its peak. Tokeshi (1986) followed this procedure in an analysis of nine species of chironomid larvae co-occurring in a river in eastern England. Two null models were used. In the first, activity peaks for each species were located randomly through the year, with the distributions overlapping circularly (across the year) if necessary. In the second, peaks were placed randomly during nonwinter months, to reflect an obvious temperature constraint on activity that was unrelated to interspecific competition. Compared to both null distributions, overlap in the observed chironomid assemblage was significantly greater than expected. These null models are similar to those used in the analysis of flowering phenology (Poole and Rathcke 1979; Cole 1981), which we discuss later in this chapter.

An important assumption underlying the analysis of temporal activity patterns is that animals that feed at different times have different diets. This assumption can be tested by examining the correlation between activity patterns and diet (Jaksić 1982). For example, diurnal and nocturnal predators may differ in their diets and thereby face less competition for food than predators with identical activity profiles. The null hypothesis here is that dietary overlap between "matched" species pairs that forage at the same time (diurnal-diurnal or nocturnal-nocturnal) is no different than that for "mixed" species pairs that forage at different times (diurnal-nocturnal). The alternative hypothesis is that competition has promoted temporal segregation, so that matched species pairs overlap less in diet than mixed species pairs (Huey and Pianka 1983).

Jaksić (1982) tested these hypotheses for dietary overlaps of diurnal falconiform and nocturnal strigiform raptors. Overlaps of all possible species pairs were compared using standard nonparametric statistics. In no case was there a significant difference in dietary overlap of mixed versus matched species pairs. Thus, temporal partitioning did not reduce exploitative competition for food resources, although it may have alleviated interference competition (Jaksić et al. 1981).

However, conventional statistics may be unsuitable for testing the mixed-matched dietary overlap hypothesis (Pimm 1983). First, none of the pairwise dietary overlaps are independent—the overlap between species A and B is not independent of the overlap between A and C and between B and C. Second, the overlap distances are geometrically constrained so that the maximum distance between any pair of species is 1.0. Finally, the analysis is likely to be sample-size dependent: the more species there are in the comparison, the closer, on average, are the nearest neighbor distances in dietary niche space. For all these reasons, a null model is necessary to properly test the mixed-matched dietary hypothesis.

Suppose there are n nocturnal and m diurnal species. Then there are mn mixed comparisons and $0.5[n(n - 1) + m(m - 1)]$ matched comparisons of species pairs. Pimm (1983) suggested randomly assigning the $m + n$ labels of nocturnal or diurnal to each species and then calculating dietary overlaps of mixed and matched pairs for this random assemblage. Repeating the procedure many times gives the mean and sample variance of the distribution of dietary overlap for each nearest neighbor, which can then be compared to the actual

Figure 5.2. Dietary overlaps for synchronous and asynchronous lizard predators in the deserts of Africa (upper panel) and Australia (lower panel). Synchronous species pairs forage at the same time of day. The histograms are the results of 200 randomizations, and the triangles show the observed values. Analyses are given for the first four nearest neighbors in niche space. Note that synchronous predators show more overlap and asynchronous predators less overlap than expected. These patterns are opposite to what one would expect if temporal partitioning of food resources were important. From Huey and Pianka (1983). Reprinted by permission of the publisher from *Lizard Ecology: Studies on a Model Organism.* R. B. Huey, E. R. Pianka, and T. W. Schoener (eds). Cambridge, Mass.: Harvard University Press. Copyright © 1983 by the President and Fellows of Harvard College.

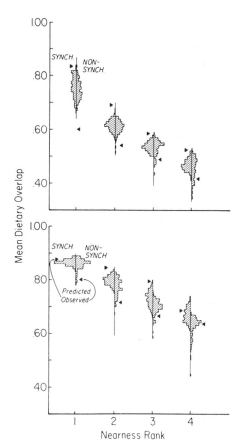

values. If the mixed-matched dietary hypothesis is correct, matched species pairs should overlap in diet less than expected, and mixed species pairs should overlap more than expected. Moreover, the percentage of first nearest neighbors in niche space that are matched should be less than that predicted by the null model.

Huey and Pianka (1983) used Pimm's (1983) recipe to examine dietary differences between nocturnal and diurnal predators in assemblages of lizards, raptors, and water snakes. For both African (Kalahari) and Australian lizards, significantly more first- and second-nearest neighbors in dietary similarity were synchronous than were asynchronous in their activity times. Similarly, synchronous pairs of species tended to overlap in diet more often than predicted, and asynchronous pairs less often than predicted, by the Monte Carlo simulation (Figure 5.2). These patterns are opposite to the predictions of the mixed-matched dietary hypothesis, suggesting that lizard food resources are not being partitioned by species that are active at different times of day. For a large data set on raptor diets (Craighead and Craighead 1956), Huey and Pianka (1983) found that overlaps of synchronous versus nonsynchronous predators did not differ significantly from predictions of the null model. Finally, for dietary data on four species of water snakes (Mushinsky and Hebrard 1977a,b), dietary overlaps of synchronous species were higher than expected, although there were too few species in the assemblage for a statistical test.

These analyses indicate that the degree of synchrony in activity periods is unreliable as an indicator of dietary overlap. The null model simulations contradict widely held beliefs that activity times allow vertebrate predators to partition food resources, and caution against the use of time as a niche dimension in competition analyses. Alternative explanations for the evolution of nocturnal and diurnal feeding strategies include predator avoidance (Lima and Dill 1990), alleviation of interference competition (Carothers and Jaksić 1984), and physiological thermal constraints (Porter et al. 1973).

Although there is little evidence for temporal partitioning by predators on a daily time scale, partitioning of food resources on a seasonal basis may be slightly more plausible. For example, Vannote and Sweeney (1980) hypothesized that competition for food within functional feeding guilds of stream insects will lead to a temporally staggered sequence of maximum resource use by species. Georgian and Wallace (1983) tested the prediction by measuring seasonal production of six species of periphyton-grazing insects in an Appalachian stream. Peak production for each species followed an orderly sequence, with very little overlap between species. Based on the Poole and Rathcke (1979) test (described later in this chapter), production peaks for each species showed an unusually large degree of separation ($p < 0.1$). Overlaps based on density and biomass were generally higher than those based on production.

PHENOLOGICAL OVERLAP IN PLANT COMMUNITIES

Robertson (1895) first proposed that pollen transfer by animals was a potentially limiting resource that could lead to staggered phenologies of flowering plants. However, at least three hypotheses may explain a staggered sequence of flowering times in a community (Waser 1983): (1) pollinator preference, in which one plant species attracts pollinators away from other species, leading to reduced reproductive success (Mosquin 1971; A. Lack 1976); (2) interspecific pollen transfer, in which pollen is exchanged between simultaneously flowering species, causing pollen loss, reduction of receptive stigma surfaces, and reduced reproductive success (Thomson et al. 1981); (3) formation of mal-

Figure 5.3. A randomly generated 20-species flowering phenology (**A**). Overlap patterns in this assemblage can be used as a null expectation for overlaps in the absence of competitive interactions. Phenology in a real assemblage is shown in (**B**) (see Figure 5.4). From Gleeson, S. K. 1981. Character displacement in flowering phenologies. *Oecologia* 51:294–295, Figure 1. Copyright © 1981 by Springer-Verlag GmbH & Co. KG.

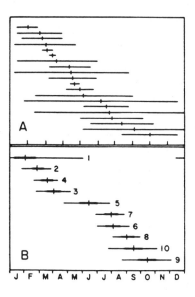

adapted hybrids, in which pollen exchange between related species reduces fitness (Levin 1971). Mechanism (1) is implicit in most ecological studies of phenological overlap. Mechanism (2) is a form of interference competition that can lead to segregation in flowering times even when pollinators are not a limiting resource, and can affect wind-pollinated species as well. All three mechanisms assume that an increase in the abundance of one plant species reduces pollination of other species that share common pollinators. This assumption notwithstanding, rare plant species may sometimes benefit from the presence of other, common species acting as "magnets" for pollinators (Thomson 1978; Schemske 1981).

Whereas temporal segregation of animal foragers does not necessarily reduce dietary overlap, segregation of plant flowering times will reduce overlap in shared pollinators. However, the converse is not necessarily true—high overlap in flowering times need not imply strong competition for pollinator visits. For example, Thomson (1982) found that overlaps in flowering times of subalpine meadow plants were unrelated to relative visitation rates by pollinators. Thus, phenological overlap was not a good indicator of competition for pollinator visits.

In spite of an extensive catalog of flowering phenology studies, the evidence for staggered flowering times in most plant communities is weak (Waser 1983; Rathcke and Lacey 1985; Wheelright 1985). Before the advent of null models, staggered flowering patterns were evaluated visually, not statistically (e.g., Heinrich 1976; Stiles 1977). But appearances can be deceiving. For example, Figure 5.3a looks, to our eyes, like a staggered flowering sequence that might be the result of interspecific competition. But this sequence of flowering times was generated by a random draw of numbers from a uniform distribution and represents a pattern that might be expected in the absence of competition for pollinators (Gleeson 1981).

When flowering phenologies are compared to appropriate null models, the results may be surprising and controversial (Rathcke 1984). Poole and Rathcke (1979) proposed the first statistical test of flowering overlap patterns. Their test considered the spacing of peak flowering time for each species and therefore did not directly test for overlap. Analyses of the spacing of flowering peaks in plant communities are identical to analyses of the spacing of body sizes in an animal community (Pleasants 1980), which we discuss in Chapter 6.

The Poole and Rathcke (1979) test summarized overlap as a single index, the sample variance of the distance between adjacent flowering peaks. For the first and last flowering species in the assemblage, distance is measured from the peak to the boundary of the growing season. The null hypothesis is the equivalent of assigning each species a random uniform value, ranging from 0.0 to 1.0, for its flowering peak within the growing season. If competition has led to a regular spacing of peak flowering times, the observed (population) variance in the position of the flowering peaks, P, should be significantly smaller than expected. Under the null hypothesis, the expectation of P for a set of k species is

$$E(P) = \frac{k}{(k+1)^2 (k+2)} \tag{5.1}$$

The ratio of observed to expected variance ($P/E(P)$) is an index that corresponds to flowering peaks that are aggregated ($P/E(P) > 1$), random ($P/E(P) = 1$), or staggered ($P/E(P) < 1$) within the growing season. Although Poole and Rathcke (1979) compared the quantity kP to a chi-squared distribution, it is more appropriate to compare the results to a randomization test (Williams 1995). De Vita (1979) developed a similar null model for analyzing resource utilization peaks of species (see Chapter 4). These tests ultimately derive from MacArthur's (1957) broken-stick model, in which points are randomly placed on a unit interval to simulate the relative abundance of species in an assemblage (see Chapter 3).

A case history illustrates the use of the Poole and Rathcke (1979) test and a typical cycle of reanalysis that has accompanied many null model investigations. Poole and Rathcke (1979) applied their test to Stiles's (1977) data on flowering times of 11 hummingbird-pollinated plant species in a Costa Rican rain forest (Figure 5.4). Stiles (1977) had claimed that flowering peaks exhibited an orderly, staggered sequence, but the Poole and Rathcke (1979) test

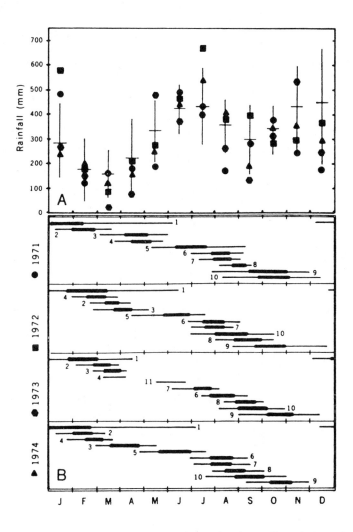

Figure 5.4. Flowering times of 11 species of hummingbird-pollinated plants (lower panel). Numbers denote individual plant species: (1) *Heliconia pogonatha;* (2) *Passiflora vitifolia;* (3) *Heliconia wagneriana;* (4) *Jacobinia aurea;* (5) *Costus ruber;* (6) *Heliconia* sp. 18; (7) *Heliconia* sp. 16; (8) *Aphelandra sinclairiana;* (9) *Costus malortieanus;* (10) *Heliconia* sp. 3; (11) *Malvaviscus arborea.* The upper panel gives the mean and standard deviation of monthly rainfall, with symbols for each of the 4 years of the study. The rainfall data were used to divide the data into wet- and dry-season plants. Depending on the data partition and the null model used, this flowering sequence has been described as aggregated (Poole and Rathcke 1979), random (Gleeson 1981), or segregated (Cole 1981). From Stiles, F. G. 1977. Coadapted competitors: the flowering seasons of hummingbird-pollinated plants in a tropical forest. *Science* 198: 1177–1178. Copyright © 1977 American Association for the Advancement of Science. Reprinted with permission.

revealed that flowering peaks in four consecutive years were significantly aggregated, not staggered. However, these results appear to have been inaccurate due to a computational error (Robert W. Poole, personal communication, cited in Gleeson 1981). Gleeson (1981) recalculated the test and found that the pattern actually was staggered ($P/E(P) < 1$), but not significantly so. In any case, the results did not strongly support the original claim of staggered flowering times.

Both Stiles (1979) and Cole (1981) argued that Poole and Rathcke's (1979) analysis was invalid because different groups of species flowered during distinct wet and dry seasons in the Costa Rican rain forest. Cole (1981) reanalyzed flowering times separately for wet- and dry-season species and found significant staggering with the Poole and Rathcke (1979) test.

Cole (1981) argued that the Poole and Rathcke (1979) test was problematic for two reasons: (1) boundaries of the growing season are incorporated into the distance measure for the two terminal species of an assemblage; (2) the test measures not overlap in flowering times, but regularity in the spacing of peak flowering times. Species could have a regular spacing of flowering peaks but still overlap highly in flowering times. Alternatively, species could have clumped flowering peaks but still have little overlap in flowering times. Neither pattern would be revealed by the Poole and Rathcke (1979) test.

Cole (1981) proposed a different metric, which represents the flowering period as a line segment rather than representing the flowering peak as a single point. For the null hypothesis that the flowering period of each species occurs randomly and independently within the growing season, the expected amount of overlap between any given pair of species ($E(d)$) is

$$E(d) = L_2 \frac{LL_1 - L_1^2 - L_2^2/3}{(L - L_1)(L - L_2)}$$ (5.2)

$$L > (L_1 + L_2)$$
$$L_1 > L_2$$

where L is the length of the growing season, L_1 is the length of the first segment, and L_2 is the length of the second segment. This same model has been developed in the context of niche overlap (Sugihara 1986; see Chapter 4) and the overlap of species spatial ranges (Pielou 1977; Dale 1986; see Chapter 9).

Statistical analysis is problematic. Cole (1981) suggested comparing observed and expected overlaps of all possible species pairs and using a binomial test to evaluate the number of species pairs above and below the expectation. By this test, overlap for Stiles's (1977) data was unusually low ($p = 0.02$). The binomial test assumes that the probability distributions are symmetric and that the species pairs are independent of one another. Cole (1981) showed by simulation that the symmetry assumption was not critical, but nonindependence of species pairs is a serious problem. Similar comments apply to tests of body size ratios (Case and Sidell 1983; Schoener 1984) and co-occurrence data (Wright and Biehl 1982) that compare all possible species pairs. In contrast to Cole's (1981) test, the Poole and Rathcke (1979) test has relatively weak statistical power (Simberloff and Boecklen 1981), but it summarizes the pattern of peak spacing for an entire assemblage in a single number, so it is not burdened by nonindependent comparisons of individual species pairs.

Fleming and Partridge (1984) investigated phenological overlap with a simulation of Cole's (1981) model. They assumed that the flowering period for each species was fixed in length, and then randomly placed each interval on a line segment. The end points of this line segment corresponded to the observed beginning and end of the flowering season. In addition to pairwise overlap, Fleming and Partridge (1984) measured the n-wise overlap of each species with the aggregate phenology of the remaining $n - 1$ species. The n-wise overlap might provide a better measure of the effects of diffuse competition (Pianka 1974) than the pairwise overlap. Both measures gave similar results, although the null hypothesis was rejected more often with pairwise overlap. Using these methods, Fleming and Partridge (1984) analyzed a variety of published phenologies and found that random or aggregated patterns were the rule. Their test has subsequently been used to assess phenological overlap of other tropical plant assemblages (Fleming 1985; Murray et al. 1987), the timing of seedfall in a guild of ant-dispersed herbs (Kjellsson 1985), and the spatial distribution of parasitic helminths along bat guts (Lotz and Font 1985), all of which were random or aggregated.

However, these measures of phenological overlap may be misleading. Pleasants (1990) tested the statistical power of the pairwise and n-wise overlap measures against a hypothetical phenology that was strongly segregated. These indices did not reveal significance for assemblages that were obviously structured by competition (Type II error), whereas low overlap was revealed for a hypothetical assemblage that was not ordered by competition (Type I error). Rather than comparing individual species pairs, Pleasants (1990) recommended calculating the average pairwise overlap for the entire assemblage and comparing this single number to the values emerging from the simulation. This is the same metric used in niche overlap studies (Inger and Colwell 1977; Pianka 1980), and it did not suffer from Type I and Type II errors. As we noted for the Poole and Rathcke (1979) test, mean pairwise overlap avoids nonindependent comparisons. Mean pairwise overlap may not reveal some low-overlap patterns (Thomson and Rusterholz 1982), but if both the mean and the variance of overlap are calculated, comparisons with null models will usually be valid (Winemiller and Pianka 1990).

Ashton et al. (1988) pointed out a more serious problem with Monte Carlo simulations of Cole's (1981) model. If the boundaries of the flowering season are determined by the observed first and last flowering species (which is usually the case), the simulated flowering season will always be too short because the segments are thrown randomly between these two boundaries. This "edge effect" (Haefner et al. 1991) biases the test toward finding staggered (low-overlap) patterns. It is therefore noteworthy, and worth repeating, that most simulation studies have detected random or aggregated patterns, which are in the opposite direction of this inherent bias.

Ashton et al. (1988) suggested a simple scaling procedure that adjusts the simulated flowering phenologies to the correct growing season. First, randomize the placement of the flowering *peaks* within the line segment, as in the Poole and Rathcke (1979) test. Then expand the scale of the segment to encompass the starting time of the first species and the ending time of the last. This scaling ensures that the simulated flowering times are randomly placed within the growing season. Overlap in the null assemblage can then be compared to the real data. Using this procedure, Ashton et al. (1988) detected a significant staggering of flowering times in tropical dipterocarps. An additional null model showed that mass flowering years were associated with droughts and the occurrence of El Niño events.

Staggered flowering times have also been detected in meadow plant communities of the Rocky Mountains. Pleasants (1980) divided the assemblage into guilds based on the identity of the dominant species of bumblebee pollinator. Of 11 guild comparisons, mean pairwise overlaps were significantly less than expected in five, and marginally less than expected ($0.05 < p < 0.15$) in five others. However, these simulations followed Cole's (1981) procedure, so they were biased against the null hypothesis (Ashton et al. 1988). In addition, previous null model tests of flowering times in a different set of sites in the Rocky Mountains did not reveal a significant reduction in temporal overlap (Thomson 1982).

Phenological studies indirectly assess competition for pollinators by assuming it is more severe with increasing temporal overlap. Armbruster (1986) addressed competition more directly by examining species co-occurrence and shared pollinators in assemblages of the euphorb *Dalechampia*. His study is a botanical analog to the mixed-matched dietary hypothesis for predator assemblages. Armbruster's (1986) analysis is noteworthy for its use of both "ecological" and "evolutionary" null hypotheses. These null hypotheses are similar in spirit to tests for mechanisms of ecological assortment and evolutionary divergence (Case and Sidell 1983) in producing patterns of character displacement (see Chapter 6). The ecological null hypothesis was that sympatric species

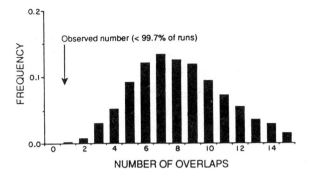

Figure 5.5. Frequency distribution of pollinator niche overlaps generated by a null model for Australian triggerplants (*Stylidium*). From Armbruster et al. (1994), with permission.

were assembled at random with respect to the pollinator species utilized. The evolutionary null hypothesis was that each population evolved pollinator associations at random with respect to those of sympatric congeners. A mixed model contained elements of both ecological and evolutionary models. Overall, there was a marginal tendency toward reduced overlap in shared pollinators, although the results depended on the type of null model used, whether source pool species were equiprobable colonists or not, and how local sympatry was operationally defined.

A similar analysis revealed much more striking patterns in an assemblage of 31 species of triggerplants (*Stylidium* spp.). At 25 sites in western Australia, there was only one overlap of discretely defined pollinator niches for 86 comparisons of sympatric species pairs (Armbruster et al. 1994). In contrast, the ecological, evolutionary, and mixed null models generated an expectation of approximately four to seven pollinator niche overlaps (Figure 5.5). Nine species of *Stylidium* in this assemblage exhibited intraspecific variation in column reach, which determines pollen placement. A significant pattern of character displacement in the presence of sympatric congeners also suggested that competition for shared pollinators structured this assemblage.

These examples of reduced overlap in pollinators or flowering times are exceptional. Most tests have revealed aggregated or random phenological overlap, compared to the null hypothesis of equiprobable flowering periods within a uniform growing season. Detailed studies of phenology in temperate (Parrish and Bazzaz 1979; Anderson and Schelfhout 1980; Rabinowitz et al. 1981) and tropical (Wheelright 1985) plant communities have not revealed unusually low temporal overlap. For example, Rathcke (1988a) measured the flowering periods of 14 species of temperate shrubs over five years. Flowering phenologies were significantly aggregated within a season and consistent across years. Although aggregation might increase competition for pollinators, field experiments showed that seed production of only four of the 14 species was limited by pollination, and of these, only one was likely to have suffered competitive effects (Rathcke 1988b).

CONSTRAINTS

The independent placement of species flowering times within a uniform growing season is the appropriate null hypothesis for tests of phenological overlap. However, even within an appropriately defined growing season, there may be other types of constraints on flowering phenology. For example, the flowering interval for a species may be correlated with the time of the flowering peak in the growing season (Ashton et al. 1988), and null models might be made more sophisticated by incorporating such constraints. Divergence in flowering times may also be constrained by plant mating systems (Lindsey 1982; Flanagan and Moser 1985), seed predators (Augsburger 1981), seed production (Roach 1986), and pollinator attraction (Augsburger 1980). Some of these forces may promote convergence rather than divergence of flowering times.

A more fundamental limitation to flowering phenology may be inherent phylogenetic constraints on flowering time. Independent of ecological forces, the flowering time of a species may fall within certain limits that are characteristic of its clade. Kochmer and Handel (1986) used phylogeny as a "null hypothesis" in a comparative study of flowering times of animal-pollinated angiosperms of North and South Carolina and temperate Japan. Flowering times were similar on the two continents but differed significantly for species in different plant families. Each plant family had a characteristic flowering time and skewness, and there were negative correlations between skewness and mean family flowering times. These phylogenetic "fingerprints" were more pronounced than differences in flowering times among plant life forms (e.g., trees versus shrubs). The results suggest that, regardless of local competitive pressures, the flowering times of plant species were limited by phylogeny. Within these limits, phenology may still be shaped by competition, mutualism, and other ecological interactions, although Kochmer and Handel's (1986) analyses were too coarse to evaluate such effects. In any case, the use of phylogeny as a null hypothesis is a promising avenue for future studies of phenology and other community-level patterns (Harvey and Pagel 1991).

NONEQUILIBRIUM ANALYSES

The preceding analyses all make the implicit assumption that flowering times or activity periods of species have reached an ecological or evolutionary equilibrium. The equilibrium assumption underlies much of the deterministic mathematics of community ecology theory (e.g., MacArthur 1972), but its relevance to many real communities is questionable (e.g., Boecklen and Price 1991). Equilibrium and nonequilibrium communities may be structured by different mechanisms (Wiens 1984). For example, predictable patterns of resource availability may lead to specialization and resource partitioning by competitors in an equilibrium community (Schoener 1974a). In phenological studies, equilibrium communities would exhibit the same patterns of temporal overlap from one year to the next (e.g., Stiles 1977; Rathcke 1988a). In contrast, if the availability of resources fluctuates through time, competitive effects may be intermittent and may only be important during occasional "resource crunches" (Wiens 1977). For phenological studies, nonequilibrium communities would be characterized by variable patterns of temporal overlap and sets of shared pollinators.

What would constitute a valid null model for assessing the equilibrium status of a community? In Chapter 10, we consider this problem in the context of community stability and food web models. Here, we address a more restricted question: Do co-occurring species exhibit compensatory fluctuations in abundance, activity, or phenology? Compensatory change might suggest competitive interactions as species covary negatively in abundance. Alternatively, positive covariation might result if species tracked shared resources that fluctuate in abundance (Schluter 1984).

The data for such an analysis would consist of a matrix with rows representing species and columns representing census dates. The entries in the matrix are the abundance (or activity) of each species at each census. Patterns of covariation in this matrix can be quantified by comparing the sum of the individual species variances to the variance of their sums (Pielou 1972a; Robson 1972). The latter variance includes the average covariation between species pairs, which is a good measure of compensatory fluctuations. The ratio of the second variance to the first, V, reveals whether species are fluctuating independently ($V = 1$), concordantly ($V > 1$) or compensatorily ($V < 1$). Järvinen (1979) calculated the reciprocal of V for censuses of avian communities at different latitudes. This index was not consistently different for northern versus southern assemblages, contradicting the hypothesis that compensatory fluctuations stabilize species-rich tropical communities (McNaughton 1977).

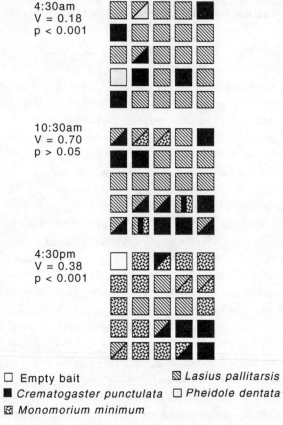

4:30am
V = 0.18
p < 0.001

10:30am
V = 0.70
p > 0.05

4:30pm
V = 0.38
p < 0.001

☐ Empty bait   ⧅ *Lasius pallitarsis*
■ *Crematogaster punctulata*   ☐ *Pheidole dentata*
▨ *Monomorium minimum*

Figure 5.6. Spatial and temporal segregation of common grassland ants as measured
by the variance ratio (Schluter 1984). Each matrix shows the species occurrences at 25
tuna-fish baits placed in a 5 × 5-m grid that were censused for 24 consecutive hours in
Caddo County, Oklahoma, July 1992. The variance ratio indicates significant spatial
partitioning at certain times of the day. Symbols indicate the presence of particular species at individual baits. Unpublished data from Marc C. Albrecht.

James and Boecklen (1984) refined this approach in an analysis of seven
years of breeding bird census data from Maryland woodlands. To estimate the
variance components, they assumed that individual birds were distributed
according to a Poisson process. *V* for this assemblage was 0.65, which was in
the direction of negative covariation, although still within the limits expected
by chance ($p \approx 0.28$). The covariance matrix revealed one pair of species
(Cardinal–Red-eyed Vireo) with a large positive covariation, followed in order
of decreasing magnitude by pairs with positive or negative covariation. Al-

though the abundances of particular pairs of species were correlated, there was no evidence over the 7-year study for strong compensatory fluctuations in the assemblage as a whole.

Schluter (1984) developed significance tests for the variance ratio. The product of the variance ratio and the number of censuses (VT) has an approximate chi-squared distribution with T degrees of freedom. Simulated data showed an acceptable fit to the chi-squared distribution, so the variance ratio can be evaluated without the use of a simulation. McCulloch (1985) showed that, for presence-absence data, the variance ratio is a multiple of Cochran's Q statistic (Cochran 1950), which has been used as a null hypothesis to test equiprobable colonization of aquatic taxa in experimental ponds (Wilbur and Travis 1984). Hastings (1987) found that the variance ratio did not always reveal significant patterns for a simple competition model in which the probability of extinction was proportional to species richness. The variance ratio will reveal cases where the average pairwise correlation between species is negative (McCulloch 1985), although, like all statistical tests, the variance ratio is sensitive to sample size and sampling error. Perhaps for this reason, a literature survey of species co-occurrence matrices revealed mostly random or aggregated spatial patterns as measured by the variance ratio (Schluter 1984).

An interesting exception can be found in the co-occurrence pattern of ant species at tuna-fish baits in an Oklahoma grassland (Marc C. Albrecht, unpublished data). Spatial occurrence, as measured by the variance ratio, was strongly negative. However, the spatial pattern changed on an hourly basis, as different associations of species emerged because of diel foraging patterns (Figure 5.6). Most authors have used the variance ratio as an index of spatial co-occurrence (see Chapter 6), and more long-term community studies such as James and Boecklen's (1984) are needed to evaluate the compensatory fluctuations hypothesis.

RECOMMENDATIONS

To compare the diets of synchronous and asynchronous predators, we recommend Pimm's (1983) Monte Carlo simulation of the mixed-matched dietary hypothesis. The Poole and Rathcke (1979) test, with modifications by Williams (1995), is acceptable for simple analyses of flowering peaks, although some of the character displacement tests described in Chapter 6 may be more powerful. If the data consist of flowering intervals for each species, we recommend the modification of Cole's (1981) test by Ashton et al. (1988). The variance ratio (Schluter 1984) is appropriate for testing the hypothesis of compensatory fluctuations of abundance or activity through time.

6
SIZE RATIOS

The analysis of size ratios of coexisting species has been a major focus in evolutionary ecology for more than three decades. The idea that body size differences follow empirical "rules" and may reflect resource partitioning has arisen several times in the ecological literature. Dyar (1890) described a constant increment of hard part length for insects at each molt, so that body size ratios of successive molts within species would approximate 1.28 (Enders 1976). Both Huxley (1942) and Lack (1947) suggested that body size differences among predators should evolve to reduce the effects of competition for the same foods (Carothers 1986). Brown and Wilson (1956) described several examples of character displacement—species pairs whose body sizes differed more in sympatry than in allopatry. Empirical evidence for character displacement comes from studies of birds (Diamond et al. 1989), lizards (Losos 1990), fish (Schluter and McPhail 1992), mud snails (Fenchel 1975), and other taxa. A number of criteria are necessary to unequivocally establish character displacement in such natural experiments (Grant 1972a; Schluter and McPhail 1992).

Whereas character displacement analyses describe intraspecific variation in multiple assemblages, many size ratio tests compare coexisting species within a single assemblage. This practice can be traced to Hutchinson's (1959) seminal paper "Homage to Santa Rosalia." Hutchinson found that body size ratios of several pairs of sympatric bird and mammal species ranged from 1.1 to 1.4. The mean ratio, roughly 1.3, was "tentatively" interpreted as the amount of separation necessary to permit coexistence of species at the same trophic level.

This modest suggestion spawned a vast amount of ecological research. Ecologists measured size overlap in other assemblages, either confirming the "1.3 rule," describing other axes of niche differentiation that "explained" size ratios less than 1.3, or invoking interference competition between species to explain size ratios greater than 1.3 (reviews in Roth 1981; Simberloff and Boecklen 1981; Simberloff 1983b). Both Hutchinson's rule and Dyar's constant were thought to reflect the same underlying pressure for divergence because of limited resources (Maiorana 1978).

Three patterns have been sought in reference to Hutchinson's rule (Simberloff 1983b): (1) minimum size ratios, below which species cannot coexist; (2) constant size ratios, in which the species in a community display an orderly spacing; (3) unusually large ratios in island assemblages, which are thought to be experiencing more severe competition than comparable mainland assemblages.

ASSUMPTIONS

Simplistic analyses of these patterns depend on a number of assumptions:

1. Morphology is linked to resource consumption, and the appropriate morphological features of the organisms have been measured. Ratio analyses assume a linear and proportional mapping of morphology onto the resource axis. Although analyses of size ratios are frequently based on body size or trophic structures (bill depth, mandible length), it is by no means obvious what the appropriate morphological variables are that reflect resource use (Wilson 1975). For example, Carothers (1982) found that resource partitioning in a guild of Hawaiian honeycreepers depended on the morphology of the tongue rather than the size or shape of the bill. Moreover, character displacement may occur among distantly related taxa that do not have comparable body parts but nevertheless compete for limiting resources, such as Galápagos ground finches and carpenter bees that use flower nectar as a food resource (Schluter 1986a).

Nonetheless, analyses of body size ratios are usually restricted to small groups of closely related species. A frequently cited example is Ashmole's (1968) study of five species of tropical terns. However, different measurements of body size (body weight, tarsus length) and appendages (bill length, bill cross-sectional area) generated different size ratios and even different orderings of species (Figure 6.1). Hendrickson (1981) found that the choice of metric also affected the outcome of null model tests: birds of the Tres Marias Islands showed evidence of character displacement in wing length but not in bill length, which may be more directly related to resource use (Strong and Simberloff 1981). Because body size and shape are intimately related (Mosimann and James 1979), multivariate analyses of morphological displacement may be more appropriate than analyses of single characters such as bill size or body weight. We review these approaches later in this chapter.

2. The underlying resource spectrum is symmetric. This assumption underlies mathematical models of both character displacement (Slatkin 1980) and

Figure 6.1. Size ratios and species sequences depend on the particular morphological variable measured. Morphometric measurements of five species of sympatric tropical terns (Ashmole 1968). As = *Anous stolidus;* At = *Anous tenuirostris;* Ga = *Gygis alba;* Pc = *Procelsterna cerulea;* Sf = *Sterna fuscata.* From Wiens (1982). Reproduced with the permission of the Finnish Zoological and Botanical Publishing Board.

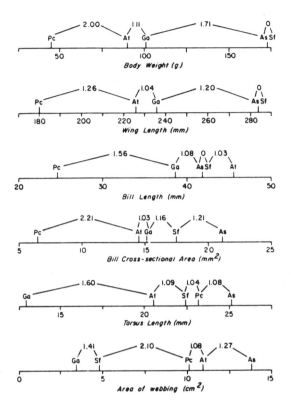

niche shift (MacArthur and Levins 1967), but it has rarely been verified in nature and may not be true (Schluter and Grant 1984). Symmetry of the resource spectrum affects the amount of divergence (Slatkin 1980) and hence the pattern of observed size ratios in a group of competitors.

3. The environment is stable and the system has reached an ecological and evolutionary equilibrium. If the environment is variable, divergence of competitors may not be pronounced, because specialization on a particular part of the resource spectrum will no longer be favored by selection (Gotelli and Bossert 1991) or promoted by extinction of overlapping species (Turelli 1978b). More importantly, if the system has not reached an equilibrium, then species composition will change through time, and the derived morphological "patterns" may be more apparent than real (Wiens 1981).

4. Competition occurs only among adult organisms. Size ratio analyses of adult animals ignore ontogenetic shifts in body size and resource use (Werner and Gilliam 1984), and the potential for different age classes to function as ecological species (Polis 1984). The ontogenetic perspective was important in early analyses of Dyar's constant (Enders 1976) but has been neglected in most community studies. Interestingly, Hutchinson (1959) appreciated the importance of body size shifts during ontogeny. In addition to the "1.3 rule," he predicted that the larger of a pair of species of coexisting corixid beetles would breed earlier in the season to have enough time for growth to achieve its size advantage.

5. Sexual dimorphism in body size is not important. When species are sexually dimorphic in body size, differences between the sexes have been either averaged (e.g., Schoener 1984) or ignored, by restricting the analysis to a single sex (e.g., Hines 1982). Both approaches are unsatisfactory. Averaging body sizes may create an imaginary phenotype that does not exist in nature, whereas analyzing one sex ignores overlap and resource use by half the population. If both sexes are treated as distinct morphospecies (e.g., Dayan, Simberloff, et al. 1989, 1990), body size ratios are difficult to interpret, because overlap within a species may not be statistically or biologically equivalent to overlap between species (see Epilogue). Sexual dimorphism in body size is typically correlated with dimorphism in trophic appendages and feeding ecology (Shine 1989), and clearly needs to be considered in studies of resource partitioning. Unfortunately, there has been little theoretical research in this area (Slatkin 1984), and quantitative models for character displacement and sexual dimorphism in a suite of species are still needed (Dayan et al. 1990).

6. Abundances of species are approximately equal. The intensity of competition depends not only on the amount of overlap in resource use, but also on the densities of the two competing species. If one of the species is rare, it may overlap completely with its competitor but not contribute much to resource depletion. The relative abundance of competing species consequently is important in determining the degree of divergence of populations (Slatkin 1980). Some authors have restricted their analyses to "common" players (e.g., Bowers and Brown 1982) on the grounds that these "core" species (Hanski 1982a) are equilibrial and are more likely to be experiencing competition. At a regional level, Hanski (1982b) found some evidence that bumblebee proboscis lengths of core species were nonrandomly spaced, although this pattern was not confirmed by detailed analyses of local assemblages (Ranta 1982).

Given this list of restrictive and often unrealistic assumptions, why were size ratio analyses so popular and uncritically accepted in ecology? Wiens (1982) suggested several reasons. First, some communities seemed to conform to the

1.3 rule, and these examples reinforced the predictions of simple models of limiting similarity (MacArthur and Levins 1967). Second, size ratio studies were guided by an adaptationist view of organisms (Gould and Lewontin 1979)—traits such as bill length or body size represented adaptive "solutions" to ecological problems (limiting food resources). Third, it is far easier to measure morphological traits from museum collections than it is to conduct field studies to quantify food habits, dietary overlap, and ecological interactions (Wiens 1991a). Finally, size ratio analyses reflected a view that ecological systems were ordered and deterministic and that the underlying mechanisms would be revealed in simple rules that governed the assembly of communities.

MODELS OF BODY SIZE DIVERGENCE

In parallel with empirical studies of character displacement, theoretical models also indicated the potential for divergence of competitors. Three basic mechanisms, two evolutionary and one ecological, could cause divergence of species in sympatry. First, evolutionary divergence of body sizes might be favored if it prevented hybridization (Bossert 1963). This mechanism has received little attention from animal ecologists, although it may be important in the divergence of morphology or phenology of closely related plant species (Levin 1971; see Chapter 5). Second, coevolutionary divergence might occur in sympatry through selection against intermediate phenotypes (Bulmer 1974). This evolutionary mechanism has been invoked for cases in which a species shows intraspecific variation in body size that is related to the presence or absence of competitors (Grant 1972a).

Finally, divergence may occur in the absence of evolutionary change through purely ecological mechanisms. Models of limiting similarity (MacArthur and Levins 1967) depict species resource utilization spectra as fixed, with no potential for evolutionary change. Species that overlap too much in resource use (and presumably in body size) will be driven to extinction; species that are widely separated along the resource axis survive, and the assemblage can subsequently be invaded by species with intermediate phenotypes. Through time, size assortment via colonization and extinction may lead to a community with a constant spacing of body sizes (Abrams 1986).

For both the evolutionary and the ecological models, divergence of competitors is by no means guaranteed, even in the face of persistent competition. Intrinsic factors, such as the amount of genetic variation underlying the trait (Slatkin 1980), and extrinsic factors, such as the variability of the environment

(Turelli 1978b), affect the degree of displacement. The terminology has been confused in this literature, as character displacement has been used to describe both the pattern and the mechanism of divergence. Strong et al. (1979) defined "community-wide character displacement" as any pattern of overdispersed body sizes, generated by either ecological or evolutionary mechanisms. In contrast, Case and Sidell (1983) developed null models to distinguish between "size-assortment" (ecological limits to similarity) and "size adjustment" (coevolutionary character displacement). Rummel and Roughgarden (1983) also distinguished between invasion-structured and coevolution-structured competitive communities.

ALTERNATIVES AND ARTIFACTS

In the early size ratio literature, competition was the only framework used to interpret patterns, and there was a distressing ignorance of alternative mechanisms. Yet, competitive interactions are only one of many forces that control body size. Selective responses to predation and the presence of enemy-free space may control the pattern of body sizes in an assemblage (Jeffries and Lawton 1984). Alternatively, body sizes of coexisting species may be phylogenetically constrained (Elgar and Harvey 1987) for reasons that have nothing to do with current or past biotic interactions. Finally, the ratios themselves may be mathematical artifacts that merely reflect the underlying distribution of body sizes in an assemblage (Tonkyn and Cole 1986; Eadie et al. 1987). For example, size ratios of tricycle wheels, iron skillets, and musical recorders also follow Hutchinson's rule (Horn and May 1977), suggesting that the size ratios observed in natural communities may have no biological significance. Before ecological mechanisms are attributed to body size ratios, their mathematical, and hence nonbiological, properties need to be understood.

STATISTICAL PROPERTIES OF RATIOS

The expected ratio in a large assemblage depends on the underlying distribution of body sizes and on the end points of possible body sizes (Tonkyn and Cole 1986). In ecological models of limiting similarity, this distribution represents the body sizes of existing phenotypes that could colonize a community. In evolutionary models of character displacement, this distribution represents the probability that a particular body size will evolve. Tonkyn and Cole (1986) assumed that the distribution of available body sizes was either uniform or

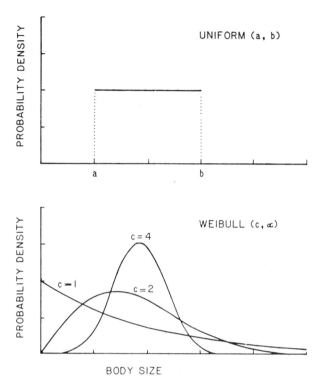

Figure 6.2. Hypothetical body size distributions ultimately determine the distribution of overlap ratios in null assemblages. From Tonkyn, D. W., and B. J. Cole. 1986. The statistical analysis of size ratios. *American Naturalist* 128:66–81. Copyright © 1986 by The University of Chicago. Reprinted by permission of the publisher.

unimodal, as fit by a Weibull distribution. The Weibull and the uniform captured the range of biologically realistic distributions, including many curves that could be characterized as log normal (Figure 6.2).

Regardless of the shape of the body size distribution, there were two general properties of size ratios for the theoretical assemblage. First, the most common size ratio for a pair of adjacent species was the minimum ratio of 1.0. The frequency of larger ratios in the assemblage decreased monotonically from this peak, and the shape of the curve was concave upward (Figure 6.3). Second, the more species in the assemblage, the smaller the expected body size ratio. This second property probably explains, in part, why ratios for island communities are often larger than those for corresponding mainland communities (Simberloff 1983b). By chance alone, we expect an island assemblage with few species to have larger size ratios

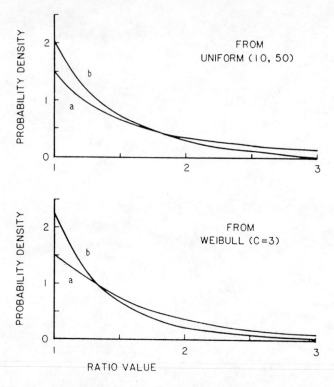

Figure 6.3. Expected ratio distributions for randomly assembled communities. The shape of these curves does not depend greatly on the body size distributions in Figure 6.2. a = two-species guilds; b = four-species guilds. From Tonkyn, D. W., and B. J. Cole. 1986. The statistical analysis of size ratios. *American Naturalist* 128:66–81. Copyright © 1986 by The University of Chicago. Reprinted by permission of the publisher.

than a corresponding mainland community, for the same reasons that we expect island species/genus (S/G) ratios to be lower (see Chapter 1).

Because these predictions hold for any set of species that are drawn randomly, they constitute a simple null model for the distribution of ratios in a large assemblage. In contrast, a community that is competitively assembled should show a unimodal distribution of ratios, in which the mode represents the limit to similarity (Tonkyn and Cole 1986). Expected ratios would be the same for large communities as for small and perhaps would even increase in large communities because of diffuse competition (Pianka 1974).

Tonkyn and Cole (1986) examined two large data sets of size ratios, one compiled by Schoener (1965) for guilds of sympatric, congeneric bird species

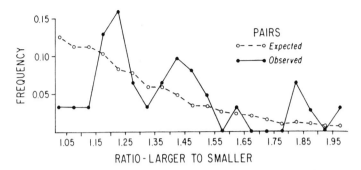

Figure 6.4. Expected and observed body size ratios for pairs of sympatric bird-eating hawks. Note the lack of very small size ratios in the observed assemblages compared to the null model. See also Figure 6.3. From Schoener, T. W. Size differences among sympatric, bird-eating hawks: a worldwide survey. In: *Ecological Communities: Conceptual Issues and the Evidence.* D. R. Strong, Jr., D. Simberloff, L. G. Abele, and A. B. Thistle (eds). Copyright © 1984 by Princeton University Press. Reprinted by permission of Princeton University Press.

(410 ratios) and one by T. Tomasi (unpublished) for guilds of sympatric, insectivorous bats (61 ratios). For both data sets, the distribution of observed ratios was monotonically decreasing and concave upward, in good agreement with the null hypothesis. For Schoener's (1965) data, mean ratios also decreased with increasing guild size, as predicted by the null model. These results contrast with the appearance of the histogram of ratios for sympatric bird-eating hawks, also compiled by Schoener (1984). The histogram of the hawk ratios, while not unimodal, was certainly not decreasing monotonically (Figure 6.4). Schoener's (1984) Monte Carlo procedures, described later, also confirmed that these ratios deviated significantly from null expectations.

THE 1.3 RULE AS AN ARTIFACT

Roth (1981) adapted conventional statistical tests for evaluating whether ratios are significantly different from any expected value. Even without such tests, it is clear that some communities show no constancy in ratios or tendency toward a particular ratio (Wiens and Rotenberry 1981a). Nevertheless, the 1.3 rule has received such widespread attention that it is worth considering the hypothesis in some detail.

Eadie et al. (1987) offered the most satisfying general explanation for why ratios should tend toward this magic number. They showed that ratios of approximately 1.3 are expected if the underlying distribution of body sizes is log normal, and if the variance about that distribution is relatively small. Both assumptions have empirical support. For 35 of 41 comparisons, body size data could not be distinguished from a log normal distribution (Van Valen 1973). The log normal distribution of body sizes could, itself, be a consequence of competition for food (Schoener 1965). However, the log normal characterizes so many biological (and nonbiological) systems (Koch 1966), that this seems unlikely.

The variance of body sizes in most log normal distributions is small, usually less than 1.0. Again, competition is not the most likely explanation. Instead, Eadie et al. (1987) pointed out that a log normal variance in body size of 1.0 implies a 400-fold range of body sizes on an arithmetic scale. Given that size ratios are usually calculated for small sets of closely related species, a small variance in body size is assured. If there is any tendency for body size ratios to conform to a value of 1.3, the analysis of Eadie et al. (1987) provides the most likely explanation, as well as accounting for 1.3 ratios in collections of inanimate objects (Horn and May 1977).

NULL MODEL APPROACHES

Although the 1.3 rule has not stood up to detailed analysis, the hypothesis that body size differences are constrained by competition is still viable and deserves testing. Null models can be used to generate expected body size ratios in the absence of competitive interactions. Three different strategies have emerged for testing body size ratios. The first approach, pioneered by Simberloff and Boecklen (1981), adapts conventional statistical tests to examine patterns of regularity or unusual minima in size ratios. A single body size value for each species is used, and intraspecific variation in body size is not considered. The tests apply to a single assemblage of co-occurring species.

The second approach, pioneered by Strong et al. (1979), considers intraspecific variation in body size data among a set of communities, usually on islands. These data form the basis for a Monte Carlo simulation in which different species populations are sampled to generate null communities and size ratios that would be expected in the absence of competition. Intraspecific variation in body size among populations is preserved.

The third approach, pioneered by Schoener (1984) and by Hopf and Brown (1986), tests size spacing patterns in multiple communities containing the same guilds and usually some of the same species. These tests are more powerful than analyses of single communities, although they may be complicated by variation in species number and the repeated occurrence of certain species in multiple assemblages (James H. Brown, personal communication).

All three approaches are controversial. The papers by Simberloff and Boecklen (1981) and by Strong et al. (1979), in particular, provoked a number of responses. After reviewing these exchanges, we consider null models of morphometrics that rely on multivariate analyses of size and shape of organisms. Finally, we review three case studies that were published in the wake of the original controversy. These studies incorporate additional data on geographic variation in morphology (Dayan, Tchernov, et al. 1989), experimental field manipulations (Juliano and Lawton 1990b), and field measurements of resource use (Schluter and Grant 1984) to provide insight into patterns of body size overlap.

RATIO TESTS FOR SINGLE ASSEMBLAGES

Simberloff and Boecklen (1981) systematically tested literature claims of unusual ratio constancy or minima. Their tests arranged the logarithms of body masses of each species as points along a line, with the largest and smallest species in the assemblage representing the end points of the line. A hypothesis of constant size ratios on a linear scale means equal spacing on a logarithmic scale. For an assemblage of $n + 1$ species, there are n line segments, $n-1$ interior points, and $n(n - 1)/2$ ratios of line segments that can be formed. If size ratios are unusually constant, then the segments will be very similar in length, so that ratios *of segments* would be unusually small. The Barton and David (1956) test gives the probability that the ratio between two specified segments (small segment/large segment) is smaller than observed. Simberloff and Boecklen (1981) tested three segment ratios for each assemblage of more than three species. Examining more than one ratio ensured that the results were typical for the assemblage but introduced a problem of nonindependence. For assemblages with three species, there are only two segments, and their ratio defines the placement of the interior species.

The Barton and David (1956) test does not handle ties (which give line segments of length zero), although identical body sizes in an assemblage should be counted as evidence against the hypothesis of ratio constancy. For cases of ties, Simberloff and Boecklen (1981) substituted other ratios from the assemblage. The Poole and Rathcke (1979) test, described in Chapter 5, was more appropriate for data with many ties, although it was less powerful than the Barton and David (1956) test. The Barton and David (1956) test was also superior to the ratio tests of constancy proposed by Roth (1981), which require a minimum of six species for statistical power (Simberloff 1983b).

For claims of ratio minima, Simberloff and Boecklen (1981) adapted the Irwin (1955) test, which gives the probability that the minimum segment for the assemblage is smaller than observed. Both the Barton and David (1956) and the Irwin (1955) tests are appropriate for analyzing body size distributions in a single assemblage. For multiple assemblages, Simberloff and Boecklen (1981) tested the probability of obtaining an observed minimum segment for a set of sites (Pielou and Arnason 1966). All of these statistics are tests for evolutionary character displacement, because the null hypothesis is that any evolutionary arrangement of body sizes within the observed limits is possible.

Simberloff and Boecklen (1981) applied these tests to a variety of published studies claiming constant or minimum size ratios. They also devised statistical tests for related claims about ratios. For example, Schoener (1965) suggested that size differences must be more extreme when food is rare, so that ratios would increase, rather than remain constant for large-bodied species. Similarly, Oksanen et al. (1979) argued that ratios much larger than 1.3 for waterfowl assemblages were the result of interference competition between species (but see Nudds et al. 1981). Simberloff and Boecklen (1981) tailored several null models to investigate these and other ratio claims.

Simberloff and Boecklen (1981) examined three segment ratios for each assemblage and defined a "significant effect" as $p < 0.05$ for more than one ratio. For 21 literature claims of ratio constancy, four were sustained at the 0.05 level and 11 were sustained at a p value of 0.30. By chance, one would have expected to find one significant claim at the 0.05 level and six at the 0.30 level. A few assemblages were nonrandom in the opposite direction: too many small ratios to be explained by chance. Of 18 claims of large minimum size ratios, only one was sustained at the 0.05 level and 13 were sustained at a p value of 0.30. Simberloff and Boecklen (1981) concluded that "evidence presented to date that sizes are competitively determined is weak, and that in particular the '1.3 rule' was probably always a red herring and has certainly outlived its usefulness to evolutionary ecologists."

CRITICISMS OF RATIO TESTS

Losos et al. (1989) disagreed with Simberloff and Boecklen's (1981) interpretation of these results. They reanalyzed a subset of the studies that included data for more than one assemblage. Combining probabilities within these studies, Losos et al. (1989) found that 47% of ratio claims of constancy were supported at the $p = 0.05$ level and more than 70% at the $p = 0.30$ level. They concluded that there was substantial evidence for ratio constancy and unusual size minima, although the patterns may not be strong in any single assemblage. Whether or not published studies represent a random subset of natural assemblages, the evidence for non-random size ratios is certainly much weaker than claimed in most of the original papers.

Other objections to the Barton and David (1956) test have been statistical. The most common complaint has been that the assumption of a (log) uniform body size distribution biases the test against rejecting the null hypothesis (Case et al. 1983; Colwell and Winkler 1984; Schoener 1984). However, when body sizes were drawn randomly from a more realistic log normal distribution, the Barton and David (1956) test was slightly liberal for small assemblages and slightly conservative for large assemblages; overall differences were trivial and the performance was consistent and unbiased (Boecklen and NeSmith 1985). The Irwin (1955) test also performed well with a log normal distribution (Losos et al. 1989). These results are consistent with Tonkyn and Cole's (1986) finding that the expected distribution of ratios is insensitive to the distribution of body sizes. For a log normal distribution of body sizes, Sinclair et al. (1985a,b) derived test statistics for constant ratios and large minimum ratios. Given that most ratio tests are conducted on small assemblages of similar species (Eadie et al. 1987), the log uniform probably performs just as well as the log normal distribution and is unlikely to affect the outcome of the test.

A more serious problem is that ratio tests may not be powerful enough to detect character displacement when it is happening. Losos et al. (1989) explored the power of the Irwin (1955) test by randomly assembling hypothetical communities with minimum threshold ratios. For communities of three species, the Irwin (1955) test almost never rejected the null hypothesis, even when the threshold ratio was large (>1.3). For communities of six species, the results were better, and the probability of falsely accepting the null hypothesis was never greater than 0.25, at least for small variances. The power of the Irwin (1955) test increased with large threshold ratios, large numbers of species, and small variances in body size (Losos et al. 1989). For multiple assemblages, the Barton and David (1956) test may also be less powerful than Monte Carlo simulations that are tailored to particular data sets (Schoener 1984).

Still another objection to the Barton and David (1956) test is that it relies on particular ratios for an assemblage that are arbitrary and not independent of one another, rather than summarizing dispersion of body sizes with a single "community-wide" parameter (Hopf and Brown 1986; Pleasants 1990). This criticism does not apply to the Irwin (1955) test, because the minimum ratio is a property of the entire assemblage. On the other hand, aggregate statistics do not always detect character displacement when present (Arita 1993). Although a single index is statistically desirable, it still may be appropriate to examine

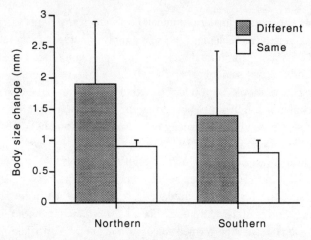

Figure 6.5. Phylogenetic evidence for character displacement in *Anolis* lizards of the Northern and Southern Lesser Antilles. Different = taxon occupied an island with a different number of species than the island occupied by its most immediate ancestor. Same = taxon occupied an island with the same number of species as the island occupied by its most immediate ancestor. Note that evolutionary change in body size is greatest when species number is different on islands with ancestral versus descendent taxa. Data from Losos (1990).

particular ratios within an assemblage when searching for ratio constancy. More recent analyses by Pleasants (1994) and Williams (1995) suggest that community-wide statistics, such as the variance of distances between body sizes (Poole and Rathcke 1979; see Chapter 5), are indeed most powerful for detecting displacement.

Finally, Tonkyn and Cole (1986) objected that ratio tests used the largest and smallest species in the assemblage to set the end points of possible body sizes. The effect of this procedure, if any, will be to bias the test toward rejecting the null hypothesis. If the actual range of possible body sizes is much greater than observed, then a pattern that appears evenly spaced by using species end points may be random or even clumped using true evolutionary end points (Simberloff and Boecklen 1981).

Using two of the species from a small assemblage to set the end points loses information, and it would be preferable to set the end points by some other criterion. An important issue in the analysis of body size patterns is to understand the evolutionary and ecological "boundaries" within which character displacement can occur. We think this is an important area of research that deserves additional attention.

Phylogeny is probably the key to understanding limits of body size evolution, and an exemplary analysis by Losos (1990) illustrates the power of incorporating phylogenetic information into null models. Islands of the Lesser Antilles support one or two species of *Anolis* lizard. On two-species islands, sympatric populations usually show substantial size differences, whereas allopatric populations on single-species islands are usually of intermediate size. A phylogenetic reconstruction (Huey and Bennett 1987) suggested that substantial evolutionary change in body size was rare and may have only occurred once within the *Anolis* clade. Nevertheless, size change was significantly greater when a descendant occurred on a two-species island than on a one-species island, supporting a model of evolutionary size adjustment (Figure 6.5). Size assortment was also revealed by a null model in which communities were randomly assembled by drawing populations from independent clades. This is essentially the same as the Strong et al. (1979) procedure, but it retains historical constraints and does not treat all island populations as equiprobable and independent of one another. Losos's (1990) approach is considerably more sophisticated and powerful than most null model tests of character displacement. However, like all comparative studies (Harvey and Pagel 1991), its application will be limited to assemblages for which reliable phylogenies exist.

MONTE CARLO TESTS

Strong et al. (1979) used Monte Carlo simulations to investigate claims of character displacement for three island avifaunas: (1) the Tres Marias Islands of western Mexico, (2) the Channel Islands of southern California, and (3) the Galápagos Islands. They compiled morphological and distributional data for the islands and for adjacent mainland areas. Mainland source pool species were limited to those that might occur in the range of habitats present in each archipelago.

For the first two data sets, Strong et al. (1979) created 100 assemblages of species from each taxonomic subfamily present on the mainland by drawing randomly the same number of species that were present in the archipelago. However, ratios for individual islands were not calculated. Instead, they averaged ratios for each morphological character in the null assemblage and treated this as the expected value in the absence of character displacement. Next, they counted the number of times the observed ratios in the archipelago exceeded the expected ratios in the null assemblages. If bill and wing length were influenced by character displacement, observed ratios should frequently have exceeded this expectation. By a binomial test, an excess of large ratios was not

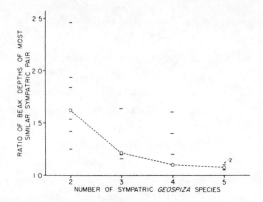

Figure 6.6. Observed (bars) and expected (open circles) minimum bill size ratios for *Geospiza* finches on the Galápagos Islands. Expected ratios were calculated by randomly sampling species and then populations. Note the lack of ratios consistently above or below the expectation. From Strong et al. (1979), with permission.

present in either assemblage, and Strong et al. (1979) concluded "a general trend of character displacement cannot be inferred from these traits."

For the Galápagos finches, Strong et al. (1979) used different procedures. They used Lack's (1947) published data on bill depth and bill length of species of *Geospiza* (ground finches) and of *Camarhynchus* (tree finches) and *Certhidea* (warbler finches) to test for character displacement. Because the Galápagos archipelago is 1,000 km offshore, there is no obvious mainland source pool for comparison with this isolated fauna. In addition, individual islands have morphologically distinct finch populations.

Strong et al. (1979) asked whether the particular combination of morphologically distinct populations on each island exhibited character displacement relative to random combinations of species and populations from throughout the archipelago. For an *n*-species island, they first chose *n* species randomly and equiprobably. Then, for each species, they randomly chose a subpopulation from the archipelago. Thus, for each island, both species identity and subpopulations were randomized, but species number was held constant. Compared to 100 random draws, there were never significantly more ratios above than below the null expectation (Figure 6.6).

Strong et al (1979) also searched for character displacement in bill shape. For each species population, they plotted bill shape (bill depth/length) as a function of bill size (length) and found that island populations for each species formed a well-defined polygon (Figure 6.7). In these simulations, Strong et al. (1979) retained species identities but randomly chose the particular island

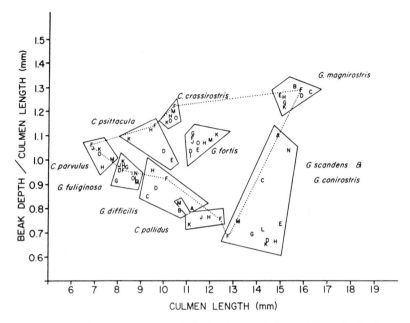

Figure 6.7. Bill shape as a function of bill size for populations of *Geospiza* finches on the Galápagos Islands. Solid polygons enclose populations of the same species. The dotted line connects coexisting species. For a pattern of overdispersion, the Euclidian distance separating these species would be unusually large. By this test, most communities were randomly spaced, or showed slight convergence. From Strong et al. (1979), with permission.

population from the archipelago list. Next, they calculated the average Euclidian distance between species of a given island. Character displacement would be expressed as unusually large Euclidian distances compared to those in randomly assembled communities.

These analyses again yielded no evidence of character displacement, although one of the islands (San Cristóbal) showed evidence of character convergence: observed Euclidian distances between species were unusually small. Analyses of the rank sum of size and shape variables also suggested a slight tendency toward character convergence, although the patterns were weak and variable from one island to the next. Strong et al. (1979) concluded, "Our approach emphasizes apparent randomness in actual communities, and that species often persist together independently of their morphological characteristics. We suggest that apparent randomness would account for a substantial proportion of variation in many real ecological communities."

CRITICISMS OF MONTE CARLO TESTS

The study by Strong et al. (1979) was important for three reasons. First, it introduced a novel method of analysis for character displacement studies (see also Gatz 1979). Second, the results indicated little evidence of character displacement in the Galápagos finches, one of the classic textbook examples. Finally, Strong et al. (1979) argued for the "logical primacy" of null hypotheses as a method for analyzing community patterns in the absence of experimental tests (see Chapter 1).

Several authors raised biological and statistical objections to the procedures and conclusions of Strong et al. (1979). Grant and Abbott (1980) leveled five major criticisms. First, they objected to analyses at the family level (Tres Marias and Channel Islands avifaunas) because these taxonomic groupings were not equivalent to ecological guilds. Second, they argued that source pools for the Tres Marias and Channel Islands should have been based on species lists of mainland areas of approximately equal size, rather than on species lists from an entire country (see Epilogue). Third, Grant and Abbott (1980) claimed that the null model assumption of equiprobable species dispersal was unrealistic. Fourth, they argued that it was somewhat circular to use the observed data to generate null distributions that were then compared to the observed data. Finally, they disagreed with the statistical tests of Strong et al. (1979), in part because the binomial did not measure the magnitude of the differences between observed and expected ratios, and because the null model simulations tacitly assumed a model of "size assortment" (Case and Sidell 1983), rather than "size adjustment" (i.e., evolutionary character displacement).

Hendrickson (1981) corrected some errors in the source pool and island lists of Strong et al. (1979). He noted that the mean was a biased measure of central tendency, and that it was more appropriate to compare observed ratios with the median of the ratios for simulated communities. Using the same null model as Strong et al. (1979), his reanalysis revealed significant patterns consistent with the character displacement hypothesis for three variables: wing length of the Tres Marias birds and bill depth and length of Galápagos *Geospiza*. Strong and Simberloff (1981) responded that two or three significant results out of a battery of more than 15 statistical tests was hardly overwhelming evidence, and that means and medians of ratios for simulated communities were quite similar. They also suggested that if character displacement were important for the Tres Marias birds, its effects should have been manifest in some measure of bill morphology rather than in wing length.

Case and Sidell (1983) examined the performance of the Strong et al. (1979) procedure for a hypothetical community that was structured by competition.

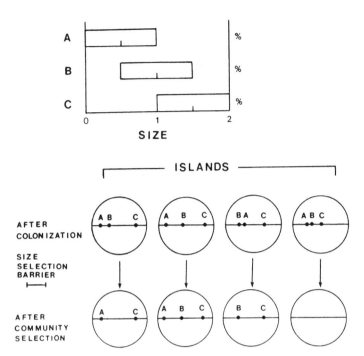

Figure 6.8. Community-wide selection following island colonization. The top figure gives body size distributions of three hypothetical colonizing species. Body sizes are drawn randomly from each distribution to seed the islands. If pairs of species are closer together than the size selection barrier, one of the pair becomes extinct. The resulting community has been randomly assembled with a limit to similarity. From Case and Sidell (1983), with permission.

They started with a three-species mainland community in which body size distributions were uniform and overlapped somewhat between species (median body size ranks: A < B < C). Next, a series of islands was colonized from this source pool by drawing a colonist randomly from each of the three size distributions. These three-species assemblages were then subjected to a size difference barrier, s. If any pair of species was closer in size than s, the interior of the two went extinct, and the assemblage collapsed to two species. This scenario of "size-assortment" corresponds to nonevolutionary models of limiting similarity (MacArthur and Levins 1967), in which communities are sorted through colonization and extinction (Figure 6.8).

If s was zero, then all three species coexisted, and the observed size distribution matched that in the source pool. As s increased, the system was dominated by two-species islands. The AC combination occurred more frequently than AB

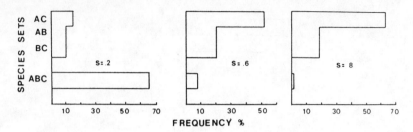

Figure 6.9. Expected frequency of different species combinations as a function of the size selection barrier (s). As the limit to similarity increases, species pair AC comes to dominate the archipelago, because species A and C are most dissimilar in size in the initial source pool. From Case and Sidell (1983), with permission.

or BC, because species A and C were most dissimilar in size in the original mainland pool (Figure 6.9). Finally, the observed island assemblage (which was competitively structured) was randomized and tested with the Strong et al. (1979) procedure.

Average size differences between species in the observed assemblage were always greater than in the null assemblage, which is consistent with a pattern of size assortment. However, the expectation from the null model closely tracked the observed assemblage; the two values were usually within one standard deviation of each other. Thus, the Strong et al. (1979) test may lack power, because the null community too closely reflected the properties of the observed assemblage. Results were similar for models in which colonizing species were sampled equiprobably versus proportionally to their frequency of occurrence, in which the body size distributions were Gaussian versus uniform, and in which species number was low versus high.

The match between the observed and expected size differences seemed to reflect the fact that different species pairs behaved differently in Case and Sidell's (1983) model. Size assortment caused a divergence in species pairs AB and BC because these species could not coexist if they were too similar in size. However, species pair AC actually showed a convergence with size assortment—the observed size difference was smaller than expected. This unexpected result was due to interactions with species B. If species A and C were too dissimilar in size, then species B persisted. The only cases in which A and C coexisted but B did not were those in which the body size differences, by chance, were less than in the source pool fauna. Because the Strong et al. (1979) test relied on average size differences (or ratios) between similar (AB or BC) and dissimilar (AC) species pairs, these patterns would be obscured, and the null model expectation would resemble the observed community.

Using a more complex evolutionary model, Colwell and Winkler (1984) also had trouble detecting significant patterns of size displacement with randomization tests. They used models of stochastic phylogenies (Raup et al. 1973) with phenotypic characters (bill length and depth) that also evolved stochastically at each speciation event. Size barriers to coexistence on islands were established, and communities were randomized according to typical null model protocols. Euclidian distances in morphological space were calculated for all assemblages, before and after competition, and before and after randomization. Three potential biases in null model tests emerged from a comparison of these hypothetical assemblages:

1. *The Narcissus effect*. Sampling from a postcompetition pool underestimated the role of competition, because its effect was already incorporated in the source pool.
2. *The Icarus effect*. Correlations between vagility and morphology sometimes obscured the effects of competition in morphological comparisons of mainland and island biotas.
3. *The J. P. Morgan effect*. The weaker the taxonomic constraint on sampling, the harder it became to detect competition.

As in Case and Sidell's (1983) analyses, the direction of the null model comparison for observed and expected distances was correct (for first nearest neighbors in morphological space): observed communities were morphologically overdispersed compared to randomized assemblages. However, the power of the randomization was weak, compared to this evolutionary model of community assembly.

In spite of these results, Monte Carlo methods may still be valid if the patterns are strong. For example, the average size ratios for coexisting beetle species in the genus *Pterostichus* were larger in undisturbed habitats than ratios in randomly assembled communities (Brandl and Topp 1985), whereas a similar analysis yielded random or small ratios for tiger beetle assemblages (Pearson and Juliano 1991). Both studies showed that the results depended greatly on the particular habitat under consideration. We suspect that habitat affinities and source pool construction are likely to be at least as important as null model structure in determining the results of ratio tests (see Epilogue).

TESTS FOR SIZE ADJUSTMENT AND SIZE ASSORTMENT

Case and Sidell (1983) proposed two tests for community-wide character displacement, based on an analysis of size differences of particular species pairs in an archipelago. Their test for size assortment ranked all possible pairs, triplets, quintuplets, etc., of species by the average difference in body size within each combination. The median of this ranking was the null expectation for the size difference of a randomly chosen species combination. Next, the number of species combinations above and below this median was tallied. If size assortment is important, there should be an excess of species combinations with large body size differences and a deficit of species combinations with small body size differences.

To test for size adjustment, Case and Sidell (1983) created random assemblages following the Strong et al. (1979) procedure, using either weighted or unweighted colonization probabilities. After randomization, they calculated average (or minimum) size ratios for the observed and randomized communities. The difference between the observed (O) and expected (E) size ratio for each assemblage was measured as a standardized deviate ($(O - E)/E$). Next, the assemblages were ranked in order from those with the largest average body size differences to those with the smallest. Finally, the standardized deviate for each assemblage was plotted against its rank.

If the assemblages in an archipelago had been structured by evolutionary size adjustment, species combinations with dissimilar body sizes (low ranking) would show little or no divergence, whereas those combinations with similar body sizes (high ranking) would show substantial divergence. Therefore, size adjustment should generate a positive relationship between the standardized deviate for each community and its rank of body size difference.

Case and Sidell (1983) applied these tests in yet another reanalysis of the Galápagos finches, after first correcting some errors in the Strong et al. (1979) and Hendrickson (1981) data sets. For both *Geospiza* and *Camarhynchus,* Case and Sidell (1983) found a significant pattern of size assortment but no evidence of size adjustment. Size assortment was also evident in four feeding guilds (frugivores, gleaning insectivores, flycatchers, and nectarivores) of the West Indian avifauna (Case et al. 1983). Null expectations were generated both by randomization of the archipelago populations and by sampling from a mainland source pool of Colombian birds in these same guilds.

Case (1983b) also applied these tests to assemblages of *Cnemidophorus* lizards in three regions of North American desert, and found evidence for size assortment of coexisting *Cnemidophorus* in the Trans-Pecos region. However, Case's (1983b) analysis excluded sites that supported the common *C. exsanguis-C. gularis* species pair. When these sites are included in the analysis, there is no pattern of size assortment (Schall 1993).

A serious shortcoming of the Case and Sidell (1983) tests is the assumption of equiprobable dispersal by species in the absence of competitive effects. Two species of dissimilar body size might not be competing with each other, but if they were both widely distributed, they would co-occur frequently, and this pattern would yield a significant result. Case and Sidell's (1983) test for size assortment further assumes that all islands are equally inhabitable for all species. The test for size adjustment does not make this assumption, because it holds observed species number constant in the simulations. Although Case and Sidell (1983) cautioned against weighting colonization probabilities by observed frequencies of occurrence, we think it is prudent to carry out weighted and unweighted analyses. If both give similar results, then the patterns are robust to assumptions about occurrence frequency. On the other hand, differing results would suggest that patterns of character displacement can be accounted for by different frequencies of occurrence of species on islands rather than by competitive structuring (see also Wilson 1995).

RATIO TESTS FOR MULTIPLE ASSEMBLAGES

Whereas ratio tests for single assemblages may be weak in statistical power, multiple assemblages may reveal consistent ratio patterns. Schoener (1984) examined size ratios of sympatric bird-eating hawks, using a worldwide list of 47 species as his source pool. For sympatric assemblages of n species, he enumerated all possible $n-1$ adjacent size ratios. Corresponding ratios in the source pool formed the null distribution. As in Tonkyn and Cole's (1986) analyses, these null distributions were concave upward and decreased from a maximum of very small size ratios (1.00–1.05). Schoener (1984) used a non-parametric Kolmogorov-Smirnov (K-S) test to compare the observed distribution of ratios with the source pool distribution. Most sets of ratios differed significantly by this test, with too many large ratios present in the sympatric groups compared to the source pool (Figure 6.4).

We note three points about Schoener's (1984) test. The first is that the K-S test does not indicate how the observed and expected distributions deviate from one another. For the hawk data, the absence or rarity of very small ratios was the most striking feature of the data. Other peaks in the observed distribution are more difficult to interpret. Second, the K-S test may be inappropriate for comparing observed and expected ratios because the two distributions are not independent of one another. Schoener (1984) controlled for this problem by removing species from the source pool that were actually present in a particular assemblage. Results were generally comparable with the original analysis, although sample sizes were seriously depleted. Schoener (1984) also obtained comparable results when the distributions were weighted by the amount of geographic overlap between particular pairs of species. Finally, Schoener's (1984) test will be powerful only for large data sets. If small numbers of species in ecological guilds are tested, it will always be difficult to detect significant patterns.

Eldridge and Johnson (1988) used Schoener's (1984) method to analyze the distribution of size differences in mixed-species flocks of sandpipers. Size ratios in observed flocks did not differ from random subsets of species that use the North Dakota migration corridor. However, the assemblage of North Dakota species had too many intermediate-sized ratios ($1.2 \leq r < 1.3$) compared to Western Hemisphere and global source pools. With respect to bill size, mixed species flocks were a random subset of a non-random source pool. Eldridge and Johnson (1988) speculated that past, but not present, competition may be important in the size structure of these assemblages.

Hopf and Brown (1986) presented an intriguing ratio test in which the ratio line segments were rescaled to a frequency of 1.0, projected from the edge of a unit simplex, and compared with the placement of random points on a "bull's-eye" target. Communities that were characterized by "even" distributions (i.e., constant size ratios) tended to fall disproportionately toward the center of the target. Hopf and Brown (1986) showed that for some assemblages, this bull's-eye test was more powerful than a modified version of the Simberloff and Boecklen (1981) protocol, although Arita's (1993) simulations suggested this will not always be true.

Two cautions should be noted for the bull's-eye test. First, the test is equivalent to using Simpson's diversity index to assess evenness of the distribution (Hopf and Brown 1986:1141), so it is vulnerable to the sample-size dependence that plagues most diversity indices (see Chapter 2). These problems are especially severe at small sample sizes, where systematic and stochastic errors of up to 20% are possible (Hopf and Brown 1986:1143). Second, the test was not designed to assess the significance of any particular assemblage, but rather to standardize the degree of evenness in body size distributions of repeated assemblages and reveal whether there was an overall trend toward evenness.

It is a difficult problem to determine how "independent" multiple assemblages really are. Only if each site contains a different set of species can we be confident that these represent distinct "natural experiments." But if some species occur repeatedly in different assemblages, the interpretation becomes more difficult. On the one hand, the recurrence of the same species combinations may, itself, be an important sign of nonrandom structuring of a community, as discussed in Chapter 7. On the other hand, certain species combinations may be the product of independent dispersal or habitat affinities that do not reflect interspecific interactions. In this case, a comparison of multiple assemblages inflates the degrees of freedom and may lead to an inappropriate rejection of the null hypothesis. The only possible solutions to this problem are to delete redundant species and repeat the analyses (e.g., Schoener 1984) or to use phylogenetic information to decide what constitutes independent species assemblages (e.g., Losos 1990).

MULTIVARIATE ANALYSES

Although much of the size ratio literature is based on simple univariate measures of body size, these may be misleading. Tests of morphological patterns frequently yield different results depending on which particular character is chosen for analysis (Hendrickson 1981; Wiens 1982). At the same time, morphological characters are highly correlated with one another (Mosiman and James 1979, Bookstein 1984). Allometric constraints lead to predictable patterns of shape that are correlated with change in body size (Cherry et al. 1982). Finally, if niche segregation occurs along several different axes, it may be necessary to measure more than one morphological variable to adequately characterize niche segregation (Pianka et al. 1979).

For all these reasons, multivariate analyses of morphological pattern may give more insight into community structure than univariate tests. Karr and James (1975) pioneered the technique of using principal components analysis (and other multivariate methods) to study a set of correlated morphological variables. The principal components are a set of orthogonal composite variables that account for the maximum amount of variation in the original data (Hotelling 1933). Because much of the variation in morphology may be explained by the first few principal component axes, the dimensionality of the original data set can be reduced (Gauch 1982).

Unfortunately, multivariate analysis has been greatly abused by ecologists (James and McCulloch 1990). The common practice of representing species as points in multivariate space, drawing polygons (or amoebas) around groups of species, and interpreting the results often amounts to ecological palmistry. Ad hoc "explanations" often are based on the original untransformed variables, so that the multivariate transformation offers no more insight than the original variables did. Because multivariate techniques maximize the amount of variation explained by a transformed axis (principal components analysis), or maximize the separation between groups (discriminant analysis), apparent patterns in multivariate space may arise from data sets created with a random number generator (Karr and Martin 1981). Consequently, it is important to compare the patterns in multivariate analysis against a properly formulated null model.

Even apparently clear-cut patterns of convergence or divergence (e.g., Fuentes 1976) may arise from neutral models that do not include these processes (Crowder 1980; but see Fuentes 1980).

Two types of community structure have been inferred from multivariate analyses of morphology. (1) Overdispersion of morphology, which is measured within a community and is assumed to reflect competition for food resources (Ricklefs and Travis 1980). It is the multivariate analog of size ratio analyses. (2) Convergence of morphology, which is measured between communities and is assumed to reflect evolutionary convergence of unrelated species that live in similar environments (Cody 1974). Convergence can be measured for a single community (the opposite of overdispersion), but it usually involves broad morphological comparisons of communities with different evolutionary histories (Wiens 1991b). Null models have been used frequently for tests of overdispersion, but have been underutilized in studies of convergence. In the following sections, we review null model tests of these hypotheses.

Overdispersion of Morphology

Gatz (1979) analyzed 56 morphological characters measured for co-occurring stream fishes of the Piedmont of North Carolina. Points representing each species were placed in a nine-dimensional factor space that was calculated from the original morphological variables. Null assemblages were constructed by choosing random points along each factor axis and then projecting them into the morphological space. For both real and simulated assemblages, Gatz (1979) calculated the Euclidian distances between all possible pairs of species and measured the number of times the observed distributions overlapped with the simulated. Compared to the null model, there were too many species pairs with unusually small or unusually large Euclidian distances.

Gatz's (1979) procedure is the multivariate analog of Lawlor's (1980b) randomization algorithm RA1 for resource utilization analyses (see discussion in Chapters 4 and 5). In RA1, resource utilizations for each species are replaced by a uniform [0,1] random number. The resulting overlaps always have a high mean and low variance (Pianka et al. 1979; Winemiller and Pianka 1990). Gatz (1979) concluded that Euclidian distances within his assemblage were nonrandom, but the comparisons were based on a rather extreme null model that did not preserve natural covariation among morphological traits.

Although Gatz (1979) attributed the nonrandomness to interspecific competition, he also explored the alternative hypothesis that phylogenetic correlates were responsible for the patterns. He analyzed Euclidian distances between sympatrically occurring members of a single family or genus and obtained

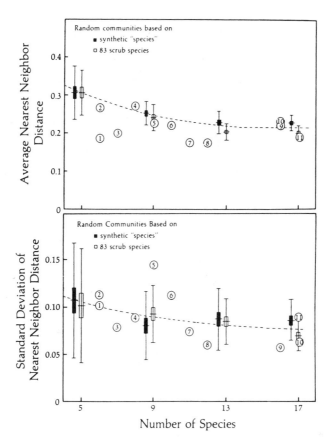

Figure 6.10. Morphological mean and standard deviation of nearest-neighbor distances for 11 shrubsteppe bird communities (Cody 1974). Each number refers to a different observed assemblage. Null distributions were based on 20 random draws of observed source pool species or construction of hypothetical "synthetic species." Means were slightly less than expected, indicating weak convergence, whereas standard deviations matched the null model predictions. From Ricklefs and Travis (1980), with permission of the American Ornithologists' Union.

comparable results with analyses of the complete assemblage. Although the randomization algorithm (RA1) was primitive, Gatz's (1979) study is noteworthy for its use of null models and consideration of phylogeny in the context of ecomorphology.

Ricklefs and Travis (1980) constructed null assemblages by either drawing species lists from a larger source pool and maintaining observed morphological features, or randomly generating "synthetic species" by substituting each factor score with a random, normal deviate, similar to Gatz's (1979) protocol. Species packing was measured by the average nearest-neighbor distance in morphological space, and the evenness of species packing was measured by the standard deviation of nearest-neighbor distances.

Ricklefs and Travis (1980) applied this protocol to morphological data for 11 temperate zone avian communities (Cody 1974). Mean nearest-neighbor distances were somewhat less than expected, whereas standard deviations usually matched the predictions of the null model (Figure 6.10). However, there were differences in the morphological structure of large and small assemblages. Species were added nonrandomly near the edge of morphological space, mostly along novel morphological dimensions. For Neotropical avian communities, the results varied widely among localities. Species packing was unusually even, and nearest-neighbor distances were overdispersed for communities on small islands in the Lesser Antilles (Travis and Ricklefs 1983). These results were consistent with guild analyses of tropical hummingbirds, which were also overdispersed in morphology (Brown and Bowers 1985; Ranta 1986).

Ricklefs et al. (1981) used similar methods to analyze the morphological structure of lizard assemblages in desert habitats. Australian assemblages were more loosely packed in morphological space than North American or African assemblages. However, the means and standard deviations of nearest-neighbor distances did not differ significantly from those of null communities that were randomly assembled from continental source pools. For North American lizard communities, observed nearest-neighbor distances were always greater than predicted by the null model, but all of these assemblages contained the same four core species and may not represent independent samples. Lizard communities from a variety of temperate-zone habitats in North America showed no evidence for overdispersion in either morphology or habitat use (Scheibe 1987).

Concordance of Morphology

Studies of concordance in morphology involve comparisons of two or more assemblages of unrelated species that evolve morphological similarity in similar environments (Cody 1973). Relatively little null model work has been done on this topic. Current tests use analysis of variance models to partition morphological variation into components of "habitat," which presumably reflect convergence due to similar environments, and components of "region," which presumably reflect unique historical or phylogenetic effects on morphology (Schluter 1986b; Schluter and Ricklefs 1993). Schluter (1990) recommended tests for a more specific hypothesis of species-for-species matching, in which ecologically equivalent sets of species are found in similar habitats at different locations. The null hypothesis here is that differences in body size of species matched between two assemblages are no smaller than would be expected by chance. Schluter (1990) found that the left-hand tail of conventional statistical distributions (chi-squared, F-ratio) matched simulated distributions in which species body sizes in a community were assigned randomly within a given range. He used the test to show that body size distributions of rodents from the Great Basin and the Sonoran Desert were "too close" to be expected by chance (but see Lomolino 1993). However, the species-for-species matching test may be unsuitable if some species occur in both locations or if species richness differs between locations. Because concordance is not necessarily the same as matching or similarity (Wiens 1991b), a broader test for convergence may require detailed comparisons of the morphology of closely related species in different habitats and different regions (e.g., Niemi 1985).

Morphology and Abundance

The studies described so far have searched for associations between morphology and coexistence. These analyses assume not only that morphology and resource use are intimately related (Miles et al. 1987), but that competitive effects are strong enough to cause the extinction (or exclusion) of species. Alternatively, there may be relationships between morphology and abundance of coexisting species that do not reflect competitive exclusion. For example, the morphology of coexisting gastropod species in a New York lake was random when compared to an unweighted null model, but significantly over-dispersed when compared to a model in which colonization probabilities were proportional to abundance (Dillon 1981).

James and Boecklen (1984) examined the relationship between abundance and morphology for an assemblage of forest birds in Maryland that was censused in seven consecutive years. Few significant patterns emerged. For example, density correlations (and nearest-neighbor distances) between species were unrelated to size and shape differences (Figure 6.11). Common species had no greater influence on the abundance of their nearest morphological neighbors than did rare species, and the density and variability of populations was not different for species near the edge versus the center of morphological space. Results were comparable for analyses at the guild level, and James and Boecklen (1984) concluded that competitive relationships did not structure the abundance or morphology of species in this assemblage. Wiens and Rotenberry (1980) arrived at a similar conclusion from a more detailed long-term study of

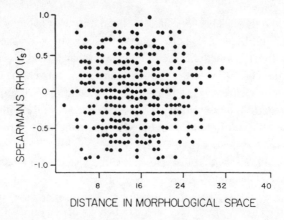

Figure 6.11. Pairwise density correlations and morphological distances for an avian assemblage in a Maryland woodland. Each point represents a different pair of species. If competition were organizing this community, morphologically similar species pairs should have shown negative density correlations. From James, F. C., and W. J. Boecklen. Interspecific morphological relationships and the densities of birds. In: *Ecological Communities: Conceptual Issues and the Evidence*. D. R. Strong, Jr., D. Simberloff, L. G. Abele, and A. B. Thistle (eds). Copyright © 1984 by Princeton University Press. Reprinted by permission of Princeton University Press.

shrubsteppe bird assemblages that included quantitative measures of habitat structure, resource availability, and dietary overlap.

In an assemblage of butterfly fishes, Findley and Findley (1985) also failed to find any relationship between morphology, diet, and abundance. These results, combined with the null model tests of Sale and Williams (1982), contradicted earlier claims of competitive structure in reef fish communities (Anderson et al. 1981). Although regional comparisons of community structure frequently are attributed to competitive effects, detailed studies of resource use, morphology, and abundance of local assemblages often do not support these explanations, even though this is the spatial scale at which strong competitive interactions ought to be most clearly expressed (Sale 1984).

Morphology and Evolutionary Extinction

One difficulty with analyzing present-day assemblages is that ecological extinctions or evolutionary shifts in morphology are not observed but must be inferred indirectly. If we knew the temporal record of species extinctions, it might be easier to evaluate the significance of morphological relationships among surviving species.

Fossil assemblages can give some insight into long-term patterns of extinction and morphology. For example, Foote (1991) tested whether species extinctions of fossil blastoids were random with respect to morphology. He measured eight morphological features of 85 species and characterized the position of each species in morphological space with a principal components analysis. Rarefaction and random sampling were then used to describe changes in taxonomic and morphological diversity in the fossil record. Generic richness of the blastoidea peaked in the Lower Carboniferous, but morphological diversity did not reach a peak until the Permian. Stochastic simulations of taxonomic and morphological evolution also yielded clades whose morphological diversity peaked later than taxonomic diversity. Because extinctions in the blastoid assemblage appeared to be random with respect to morphology, morphological diversity was maintained and even increased in the face of major taxonomic extinctions.

Morphology and Ecological Extinction

In ecological time, can extinctions be predicted on the basis of morphology or other species attributes? From the conservation perspective, there is great interest in knowing whether extinctions occur randomly with respect to body size, habitat affinity, or trophic status (Karr 1982a,b; Diamond 1983; Pimm et al. 1988). However, extinctions are difficult to measure systematically, and we must often rely on natural experiments (and null models) to study the process. A controversial study of extinctions in the Hawaiian avifauna illustrates some of the difficulties.

Moulton and Pimm (1983, 1986, 1987) argued that extinction of introduced species in the Hawaiian Islands could be predicted on the basis of body size or morphology, and that these patterns were caused primarily by competition among introduced species. For example, introduced pairs of congeneric species that both survived on at least one island ($n = 6$ pairs) differed more in bill length (22%) than congeneric pairs in which one of the pair went extinct (9%; $n = 9$ pairs; Moulton 1985). The morphology of the surviving species also appeared non-random. For three of the six major Hawaiian islands, introduced species of forest passeriformes were overdispersed in morphological space compared to random draws of species from the set of all introduced forest passerines (Moulton and Pimm 1987). Introduced finches of Oahu (Moulton and Lockwood 1992) and introduced passeriformes of Tahiti (Lockwood et al. 1993) also exhibited morphological overdispersion (Figure 6.12).

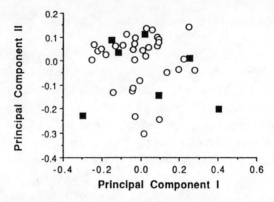

Figure 6.12. Morphological overdispersion of introduced bird species on the island of Tahiti. The surviving species (filled squares) were significantly overdispersed in comparison to random subsets of all introduced species. From Lockwood, J. L., M. P. Moulton, and S. K. Anderson. 1993. Morphological assortment and the assembly of communities of introduced passeriforms on oceanic islands: Tahiti versus Oahu. *American Naturalist* 141:398–408. Copyright © 1993 by The University of Chicago. Reprinted by permission of the publisher.

Simberloff and Boecklen (1991) challenged the Hawaiian results and argued that evidence for competition was not so clear-cut. They pointed out that most species introduced to the islands were either highly successful or consistent losers. Out of 41 species that were introduced on more than one island, 21 succeeded on all the islands to which they were introduced, 16 failed on all islands, and only four species showed mixed results. Apparently, each species was intrinsically successful or not at establishment, and successful introductions had little to do with the size or composition of the resident or introduced avifauna of the island. If this "all-or-none" hypothesis is true, then whatever patterns of overdispersion may have been present in the source pool would be retained in the subsets of introduced species on each island. Moulton (1993) countered that biases from phylogeny, errors in Simberloff and Boecklen's (1991) data matrix, and differences in the number of islands per introduction refuted the all-or-none hypothesis and reaffirmed the role of competition.

The debate rests ultimately on the quality of the introduction and extinction data. In this case, the data are a heterogeneous collection of checklists (e.g., Henshaw 1902), surveys (e.g., Donagho 1965), secondary sources (Long 1981), and records from *Elepaio,* the monthly publication of the Hawaiian Audubon Society. This information required a number of arbitrary judgment calls to quantify introduction and extinction dates; even still, some species extinction dates could only be estimated to the nearest decade.

Consequently, the patterns described by Moulton and Pimm (1983, 1986, 1987) are extremely fragile and probably would not be replicated if another investigator extracted the data from the same sources. To cite just one example from Simberloff and Boecklen (1991), two species of cardinal (*Paroaria*) both survived on Hawaii, but Moulton (1985) did not include them in the analysis of congeneric species pairs because he felt it was likely they were allopatric. With such small sample sizes, this sort of judgment call will greatly affect any statistical analysis. We think there are so many problems of misidentification, errors in taxonomy and nomenclature, irregular and incomplete censuses, and sightings of vagrants, nonbreeders, or cage-released birds that it is impossible to evaluate the ecological significance of the results.

This is not the first time that avian ecologists have been plagued by unreliable census data. Controversies over avian extinctions in the California Channel Islands (Diamond 1969; Lynch and Johnson 1974; Jones and Diamond 1976), in remnant forest patches (Whitcomb et al. 1977; McCoy 1982), and on Barro Colorado Island (Willis 1974; Karr 1982a,b) highlight the dangers of inferring extinctions from historical records or short-term censuses. Extinction data for island birds of Great Britain probably are more reliable, and Pimm et al. (1988) concluded that large-bodied species were most vulnerable to extinction. However, these conclusions hinged upon the precise way that extinctions are measured (Haila and Hanski 1993). The disappearance of species may have depended more on island attributes such as area or isolation than on intrinsic properties of species (Tracy and George 1992; but see Diamond and Pimm 1993; Tracy and George 1993).

This is not to say that it is impossible to measure avian extinctions accurately, but the task requires intensive, systematic surveys using reliable census techniques (e.g., Haila and Järvinen 1981). The lesson is obvious: no matter how sophisticated the null model, the results are meaningless if the underlying data cannot be trusted.

EMPIRICAL TESTS

The size ratio controversies have been good for community ecology. Not only have recent studies of size overlap used more rigorous statistical analyses, but they have incorporated data on geographic variation in morphology, patterns of resource use, and even experimental manipulations to understand the mechanisms behind the patterns. These approaches are illustrated in the following examples.

Ecological Character Displacement in the Red Fox

Dayan, Tchernov, et al. (1989) provided persuasive biogeographic evidence suggesting character displacement between the red fox (*Vulpes vulpes*) and Ruppell's sand fox (*Vulpes ruppelli*). These species are sympatric in the Saharo-Arabian region, where they exhibit unusually constant size ratios (1.18–1.21) in lower carnassial length, as measured by the Barton and David (1956) test applied to the sexes separately. Both species are sympatric with Blanford's fox (*Vulpes cana*), in Israel where there was also unusual constancy in size ratios of tooth dimensions for sites with all three species present (Figure 6.13).

The red fox is allopatric with Ruppell's and Blanford's foxes throughout most of the Palearctic. In regions of allopatry, tooth size is strongly correlated with latitude and temperature, with large-toothed populations in the north (Bergmann's rule). But in regions of sympatry, the slope of the relationship is significantly more shallow. Thus, size ratios of sympatric populations are unusually constant, despite strong clinal variation in tooth size. This pattern meets one of the criteria set forth in Grant (1972a) for geographic tests of character displacement. Although resource availability is not known for the foxes, the pattern of constant size ratios in the face of latitudinal variation in tooth dimensions is compelling evidence for ecological character displacement.

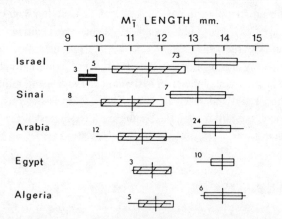

Figure 6.13. Lower carnassial lengths of three foxes in the Saharo-Arabian region. Vertical lines represent means, horizontal lines represent ranges, bars represent two standard deviations. Empty bars = red fox (*Vulpes vulpes*); shaded bars = Ruppell's sand fox (*Vulpes ruppelli*); blackened bar = Blanford's fox (*Vulpes cana*). Size ratios for these assemblages varied between 1.18 and 1.21, and were unusually constant by the Barton and David (1956) test. From Dayan, Tchernov, et al. (1989), with permission.

This study is one of several that have revealed evidence for character displacement in assemblages of mammalian carnivores. Other examples include canids of Israel (Dayan et al. 1990, 1992) and North American mustelids (Dayan, Simberloff, et al. 1989; but see Harvey and Ralls 1985). Patterns were much weaker for sympatric tropical cats (Kiltie 1984, 1988).

Competition and Morphology of Co-occurring Dytiscid Beetles

Juliano and Lawton (1990a) tested for widely and regularly distributed body forms in assemblages of co-occurring dytiscid water beetles. The morphology of each species was represented by canonical discriminant analysis of four morphometric variables. The average nearest-neighbor distance and the variance of nearest-neighbor distances were interpreted as measures of species dispersion and regularity of niche packing.

Random assemblages were constructed by sampling from the total source pool (Strong et al. 1979) and by creating synthetic species in morphological space (Ricklefs and Travis 1980). Null assemblages were constructed for the entire species list, for the abundant species, and for species in the dominant genus *Hydroporus*. The results depended on site characteristics. For seven small sites that were acidic and lacked fish, real and null assemblages were not significantly different. For two large sites that were well buffered and had fish, morphological distances between species were larger and more regular than expected by chance.

Juliano and Lawton (1990b) next tested experimentally whether these patterns were the result of interspecific competition. The null model analyses led to the prediction of competition at large, well-buffered sites, but not at small, acidic sites. At one of the small, acidic ditches, the feeding rate of dytiscid beetles was unaffected by manipulation of adult density and was unrelated to the presence of competing species, regardless of their body size. However, there was evidence of competition for food and of cannibalism in the larval stages. In a large, well-buffered canal, the feeding rate declined with increasing density, but the effect was unrelated to body size of competing species, and adults did not appear to be food-limited at natural densities.

The results suggest that nonrandom body size spacing was not necessarily related to interspecific competition. The difference in body size patterns may instead have been related to the presence of predators, although a link between prey body morphology and predator avoidance has not been established in this system. The results also suggest that competition in the larval stages was considerably more important than interactions among adults in determining community composition.

Few other studies have used this double-barreled approach of null models combined with experimental manipulations. An interesting contrast to the dytiscid beetle system is the desert rodent assemblages of North America, for which null models and field experiments have yielded consistent results. Large-scale field manipulations have demonstrated competition for limited seed supplies (Brown et al. 1979; Brown and Munger 1985), and null model simulations revealed that common species of similar body size (mass ratios < 1.5) co-occurred less frequently and overlapped less in geographic range than expected by chance (Bowers and Brown 1982). Body size distributions of local assemblages were also more uniform than in regional or continental source pools (Brown and Nicoletto 1991). Community ecology needs more of these studies that combine experimental manipulations with null model analyses.

Bill Sizes of Galápagos Finches

Bill sizes of Galápagos ground finches (*Geospiza*) are one of the most well-known and controversial examples of character displacement (Lack 1947; Bowman 1961; Grant 1972a; Strong et al. 1979; Grant and Abbott 1980). Bill sizes for each species vary dramatically between islands, and the differences seem to correspond to the presence or absence of other finch species. These patterns may be explained by competition among species (Lack 1947) or by differences in food supply among islands (Bowman 1961). The initial null models of Strong et al. (1979) revealed little evidence for character displacement, whereas the reanalysis of Hendrickson (1981) and the null models of Case and Sidell (1983) suggested nonrandomness in morphology of coexisting species. Simberloff (1983b) reassessed the early null model studies and concluded that a substantial majority of tests revealed displacement in *Geospiza* bill morphology that was consistent with interspecific competition. All of these statistical analyses were based on lists of coexisting species on islands and measurements of average bill and body sizes for finch populations on each island.

Schluter and Grant (1984) resolved the controversy with new data on seed biomass and hardness, bill depth, and finch biomass, based on many years of field work. These data were incorporated into a series of null models that attempted to explain the co-occurrence and morphology of *Geospiza*. Schluter and Grant (1984) first estimated the expected population density on each island as a function of bill size for a hypothetical solitary species of granivorous finch (Figure 6.14).

These functions correspond to resource availability curves in models of character displacement and limiting similarity. In contrast to the simplifying assumptions of theory (MacArthur and Levins 1967; Slatkin 1980), these

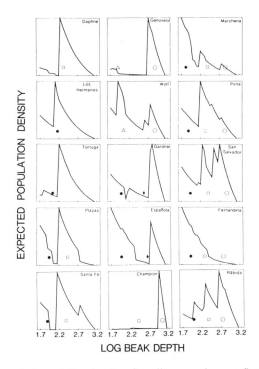

Figure 6.14. Expected population density of a solitary granivorous finch species on 15 Galápagos Islands. Points represent observed bill depths of species present on each island ● = *Geospiza fuliginosa;* □ = *G. fortis*; ○ = *G. magnirostris;* Δ = *G. difficilis;* ♦ = *G. conirostris.* Note the polymodal peaks of expected density and the wide spacing of species from one another. Such spacing was unlikely for null models that did not incorporate species interactions. From Schluter, D., and P. R. Grant. 1984. Determinants of morphological patterns in communities of Darwin's finches. *American Naturalist* 123:175–196. Copyright © 1984 by The University of Chicago. Reprinted by permission of the publisher.

empirically derived curves were not uniform or Gaussian in shape, but complexly polymodal. The modes represented bill sizes that might be expected for a species in the absence of competition. The curves formed the basis for five null models that were tested against the observed data. These null models predicted the minimum difference in bill size for communities that were assembled according to the following rules:

Model 1. Random Assembly/Evolution. Food supply set the range of permissible bill sizes, and all bill sizes were equiprobable within this range. This model is similar to the Barton and David (1956) test, although the range was set by food supply rather than by the largest and smallest species in the assemblage.

Model 2. Partly Directed Assembly. All bill sizes were possible, but the probability of persistence on an island was proportional to available food supply. Thus, for a given island, the most likely bill sizes were those that corresponded to peaks in available food supply. Differences in morphology of finch populations between islands would reflect differences in resource availability, which was essentially Bowman's (1961) explanation.

Model 3. Directed Evolution. Only bill sizes corresponding to peaks in resource availability were permissible. This model assumed natural selection optimized the mean phenotype and that each species evolved independently. Bill size differences for a pair of species might be zero if they were randomly assigned to the same resource peak. This would always happen for islands that had fewer peaks than species.

Model 4. Directed Assembly with Competitive Exclusion. Whereas the first three models assumed no species interaction, this model assumed that the presence of other species could lead to competitive exclusion. Species were allowed to colonize an island randomly, but they would persist only if their bill sizes allowed them access to at least some exclusive food resources. This is a model of limiting similarity, in which colonization and extinction dynamics determine the combinations and sizes of species that can coexist, given the constraints of the available resource spectrum.

Model 5. Directed Coevolution Under Interspecific Competition. This model assumed that natural selection adjusted the mean phenotype of a species to maximize its population size, conditional on the morphology of other species present on the island. Coevolution between birds and seed plants was not considered. For this model, Schluter and Grant (1984) enumerated expected population densities of all possible species combinations on an island, and then found the particular combination of phenotypes that maximized population sizes. Presumably, coevolution would adjust bill sizes until this optimum was reached. For islands with multiple resource peaks, multiple solutions were possible.

For each model, Schluter and Grant (1984) computed the probability of randomly obtaining the minimum observed size difference on each island. Models 1–3 included no competitive effects and could not account for observed bill size differences. Across all islands, observed bill size differences were too large to be accounted for by these null models. In contrast, there was a good fit between observed and expected bill sizes for models 4 and 5, although they were not assessed statistically in the same way as models 1–3. Schluter and Grant (1984) suggested that model 4 (size assortment) might be preferable to model 5 (size adjustment) because morphology on islands was predictable, but species combinations were not. This interpretation is consistent with Case and Sidell's (1983) analyses. On the other hand, the proximity of *Geospiza fortis* and *G. fuliginosa* to theoretical resource peaks was different in sympatry and allopatry, suggesting evolutionary size adjustment, at least for this species pair (Schluter et al. 1985). Given all the controversy surrounding the analysis of size ratios, the Galápagos *Geospiza* may represent one of the few unequivocal examples of character displacement.

RECOMMENDATIONS

For tests of single assemblages, we recommend the Barton and David (1956) and Irwin (1955) tests as simple (but conservative) measures of ratio constancy and minima. For multiple assemblages with intraspecific variation, we recommend the Monte Carlo algorithm of Strong et al. (1979), but with the modifications suggested by Hendrickson (1981) and Grant and Abbott (1980). The weighted versions of Case and Sidell's (1983) tests may also be useful for distinguishing between patterns of size adjustment and size assortment. Schluter's (1990) test should be used for patterns of species-for-species matching, and Ricklefs and Travis's (1980) procedures should be used in the analysis of multivariate data. The simulation version of Hopf and Brown's (1986) bull's-eye test is appropriate for examining size ratios in multiple assemblages. All of these tests can be greatly strengthened by incorporating independent measures of resource availability (Schluter and Grant 1984) and phylogeny (Losos 1990).

7
CO-OCCURRENCE

COMMUNITY ASSEMBLY

A pervasive theme in community ecology is that the species composition of a community is governed by deterministic "assembly rules" (Cody and Diamond 1975; Case and Diamond 1986). These rules emphasize the importance of interspecific interactions in determining which species are found in a particular assemblage (Drake 1990). We have already examined two such "rules" in this book: (1) species that overlap "too much" in phenology, resource use, or other niche dimensions cannot coexist (Chapters 4 and 5); (2) species that do coexist must differ in body size or trophic morphology by a critical minimum that allows them to exploit different resources (Chapter 6).

In this chapter, we consider related assembly rules that predict the presence and absence of particular species rather than their sizes or patterns of resource utilization. The significance and even the reality of such assembly rules have been widely debated in community ecology. Proponents have argued for the importance of resource exploitation (Diamond 1975), competitive hierarchies (Gilpin et al. 1986), and priority effects (Drake 1991) in producing assembly rules. Critics have complained that many of the rules are trivial tautologies that lack predictive power (Connor and Simberloff 1979) and that the evidence for consistent patterns of community structure, much less for assembly rules, is hardly compelling (Wiens 1980; Wilson 1991a).

Laboratory studies have provided the strongest evidence for assembly rules. For example, Gilpin et al. (1986) thoroughly explored competitive interactions among 28 species of *Drosophila*. They varied the level of food resources, the length of the experiments, and, most importantly, the initial combinations and densities of species. Competitive interactions were strong and predictable, and few species persisted until the end of the experiments. For example, experiments that started with 10 species always ended with fewer than four. With 10 initial species, there were $2^{10} = 1,024$ different possible species combinations, but fewer than a dozen of these persisted. These results contrast with nature, where dozens of *Drosophila* species may co-occur sympatrically.

Field experiments also provide some evidence for assembly rules. Abele (1984) experimentally "supersaturated" *Pocillopora* coral heads with component species of decapod crustaceans. Agonistic interactions and predation by voracious wrasses caused the fauna to "relax" to a predictable species number and composition for coral heads of a given size. Cole (1983) described assembly rules for five ant species on small mangrove islets in the Florida Keys. Two "primary species" (*Crematogaster ashmeidi* and *Xenomyrmex floridanus*) could never be introduced successfully on very small islands, perhaps because of frequent flooding. In contrast, the minimum island size occupied by two "secondary species" (*Pseudomyrmex elongatus* and *Zacryptocercus varians*) was set by the presence of primary species, which were superior competitors. The two primary species also did not coexist and formed a classic "checkerboard" pattern (Diamond 1975), in which only one of the two species, but not both, occurred on an island. Experimental transplants and behavioral arena experiments confirmed that aggressive interactions between workers prevented coexistence and that either primary species as an island resident could repulse an invader. Thus, observed species combinations could be predicted on the basis of island size and competitive relationships among colonizers.

However, the debate over assembly rules has not been concerned with such detailed experimental studies. Rather, the controversy has been over whether assembly rules can be inferred from nonexperimental data, specifically from combinations of coexisting species, usually on islands. Such data are conveniently summarized in a presence-absence matrix, which forms the fundamental unit of study in many analyses of community ecology and biogeography (McCoy and Heck 1987). Null models have been a useful tool for evaluating pattern in such matrices and for revealing the extent to which species combinations can be predicted on the basis of simple models of island colonization (Simberloff 1978a).

PRESENCE-ABSENCE MATRICES

Presence-absence matrices summarize data on the occurrence of a group of species at a set of sites (Table 7.1). The "sites" may range in size from 160-mm^2 vegetation quadrats (Watkins and Wilson 1992) to large oceanic islands (Diamond 1975) or entire continents (Smith 1983). Similarly, the set of "species" analyzed may be restricted to ecologically similar congeners (Graves and

Table 7.1
Presence-absence matrix for five fish taxa in 28 Australian springs

		Number of springs
Goby	x x x x x x x x x x x x x x x x x x x x x x x x x x x x	28
Gudgeon	x x x x x x x x x x x x x x x x x x x	19
Catfish	x x x x x x x x x x x x x x	14
Hardyhead	x x x x x x x x x	9
Perch	x x x x x x x	7
Number of species	5 5 5 5 5 5 4 4 4 4 3 3 3 3 2 2 2 2 2 1 1 1 1 1 1 1 1 1	

Each row is a different taxon and each column is a different site (= spring). Each x represents the occurrence of a taxon in a particular spring. Springs are ordered by species richness. Goby = *Chlamydogobius* sp.; Gudgeon = *Mogurnda mogurnda*; Catfish = *Neosilurus* sp.; Hardyhead = *Craterocephalus* sp.; Perch = *Leiopotherapon unicolor*. Note the nearly perfect pattern of nestedness. From Kodric-Brown and Brown (1993).

Gotelli 1993) or to ecological or trophic guilds (Heatwole and Levins 1972), or it may encompass entire avifaunas (Connor and Simberloff 1979).

In an $r \times c$ matrix, each row of the matrix represents a different species and each column represents a different site (Simberloff and Connor 1979). Each cell in the matrix (a_{ij}) contains a 0 or a 1, denoting, respectively, the absence or presence of species i on site j. The row sum R_i represents the total number of occurrences of each species; it ranges from a minimum of 1 to a maximum of c, the number of sites censused. Similarly, the column sum C_j gives the number of species censused on site j and ranges from a minimum of 1 to a maximum of r, the number of species recorded. The grand matrix sum N represents the total number of site occurrences.

ASSUMPTIONS UNDERLYING THE ANALYSIS OF PRESENCE-ABSENCE MATRICES

Before discussing the analysis of such matrices, it is important to consider the assumptions implicit in the choice of the sampling universe and hence in the dimensions of the matrix. The decision of which species to analyze is critical. If ecologically diverse assemblages are analyzed together, species interactions may not be apparent because of the "dilution effect" (Diamond and Gilpin 1982), in which many species will be compared that are not interacting with one another. Or, as Grant and Abbott (1980) have more colorfully expressed it, the analysis is "in danger of throwing the baby out with the bathwater, or, more specifically, drowning the baby in a tub that is too deep." On the other hand, if the analysis is restricted to very few species, the sample sizes may simply be too small to reveal any significant patterns, no matter what test is used (Biehl and Matthews 1984).

Equally important is the choice of which sites to include and which to exclude from the analysis. An implicit assumption in the analysis of presence-absence matrices is that individual islands serve as replicates to reveal repeated patterns of species co-occurrence. But if the islands differ in size or suitability for colonization, important adjustments to the null model are necessary. Indeed, if the islands vary too much in area, habitat, and isolation, it may be invalid to assume they share a common colonization history. Instead, it may be necessary to tailor source pools for each individual island (Graves and Gotelli 1983) or to control for island differences statistically (Schoener and Adler 1991). We suspect that many of the island archipelagoes that have been used for matrix analysis, such as the West Indies, probably should be analyzed on an island-by-island basis, rather than as "replicates" within an archipelago.

Published presence-absence matrices almost never include empty rows or columns, that is, sites with no species or species that occur on no sites. However, these "degenerate" arrangements may be very important in assessing nonrandomness of species on the sites they do occur on (Reddingius 1983). For example, suppose the source pool for a pair of islands contains many species that never occur on either island. In this case, null models that use the presence-absence matrix to construct the sampling universe will overestimate the expected number of shared species (Wright and Biehl 1982). We believe that the initial decisions about the dimensionality of the matrix may be more important in determining the results than the mechanics of the null model used.

There are other limitations of presence-absence matrices. By their very nature, these matrices do not include any information on absolute or relative abundances of species (Haila and Järvinen 1981). If abundances are known, more powerful null models of community assembly can be built (Gotelli et al. 1987; Graves and Gotelli 1993). The analysis of presence-absence matrices assumes that mechanisms controlling co-occurrence are reflected in the dominant or easily censused life-history stage (Pearson 1986). But in many assemblages, larval dispersal (Roughgarden et al. 1988) and interactions among early life-history stages (Wilbur 1988) are responsible for community patterns in the adult stage. Presence-absence matrices also require that residency criteria be unambiguous (Connor and Simberloff 1978). But it is sometimes unclear whether a species is "present" on an island. Breeding status may be difficult to establish, and nonbreeding species may have significant ecological effects on residents (Lynch and Johnson 1974; Simberloff 1976a). Finally, presence-absence matrices assume that all sites have received equal sampling effort, which may not be true even for well-studied archipelagoes (Connor and Simberloff 1978).

In spite of these limitations, the analysis of presence-absence matrices holds the promise of revealing general patterns of community structure (Pearson 1986). In some cases, prescriptions for conservation biology have been made on the basis of presence-absence matrices (Patterson 1987), so it is especially important that their analysis be on solid ground.

TWO MODES OF ANALYSIS

Using the terminology of numerical taxonomy (Sneath and Sokal 1973), there are two modes of analysis for a presence-absence matrix (Simberloff and Connor 1979). The Q-mode analysis assesses the similarity of different columns, revealing how similar sites are in the species they contain. In R-mode analysis, we compare the rows of the matrix and ask how similar species are in the set of islands they occupy. Both modes of analysis are relevant to the issue of assembly rules, although the Q-mode analysis has its roots in biogeographic studies of faunal similarity (McCoy and Heck 1987).

Q-MODE ANALYSES IN BIOGEOGRAPHY

Given a list of species for two sites, how can we quantify the degree of similarity between the sites? The sites will obviously be most similar if they share identical species lists and most dissimilar if they share no species. In analyses of biogeography, a plethora of correlated indices has been used to quantify site similarity (Simpson 1960; Cheetham and Hazel 1969; Jackson et al. 1989). For example, Jaccard's (1908) index scales similarity to range from 0 to 1:

$$J = N_C / (N_1 + N_2 - N_C) \tag{7.1}$$

N_1 and N_2 are the number of species present on each site, and N_C is the number of species common to both sites. As with measures of species diversity (Chapter 2) and niche overlap (Chapter 4), these indices are sensitive to sample size—the value of the index depends as much on the total species richness as it does on the number of shared species. Although some indices have been derived from probability theory (Goodall 1966, 1974; Baroni-Urbani and Buser 1976), most lack an underlying statistical distribution. Consequently, it is difficult to say whether a particular value of an index is statistically significant.

If such indices are to be used at all, they must be combined with simulations to assess the degree to which the index is unusually large or small (Wolda 1981). Rice and Belland (1982) used this approach to examine the similarity of moss floras in five lithophysiographic regions of Bonne Bay, Newfoundland. They combined the species lists from all five regions to generate an aggregate species pool, and weighted each species by its number of occurrences (one to five). Without such weighting, the analysis would have assumed that all species have equivalent probabilities of dispersal and persistence. From the weighted species pool, they drew randomly the observed number of species found in each region, and then calculated Jaccard's index between all possible pairs of sites. The simulations were repeated 20 times to generate 95% confidence intervals for Jaccard's index. The result was that all the observed pairwise similarities were less than expected, and half of the combinations were significantly less than expected (Figure 7.1). This suggests that the floral regions are indeed distinct, although if the regions were originally delineated solely on the basis of these species lists, the test would be circular.

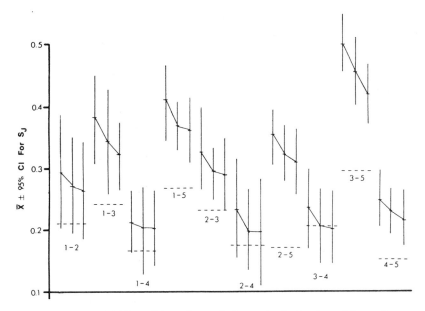

Figure 7.1. Mean and 95% confidence intervals for randomized values of Jaccard's co-efficient of similarity between all possible pairs of five floristic provinces. The triad of vertical lines represents different source pool designations for mosses of Newfoundland. The dashed line is the observed similarity between pairs of provinces. From Rice and Belland (1982), with permission.

In a biogeographic context, faunal provinces are delineated by grouping many sites together on the basis of pairwise similarities (Pielou 1979a). A variety of cluster analyses are available for this purpose, which hierarchically group sites on the basis of similarity (Jackson et al. 1989). However, all of these methods assume that the resulting "groups" are biologically meaningful. Because groupings can be made for sets of random numbers, some method is needed for distinguishing groups that are more similar than expected by chance. Strauss (1982) described randomization techniques to ensure that, whatever the clustering algorithm, the clusters are actually more similar than expected by chance. In an evolutionary context, similar bootstrapping methods have been used to assess the significance of phylogenetic reconstructions (Felsenstein 1985).

Q-MODE ANALYSES IN ECOLOGY

In ecological studies, pairwise similarities have also been used to relate faunal similarities to other site characteristics. For example, Terborgh (1973a) regressed pairwise similarities for West Indian avifaunas against interisland distances. He concluded that island size and position explained between 80 and 93% of the variation in avifaunal composition, and attributed the remainder to habitat differences and species interactions. Power (1975) regressed interisland similarities of Galápagos bird and plant species against physical characteristics of the islands. He concluded that bird similarity among islands was explained by plant similarity, but that plant similarity was explained by interisland distance, along with island area and elevation. For Galápagos finches, Abbott et al. (1977) also used similarity indices to evaluate the effects of floral composition on avifaunal composition. All of these analyses are problematic because the similarity indices are ad hoc and because the pairwise points in the regression analysis are not independent of one another.

A Simple Colonization Model (Null Hypothesis 0)

In an unpublished presentation, Johnson (1974; cited in Simberloff 1978a) pioneered a different approach. He used the number of shared species as a simple index of similarity between sites and then asked what the expected number of shared species is under the simplest colonization model (Null Hypothesis 0). If two islands with m and n species, respectively, are colonized randomly by a pool of P equiprobable species, the expected number of shared species (E_{ss}) is

$$E_{ss} = mn / P \tag{7.2}$$

with a variance (from Connor and Simberloff 1978) of

$$\sigma_{ss}^2 = \frac{\sum_{i=0}^{m} \binom{P-n}{i}\binom{n}{m-i}(m-i-E_{ss})^2}{\binom{P}{m}} \tag{7.3}$$

As a standardized index of site similarity, Connor and Simberloff (1978) recommended

$$(\text{Observed}_{ss} - E_{ss})\big/ \sqrt{\sigma_{ss}^2} \tag{7.4}$$

For the 29 Galápagos Islands, there are $\binom{29}{2}$ = 406 island pairs. Of these, the observed number of shared species exceeded the expected in 369 cases. Connor and Simberloff (1978) obtained similar results at the generic level for Galápagos plants, and Simberloff (1978a) found that all pairs of nine mangrove islands in the Florida Keys shared more insect species than expected if species had equal colonization probabilities. Note that this hypothesis does not assume that all islands are identical, because differences in species richness among islands are maintained in this model.

A Small-Island Limitation Model (Null Hypothesis I)

Johnson (1974) noted that habitat availability might be responsible for the fact that most sites shared more species than expected compared with Null Hypothesis 0. In particular, species may be missing from small islands if these islands lack critical habitat. A modified protocol also placed species randomly and equiprobably, but the species pool for each island was composed of only those species found on islands of that size or smaller. In this case, the expected number of shared species is mn/P_n where P_n is the number of species in the pool of the larger island ($m \leq n$). Incorporating this small-island limitation improved the fit of the Galápagos plant data to the expected values: 285 of the 406 pairs of islands shared more species than expected. If species number (rather than island size) characterized the lower minimum, 259 of the 406 pairs of islands shared more species than expected.

Limits at the upper size end are also possible. Diamond (1975) hypothesized that certain "supertramp" species were restricted to species-poor communities by diffuse competition. To incorporate this constraint into the null model, the species pool would consist of all species that occurred on islands of a particular size or larger. The extent to which the probability of occurrence of a species is related to community size, island area, or other site attributes is the "incidence function" of the species (Diamond 1975). Incidence functions may serve as realistic constraints in null models of species co-occurrence. They may also represent a type of "assembly rule" that can be tested against other colonization models, as we describe later in this chapter.

A Nonrandom Dispersal Model (Null Hypothesis II)

Null Hypothesis 0 is unrealistic, in part because it assumes species are identical. But even if colonization were stochastic, species would be expected to occur at different frequencies on islands because they differ in their abilities to disperse and persist. Dispersal and persistence abilities are probably a function of many species-level attributes, including population size (Terborgh and Winter 1978) and variability (Karr 1982a), body size (Pimm et al. 1988), and geographic range (Graves and Gotelli 1983; Jablonski 1986). When species occurrence probabilities can be measured independently, they can be a powerful tool in null model analyses. But for most archipelagoes, this information is lacking. One must either assume (unrealistically) that species occurrence probabilities are equal or somehow estimate those probabilities from the matrix itself.

The "occurrence distribution" (Connor and Simberloff 1978) has been used to weight species, so that the probability of occurrence of a species is proportional to its frequency of occurrence (Abele and Patton 1976). Many critics have objected that this procedure is circular—the incidence data are used to estimate probabilities of occurrence, which are then used to test the pattern of co-occurrence (Grant and Abbott 1980; Diamond and Gilpin 1982; Case and Sidell 1983). However, constraining marginal totals does not uniquely determine the pattern of co-occurrence in the data (Manly 1991). As in contingency table analysis (Fienberg 1980), some arrangements of the data may be highly improbable given a set of marginal constraints (Connor and Simberloff 1983), and this should be true whether or not the marginals themselves are influenced by competition (Simberloff 1978a). As we shall see, the consequences of marginal constraints on the resolution of co-occurrence patterns depend greatly on whether the constraints are absolute or probabilistic.

Analytic expressions for Null Hypothesis II are not known, so the expected number of shared species must be determined with a simulation. In such a simulation, species are drawn from an aggregate source pool for the archipelago, with probabilities weighted by species occurrences. As in Null Hypotheses 0 and I, the observed number of species on each island is maintained as an absolute constraint. For the Galápagos plants, 338 of the 406 island pairs had more shared species than expected under Null Hypothesis II (Connor and Simberloff 1978). Johnson (1974) performed a mixed-model simulation that simultaneously incorporated both the small-island limitation (Null Hypothesis I) and the weighted species pool (Null Hypothesis II). For the Galápagos plant data, this was the only analysis in which there were too many island pairs with fewer shared species than expected. However, only about 5% of the pairwise comparisons were statistically significant (Figure 7.2).

From this result, Simberloff (1978a) concluded that the mixed model "might not be far from an accurate description of colonization in this archipelago." He also reasoned that an archipelago structured by competition should show a predominance of island pairs with fewer shared species than expected. However, he warned that shared species number is a weak statistic for detecting diffuse competition, because it says nothing about taxonomic or ecological relationships of the species that do co-occur.

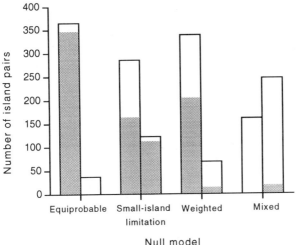

Figure 7.2. Four null models of shared plant species between pairs of Galápagos Islands. For each model, the left-hand bar represents the number of island pairs that shared more species than expected and the right-hand bar represents the number of island pairs that shared fewer species than expected. The hatched region represents the number of pairs that deviated at the 5% level of significance. "Equiprobable" is the model in which all species had equal colonization probabilities. "Small-island limitation" allowed for equiprobable colonization but restricted species occurrences to the minimum island size observed. "Weighted" assigned colonization probabilities for each species proportional to the number of island occurrences. "Mixed" model included both the small-island limitation and weighted colonization probabilities. If species occurrences were independent of one another, the height of the two bars would be approximately equal, and roughly 2.5% of each bar would be shaded. Note the predominance of island pairs that shared more species than expected for the first three null models. Data from Simberloff (1978a).

Criticisms of Ecological Q-Mode Analysis

Wright and Biehl (1982) argued that shared-island analyses may not reveal competitive effects, because many of the pairwise island comparisons are between islands that have the same species sets. Consequently, the shared-species analysis would fail to detect a highly significant "checkerboard distribution" in which a pair of species never occur together on the same island (Diamond 1975). The problem is not as severe if more than a single pair of species occurs in a checkerboard. With an assemblage composed of several competitive guilds, some shared species patterns may be improbable, although it will still be difficult to detect competition from these sorts of data (Connor and Simberloff 1984).

Hamill and Wright (1988) pointed out two other complications with Q-mode analysis. First, the number of species pairs should be tallied above and below the simulated median, not the simulated mean (see also Hendrickson 1981). Second, because the pairs of islands are not independent, it is not appropriate to ask whether more than 5% of the pairs are significantly different from the expectation. They recommended examining shared species among randomly selected, independent pairs of islands, rather than among all possible pairs. These island pairs could be compared to randomizations for each, rather than to a single randomization of the entire presence-absence matrix. With these refinements, Hamill and Wright (1988) found a good agreement between observed and expected number of shared species for the Galápagos avifauna. In contrast, Connor and Simberloff's (1978) analyses suggested a significant excess of shared species among islands. Neither analysis implicated a role for interspecific competition in the distribution of the Galápagos avifauna, although these studies did not consider body size differences among coexisting species (see Chapter 6).

We think that using Q-mode analysis to detect competition is a case of the right answer to the wrong question. Q-mode analysis should be used as a biogeographic tool to group sites on the basis of similarity in species composition, rather than to infer species interactions on the basis of dissimilarity. The analysis is trivial for a single pair of species, but for larger assemblages, Equation 7.4 is a natural index for classifying pairs of sites on the basis of species similarity. Of course, such an analysis depends on the assumption of a common species pool and on whether small island constraints and species weighting are retained, but these assumptions are implicit in any similarity analysis. By generating an explicit null expectation and allowing for increasingly complex colonization models, Q-mode analysis provides a reliable framework for comparing species composition of sites (McCoy and Heck 1987). If the question is one of species interactions, then an R-mode analysis, which compares species in the sites they share, is more appropriate.

ASSEMBLY RULES

Missing Species Combinations

Most analyses of presence-absence matrices have examined the number of shared sites for a set of species. These R-mode analyses have emphasized the detection of nonrandom patterns of species association. Two broad classes of interactions can lead to distinctive species combinations. (1) *Interactions of species and sites*. These include site characteristics, such as island area, isolation, and habitat availability, and species characteristics, such as dispersal, persistence, and habitat affinities. Even if species colonize sites independently of one another, interactions between species and sites may lead to characteristic species combinations. (2) *Interactions between species*. Competition, predation, and mutualism between particular species pairs and among larger groups of species will also lead to nonrandomness. Biotic interactions may lead to "forbidden combinations" of species (Diamond 1975) and also to combinations of species that are unusually stable and occur more frequently than expected.

The search for assembly rules of community organization is predicated on the assumption that biotic interactions are strong enough to produce discernible patterns. The null model approach has been to build colonization models that incorporate only species-site interactions (autecological factors) and to compare their predictions to the empirical data. The goal is to provide a baseline for recognizing nonrandom patterns caused by species interactions. Because a variety of forces can lead to either positive or negative species associations (Schluter 1984), it is a challenge to properly frame and interpret null models for assessing species interactions. Even if a pattern can be shown by a null model analysis to be nonrandom, it may not be possible to determine the underlying cause (Simberloff and Connor 1981).

Statistical Tests for Missing Species Combinations

The pioneering work of E. Chris Pielou (Pielou and Pielou 1968; Pielou 1972a) on the R-mode analysis of species associations was ignored and uncited for over a decade (Simberloff and Connor 1981). Pielou and Pielou (1968) noted that for presence-absence matrices with r species (= rows), there are 2^r possible species combinations (including the combination of none of the r species being present). With enough replicated sites, the observed and expected frequencies of these combinations can be compared with a chi-squared test. This comparison holds the row totals of the presence-absence matrix constant. The null hypothesis is that the observed frequency of different species combinations is no different than expected by chance, given that some species in the collection are common and others are rare.

Unfortunately, this test is rarely practical, because the number of species combinations is usually very large compared to the number of sites. Pielou and Pielou (1968) instead advocated a simulation procedure in which each species is placed randomly and independently in sites. From these simulations, one can obtain the expected number of different species combinations.

The observed number of combinations may be less than this expectation either because (1) some sites are uniformly better than others for all species, or because (2) species associate nonrandomly with one another or with different sites. In either case, there will be fewer combinations of species than expected under the null model. By carefully comparing the number of occupied sites with the curve generated by the null model, it may be possible to distinguish between segregative and nonsegregative association. Pielou and Pielou (1968) did this for 13 collections of insect and spider fauna associated with *Polyperus* fungus brackets. The number of combinations did not differ from the expected in five collections. In the remaining eight, there were fewer associations than expected, although there was evidence for segregative association in only three of the samples.

Two restrictions are important in Pielou and Pielou's (1968) analysis. First, all sites are assumed equiprobable. If this assumption can be relaxed, it may be easier to reveal the effects of species interactions. Second, the analysis requires an estimate of the frequency of unoccupied sites. Unfortunately, these data are not usually collected, and ad hoc procedures for dealing with empty sites (e.g., Siegfried 1976) may not be valid (Simberloff and Connor 1981).

Whittam and Siegel-Causey (1981a) expanded on Pielou and Pielou's (1968) method and used a contingency table analysis to test for species associations in Alaskan seabird colonies. Rather than looking just at the number of species combinations, Whittam and Siegel-Causey (1981a) used a series of hierarchical log linear models to tease apart positive and negative species associations. Observed species combinations differed in frequency from those expected under a model of independent assortment. Models that best fit the data included mostly positive two-way associations between species (Figure 7.3). Higher-order interactions were uncommon, and positively associated pairs of species tended to overlap in diet. These sophisticated analyses derive their strength from very large sample sizes [20 species, 902 colonies (= sites), and 19 diet categories] and provide considerable insight into species interactions.

Pielou (1972a) developed a second type of R-mode analysis. She analyzed the variance of the row sums in the presence-absence matrix, that is, the variance in the frequency of occurrence of each species. If the species are distributed independently of one another, then the row sums will behave as a series of random variables, with a covariance of zero. As described in Chapter 5, the ratio of variance in total species number in sites to the sum of the variances of individual species provides a simple test for positive or negative covariance in a presence-absence matrix. The variance ratio was derived inde-

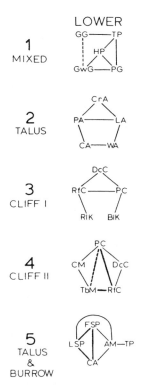

Figure 7.3. Complex species associations in Alaskan seabird colonies, as detected by contingency table analysis. For each of five habitat types, the diagram summarizes statistically significant interactions. Solid line = positive pairwise interaction; dashed line = negative pairwise interaction; heavy line = negative three-way interaction. GG = Glaucous Gull (*Larus hyperboreus*); TP = Tufted Puffin (*Fratercula cirrhata*); HP = Horned Puffin (*Fratercula corniculata*); GwG = Glaucous-winged Gull (*Larus glaucescens*); PG = Pigeon Guillemot (*Cepphus columba*); CrA = Crested Auklet (*Aethia cristatella*); PA = Parakeet Auklet (*Cyclorrhynchus psittacula*); LA = Least Auklet (*Aethia pusilla*); CA = Cassin's Auklet (*Ptychoramphus aleuticus*); WA = Whiskered Auklet (*Aethia pygmaea*); DcC = Double-crested Cormorant (*Phalacrocorax auritus*); RfC = Red-faced Cormorant (*Phalacrocorax urile*); PC = Pelagic Cormorant (*Phalacrocorax pelagicus*); RlK = Red-legged Kittiwake (*Rissa brevirostris*); BlK = Black-legged Kittiwake (*Rissa tridactyla*); CM = Common Murre (*Uria aalge*); TbM = Thick-billed Murre (*Uria lomvia*); FSP = Fork-tailed Storm Petrel (*Oceanodroma furcata*); LSP = Leach's Storm Petrel (*Oceanodroma leucorhoa*); AM = Ancient Murrelet (*Synthliboramphus antiquus*). From Whittam and Siegel-Causey (1981a), with permission.

pendently by Järvinen (1979) in the analysis of temporal fluctuations and by Schluter (1982) in the analysis of spatial distributions.

The variance ratio and related tests do not focus on assembly rules per se or missing species combinations, but on the average amount of association between each species and all others in the matrix. Schluter (1984) analyzed several published presence-absence matrices with the ratio test and found that positive covariation, rather than neutral or negative co-occurrence, was the most common pattern. However, the variance ratio test assumes that species number per site can vary freely, which may account for the predominance of positive aggregations.

Simberloff and Connor (1981) thoroughly reviewed the literature on missing species combinations. They used Maxwell-Boltzmann statistics to calculate the probability of observing a particular number of missing species combinations in an archipelago. The Maxwell-Boltzmann analysis assumes that each combination of species is an equiprobable group of colonists. An alternative analysis assumes that the probability of a particular combination is proportional to the product of the colonization probabilities of the component species. Thus, combinations that include common (= widespread) species are more probable than combinations with rare species. This proportional weighting always raises the observed tail probability. If some combinations are more likely than others, the number of combinations expected under the null model decreases.

Simberloff and Connor (1981) investigated claims that missing species combinations were nonrandom for assemblages of plants (Abbott 1977), birds (Siegfried 1976; Abbott et al. 1977), and mammals (Grant 1972b; M'Closkey 1978; King and Moors 1979). Few significant patterns emerged from these analyses—in most cases, the observed number of missing species combinations was about what one would expect, given a random sample of all species in the archipelago.

One notable exception was the Galápagos finches, which had fewer multispecies combinations than expected. With six species of *Geospiza,* there are $\binom{6}{3} = 20$ possible three-species combinations. But only two of the 20 possible combinations were found on the islands ($p = 0.000002$; weighted $p = 0.001$). On the other hand, the observed number of one- and two-species combinations did not differ from the null model, and the significance of the multispecies patterns hinged upon which species and islands were included in the source pool. Nevertheless, the presence of very few species combinations of Galápagos finches is consistent with the evidence of nonrandom body size patterns in this assemblage (see Chapter 6).

Diamond's Assembly Rules

Diamond (1975) popularized the study of community assembly rules in a detailed treatise on the distribution of 141 land-bird species on New Guinea and its satellite islands in the Bismarck Archipelago. Diamond (1975) summarized many years of his own field studies on species-area relationships, incidence functions, species combinations, and resource use patterns in this archipelago. Although Diamond (1975) discussed the importance of factors such as dispersal, habitat availability, and chance colonization, he emphasized that interspecific competition within groups of related species (ecological guilds) was the most important determinant of observed species combinations.

Diamond (1975) codified and generalized his findings in a list of seven "rules" of community assembly:

1. "If one considers all the combinations that can be formed from a group of related species, only certain ones of these combinations exist in nature."

2. "These permissible combinations resist invaders that would transform them into a forbidden combination."

3. "A combination that is stable on a large or species-rich island may be unstable on a small or species-poor island."

4. "On a small or species-poor island a combination may resist invaders that would be incorporated on a larger or more species-rich island."

5. "Some pairs of species never coexist, either by themselves or as part of a larger combination."

6. "Some pairs of species that form an unstable combination by themselves may form part of a stable larger combination."

7. "Conversely, some combinations that are composed entirely of stable sub-combinations are themselves unstable."

The publication of Diamond's (1975) rules touched off an acrimonious debate over null models that has spanned more than 20 years in the ecological literature [see Wiens (1989) for an even-handed review of the controversy]. In this section, we review the null models that have been used to test Diamond's (1975) rules, and the various claims and counterclaims that have followed. We think that all of the null models proposed to date contain one or more serious flaws. Later in this chapter, we propose a hybrid model that combines the best features of each and seems to overcome the most serious deficiencies.

First, we need to consider the nature of the assembly rules. Wiens (1989) noted that Diamond's (1975) rules are statements of pattern and do not explicitly describe mechanisms, although they do require that communities be in an equilibrium state. Nevertheless, the use of terms such as "forbidden combinations" clearly implicates the role of competitive interactions and implies that the patterns are nonrandom and would not be expected in the absence of species interactions.

It has been very difficult to make these rules operational. On the one hand, the rules as stated are so broad that they would be difficult to apply to real data, much less test them (Haefner 1988b). Null model analyses have contributed considerably to the study of assembly rules by forcing the issue of precisely what patterns must be established in order to document a competitively structured community. On the other hand, Diamond's (1975) own interpretation of these rules for the Bismarck Archipelago seems so detailed, anecdotal, and nonstatistical that it resembles more an historical narrative than a test of community assembly. We agree with Simberloff (1978a) that "one is left with the uneasy feeling that the rules lack predictive power, in that all the data are required before any prediction can be made."

The Connor and Simberloff Procedure

Connor and Simberloff (1979) launched an aggressive attack on Diamond's (1975) assembly rules. They argued that Rules 2, 3, 4, 6, and 7 were either tautologies or restatements of other rules. Connor and Simberloff (1979) did test Rules 1 and 5 with a null model analysis. Rules 1 and 5 are identical, except that Rule 1 mentioned "related species" and Rule 5 was restricted to species pairs. Rule 5 described a checkerboard pattern of species occurrences, which is perhaps the simplest and most clear-cut of Diamond's (1975) assembly rules (Graves and Gotelli 1993). The requirement of a complete distributional checkerboard is especially stringent: two species might have exclusive distributions on 99 islands, but if they occurred together on a single island, the pair would not be scored as a true checkerboard. Diamond (1975) presented seven examples of pairs of closely related, ecologically similar species that were distributed as checkerboards in the Bismarck Archipelago.

The checkerboard patterns (Figure 7.4) were striking and provided the strongest evidence for Diamond's (1975) hypothesis. For two of the examples (*Macropygia* cuckoo-doves and *Pachycephala* flycatchers), the probability that the species within each genus formed a distributional checkerboard [the "shared islands" analysis of Wright and Biehl (1982)] was unusually small (Connor and Simberloff 1979).

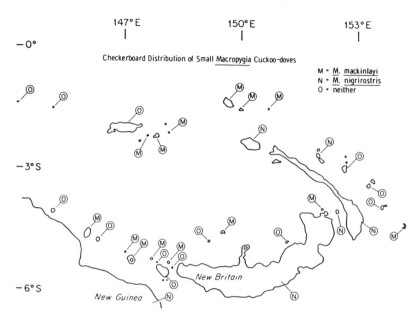

Figure 7.4. Checkerboard distribution of two *Macropygia* cuckoo-dove species in the Bismarck Archipelago. Each island supports only one of the two species. M = *Macropygia mackinlayi;* N = *Macropygia nigrirostris;* O = neither species present. From Diamond (1975). Reprinted by permission of the publisher from *Ecology and Evolution of Communities.* M. L. Cody and J. M. Diamond (eds). Cambridge, Mass.: The Belknap Press of Harvard University Press. Copyright © 1975 by the President and Fellows of Harvard College.

But even these examples may not be so clear-cut. *Macropygia nigrirostris* occurred mostly on large, species-rich islands, whereas its putative competitor (*M. mackinlayi*) occurred mostly on small and medium-sized islands with few species. If these incidence constraints were not a direct result of competitive interactions, then the resulting checkerboard may be due to independent colonization by each species of different-sized islands (Wiens 1989). Moreover, Diamond's (1975) Figure 20 of this example (and also Diamond's (1975) Figure 22 for the genus *Ptilinopus*) did not show all of the "empty islands" that supported neither species. When these were incorporated into the calculation, the p value was marginally nonsignificant (Connor and Simberloff 1983).

However, Connor and Simberloff (1979) were not satisfied with the demonstration that some pairs of species showed unusually exclusive distributions. They argued that, with $\binom{141}{2} = 9{,}870$ possible species pairs, it was not surprising that seven pairs showed exclusive distributions. Malanson (1982) made a similar point about checkerboard distributions of plant species in the hanging gardens of Zion National Park.

Because Diamond (1975) did not provide data on all guild designations for this assemblage, we cannot say how improbable it is that all five pairs would be ecologically similar congeners. In order to assert that species checkerboards are a manifestation of community assembly rules, Connor and Simberloff (1979) required that the observed number of pairs, trios, etc. of species that exhibit checkerboards be significantly greater than the expected number generated by an appropriate null model.

Diamond's (1975) Bismarck data were never published, so Connor and Simberloff (1979) instead used presence-absence data for West Indian birds and bats, and New Hebridean birds. Connor and Simberloff (1979) used a null model that randomized an observed presence-absence matrix subject to the following three constraints:

1. The row totals of the randomized matrix were maintained.
2. The column totals of the randomized matrix were maintained.
3. For each row, species occurrences were restricted to those islands for which total species richness fell within the range occupied by the species.

Constraint (1) maintained differences between species in their frequency of occurrence. Constraint (2) maintained differences among islands in the number of species they contained. Constraint (3) maintained the observed incidence function for each species (it could not occur in assemblages larger or smaller than those observed). The simulation first ordered the rows of the matrix from most common to least common species, and then randomly placed species on islands until all three constraints were satisfied.

When the matrix was sparsely filled, this algorithm was satisfactory. But if many of the species were widespread (= large row totals), it was sometimes impossible to place species late in the simulation and still maintain the constraints. In these cases, Connor and Simberloff (1979) repeatedly interchanged submatrices in the matrix so that row and column sums were not altered. After the interchanges, new matrices that were nonequivalent to the observed matrix were retained to estimate the null distribution. More recent advances in randomization algorithms (Stone and Roberts 1990; Daniel Simberloff, personal communication) have overcome this problem.

Connor and Simberloff (1979) used 10 such randomizations to construct a histogram of the mean and standard deviation of the number of pairs (or

Table 7.2

Null model analyses of co-occurrence in island faunas

Taxon	Number of possible species pairs	Observed number of checkerboard species pairs	Expected number of checkerboard species pairs	p
New Hebrides birds	99	1	0.90	>0.99
West Indies birds	1,029	621	437.0	$<10^{-8}$
West Indies bats	499	325	208.6	$<10^{-8}$

For each fauna, the table lists the total number of confamilial pairs, the expected number of checkerboard pairs, and the observed number of checkerboards. The chi-squared significance test is for the overall fit of the distribution. Note the excess of checkerboard pairs for the West Indian faunas. From Connor and Simberloff (1979) and Diamond and Gilpin (1982).

triplets) of species that shared 0, 1, 2 . . . n islands. The first bar of this histogram is the zero class and represents the expected number of species pairs that share no islands, i.e., have a checkerboard distribution. Connor and Simberloff (1979) lumped adjacent size classes that had small expected values and then compared the entire distribution of observed and expected frequencies with a chi-squared test, using $n-1$ degrees of freedom for an archipelago with n islands. They tested the fit of the observed and expected number of shared islands for pairs and trios of species at the level of the entire assemblage and within taxonomic families.

What was the outcome of these tests? For the New Hebrides bird data, the fit between observed and expected was suspiciously good ($p > 0.99$). This matrix had to be randomized by the interchange of submatrices, and Connor and Simberloff (1979) noted that the matrices randomized in this way were very similar to the observed matrix. They pointed out that there were very few arrangements of this matrix that maintained row, column, and incidence constraints. As a consequence, the evidence for competition was weak, unless one were to argue that competition was responsible for the marginal totals.

Patterns for West Indian birds and bats were quite different. In all cases, the null hypothesis was strongly rejected, and in all analyses, there were more exclusively distributed species pairs (checkerboards) than expected by chance (Alatalo 1982). Connor and Simberloff (1979) did not emphasize these highly nonrandom results (Table 7.2). Instead, they presented graphical comparisons of observed and expected species combinations in each frequency class (Figure 7.5). From these, they argued that the overall fit of the observed and

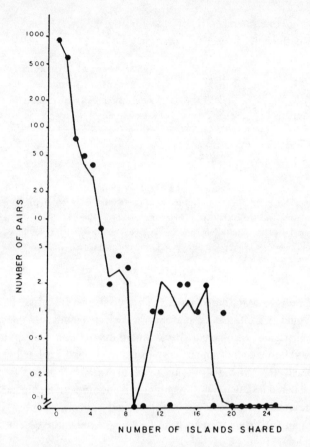

NUMBER OF ISLANDS SHARED

Figure 7.5. Observed and expected numbers of species pairs versus number of islands shared for West Indies birds. The solid line is the expected value generated by a null model that held row and column totals constant and maintained species area restrictions. Dots are the observed values. Although the logarithmic scale suggests a good fit between the observed and expected values, the difference is highly significant ($p < 0.01$) and in the direction predicted by the competition hypothesis (more species pairs that share zero islands than expected by chance). See also Table 7.2. From Connor and Simberloff (1979), with permission.

expected data was good, and that therefore Diamond's (1975) seven examples of checkerboards were not a compelling demonstration of Assembly Rules 1 and 5. For birds of the Bismarck Archipelago, and for the West Indian bird and bat faunas, Connor and Simberloff (1979) suggested that allopatric speciation and limited dispersal of single-island endemics were alternative hypotheses that did not invoke interspecific competition but might account for checker-board distributions.

The Connor and Simberloff (1979) model has been used in two additional tests. Matthews (1982) analyzed the occurrence of 13 minnow species distributed in six streams of the Ozark watershed. Although some species pairs that never co-occurred in watersheds were morphologically and ecologically similar, the observed number of checkerboard pairs matched the predictions of the null model. However, Matthews's (1982) analysis was based on a binomial distribution, sampling with replacement, whereas a more appropriate analysis uses the hypergeometric distribution, sampling without replacement (Biehl and Matthews 1984). Jackson et al. (1992) used the Connor and Simberloff (1979) model to analyze five presence-absence matrices for Ontario lake fish and also found no evidence of nonrandomness.

Criticisms of the Connor and Simberloff Procedure

Connor and Simberloff's (1979) analysis provoked several critiques (Alatalo 1982; Diamond and Gilpin 1982; Gilpin and Diamond 1982, 1984; Gilpin et al. 1984) and subsequent rebuttals (Connor and Simberloff 1983, 1984; Gilpin et al. 1984; Simberloff and Connor 1984). Here, we summarize the most important of the criticisms:

1. The dilution effect. Because Connor and Simberloff (1979) analyzed confamilial groups or entire avifaunas, competitive effects were not apparent. Diamond's (1975) choice of examples suggested that the ecological guild was the correct unit of analysis for revealing competitive effects. However, guilds must be established a priori by criteria that are independent of the co-occurrence data being tested (Connor and Simberloff 1983). Delineating guilds is not an easy task (Jaksić and Medel 1990; Simberloff and Dayan 1991), and guild designations clearly affect the outcome of null model tests.

For example, Graves and Gotelli (1993) tested the significance of checkerboard distributions in mixed-species flocks of Amazonian forest birds. There was no evidence of unusual patterns for the entire assemblage of flocking species, or for species grouped into ecological foraging guilds. Only when the analysis was restricted to congeneric species within feeding guilds was there evidence of unusual checkerboard distributions. Even at this level, the patterns were statistically significant only for null models based on abundance and population structure, rather than presence-absence data (Table 7.3). Vuilleumier and Simberloff (1980) also found that co-occurrence patterns of Andean birds were affected by the designation of ecological and taxonomic guilds in

Table 7.3
Observed and expected numbers of perfect checkerboard distributions among pairs of Amazonian bird species in mixed species flocks

			Null model								
			SPEC		ABUN		DEMO				
Level	n	Obs.	Exp.	p	Exp.	p	Exp.	p			
Flock	71	1,012	1,018.91	0.63	927.58	<0.01	992.47	0.25			
Guild											
1	27	111	122.11	0.912	94.04	0.027	114.73	0.706			
2	14	36	38.12	0.758	40.47	0.876	38.34	0.783			
3	8	10	7.29	0.137	6.37	0.046	7.28	0.123			
4	3	3	2.63	0.667	2.46	0.526	2.65	0.687			
5	10	14	11.04	0.142	10.14	0.095	9.84	0.046			
6	7	15	14.70	0.576	14.81	0.602	14.62	0.556			
7	2	1	0.89	0.887	0.88	0.879	0.89	0.893			

Fisher's combined probabilities test

(df = 14)

$\chi^2 = 10.77$ $\chi^2 = 20.91$ $\chi^2 = 13.68$

$p > 0.50$ $p > 0.10$ $p > 0.50$

Genera							
Monasa	2	0.03	1.000	0.13	1.000	0.09	1.000
Xiphorhynchus	4	0.35	0.041	0.24	0.024	0.32	0.036
Philydor	2	0.00	1.000	0.00	1.000	0.00	1.000
Automolus	3	1.28	0.045	0.09	0.014	1.30	0.052
Xenops	2	0.05	0.054	0.07	0.067	0.06	0.062
Thamnomanes	2	0.00	1.000	0.00	1.000	0.00	1.000
Myrmotherula	7	1.30	0.119	0.89	0.048	0.95	0.051
Hylophilus	2	0.19	0.189	0.02	0.020	0.14	0.142
Fisher's combined probabilities test		$\chi^2 = 24.76$		$\chi^2 = 33.43$		$\chi^2 = 27.86$	
(df = 16)		$p < 0.10$		$p < 0.01$		$p < 0.05$	

Three null models were tested: (1) SPEC (randomization of presence-absence matrices), (2) ABUN (randomization of abundance data), and (3) DEMO (randomization of abundance data with intraspecific demographic constraints). These analyses were carried out at three hierarchical levels: (1) entire flocks, (2) foraging guilds, and (3) congeneric groups within feeding guilds. Guild designations: 1 = arboreal gleaning insectivores; 2 = arboreal sallying insectivores; 3 = arboreal dead-leaf–searching insectivores; 4 = bark interior insectivores; 5 = superficial bark insectivores; 6 = arboreal omnivores; 7 = arboreal frugivores. Note that significant checkerboards were consistently revealed only for congeners within the same feeding guild. From Graves and Gotelli (1993).

the source pool. Although the designation of guilds is a crucial step in the analysis of co-occurrence matrices, it is a procedure that is quite distinct from the null model randomizations themselves.

2. *Effects of randomization constraints.* The three simultaneous constraints imposed by Connor and Simberloff (1979) were severe and made it less likely that the null hypothesis would be rejected. For example, relaxing the "incidence constraint" prevented the simulation for the New Hebrides matrix from hanging up and revealed significant negative associations between species (Wilson 1987). For a similar model with only row and column sum constraints, Wilson et al. (1992) detected no evidence of nonrandomness in the distribution of rock-pool algae, whereas both positive and negative associations were revealed in the flora of islands in Lake Manapouri, New Zealand (Wilson 1988).

However, if row and column totals are constrained, some, but not all, checkerboard distributions cannot be detected by the null model (Diamond and Gilpin 1982; Connor and Simberloff 1984). In an empirical comparison of several R-mode analyses, the Connor and Simberloff (1979) procedure was the only one that could not detect nonrandomness in presence-absence matrices for fish assemblages (Jackson et al. 1992). More formally, Roberts and Stone (1990) showed that the average number of shared islands among all species pairs cannot change in a simulation if row and column totals are constrained. Somewhat paradoxically, matrices with mutually exclusive species pairs will always contain some species pairs that co-occur more than expected (Stone and Roberts 1992).

The sample variance of the number of shared islands reflects this pattern. For the New Hebrides bird data, this variance was significantly larger than expected under the null model that held row and column totals constant, suggesting that some species pairs shared too many islands and others shared too few (Roberts and Stone 1990). Indices of "checkerboardedness" (Stone and Roberts 1990) and "togetherness" (Stone and Roberts 1992) also confirmed that there were too many exclusive and aggregated pairs of species within confamilial subsets of the New Hebridean avifauna.

Some authors (Grant and Abbott 1980; Colwell and Winkler 1984) have claimed that it is circular to constrain marginal totals, because the marginals also reflect interspecific competition. This claim has never been validated, but if it is true, then the Connor and Simberloff (1979) model will reveal only competitive effects above and beyond those expressed in the row and column sums. The hypothesis that competition sets the total number of island occurrences for a particular species (or the total number of species on a particular island) is quite distinct from the hypothesis of forbidden species combinations, and deserves to be tested in its own right. There are many reasons besides competition that species occur on many or few islands and that species number varies among islands. We agree with Connor and Simberloff (1983) that these factors need to be incorporated into null models, although imposing absolute marginal constraints may be too severe a restriction.

Finally, the debate over marginal constraints also reflects the way in which the null models are interpreted. As we noted in Chapter 1, one interpretation is that the null model is simply a statistical randomization. This interpretation is consistent with the use of absolute marginal constraints, because the question is whether the co-occurrence patterns are nonrandom, given the observed "sample" of species and islands. On the other hand, if the randomization is viewed as a model of community colonization in the absence of competition, the marginal constraints may not be appropriate. In a group of randomly colonized archipelagoes, we would not expect each replicate of an island to have exactly the same number of species, nor would we expect each species to occur on exactly the same number of islands in the different archipelagoes. We develop these ideas later in this chapter.

3. Significance tests. Connor and Simberloff (1979) compared the observed and expected distributions with a chi-squared test. However, this may be inappropriate because of the nonlinear dependence imposed by the marginal constraints. Even if the chi-squared test were appropriate, the number of degrees of freedom used by Connor and Simberloff (1979) was roughly double the "best fit" value found empirically (Roberts and Stone 1990). The same criticism applies to Gilpin and Diamond's (1982) null model, which also compared observed and expected distributions of species pairs with a chi-squared test.

The Wright and Biehl Procedure

Wright and Biehl (1982) suggested a "shared-island" test for detecting unusual species co-occurrences. For each species pair, they calculated the tail probability of finding the observed number of co-occurrences. The calculation is identical to Connor and Simberloff's (1978) "shared species" analysis, but with the rows and columns of the presence-absence matrix transposed. Wright and Biehl (1982) argued that an assemblage exhibited nonrandomness if more than 5% of the species pairs shared more islands than expected (at the 5% significance level). By this test, the New Hebridean avifauna exhibited aggregation, because 8% of the species pairs shared significantly more islands than expected by chance.

One advantage of the Wright and Biehl (1982) method is that it directly pinpoints particular species pairs that show aggregated or segregated distributions. However, assessing the statistical significance of all possible non-independent species pairs is problematic. Even if the null hypothesis is rejected for more than 5% of the pairs, this pattern can be caused by nonrandomness in the distribution of only a few species (Connor and Simberloff 1983). The same criticism applies to the shared species analysis of Connor and Simberloff (1978) and to Gilpin and Diamond's (1982) null model for R-mode analyses. An excess of species pairs that are significant at the 5% level does not mean that the patterns are biologically meaningful for all of these pairs.

A more serious problem is that Wright and Biehl's (1982) shared island model assumes that all sites are equivalent. Consequently, it confounds species-site associations with the effects of species interactions. The slight excess of New Hebrides species pairs that shared more islands than expected may simply reflect differences in island suitability.

The Gilpin and Diamond Procedure

Gilpin and Diamond (1982) developed their own R-mode analysis as an alternative to the Connor and Simberloff (1979) approach. Gilpin and Diamond's (1982) null model was based on the principles of contingency table analysis. For species i on island j, they calculated the probability of occurrence as

$$P_{ij} = R_i C_j / N \tag{7.5}$$

where R_i is the row total for species i, C_j is the column total for island j, and N is the grand total for the presence-absence matrix. Next, they calculated the expected overlap for each species pair by summing the product of these probabilities across all islands. Observed and expected overlaps for each species pair were standardized and then compared with a chi-squared test to a standard normal distribution. If the null hypothesis of independent placement were true, the histogram of normalized deviates would follow a normal distribution. Species pairs that showed unusual aggregation would appear in the right-hand tail of the distribution, and species pairs that showed unusual segregation would appear in the left-hand tail.

For the New Hebridean birds, the observed distribution of deviates was significantly different from a standard normal, and weakly skewed towards the right. The Gilpin and Diamond (1982) analysis did not reveal any significant negative associations, in contrast to the results of Wilson (1987) and of Stone and Roberts (1992). Returning to Diamond's (1975) original Bismarck data, Gilpin and Diamond (1982) found a strong excess of positive associations and a weak excess of negative associations. They examined the extreme species pairs in detail and attributed positive associations to shared habitat requirements, clumping of single-island endemics on large islands, shared geographic origins, and shared distributional strategies. Negative associations were attributed to competitive exclusion, differing distributional strategies, and differing geographic origins. Compared to Diamond's (1975) original conclusions, the null model interpretations of Gilpin and Diamond (1982) placed considerably less emphasis on competitive interactions in producing community assembly rules for the birds of the Bismarck Archipelago.

Using the Gilpin and Diamond (1982) model, Jackson et al. (1992) also found mostly positive associations between species pairs of fishes in lakes. These positive associations were usually between pairs of cold-water species with similar habitat requirements. Negative associations were usually between piscivorous fish species and their prey. Finally, McFarlane (1989) found an excess of positive associations for the Antillean bat fauna and attributed this pattern to a large number of single-island endemics in the northern Antilles.

Gilpin and Diamond's (1982) approach was important because it introduced the idea that the marginal totals may represent *expected values* rather than *absolute constraints*. In different runs of a stochastic model, we would not expect each island to support precisely the observed number of species, or each species to always occur with its observed frequency. In fact, putting a strict "cap" on the number of species that can occur on an island, as Connor and Simberloff (1979) did, could be interpreted as a competitive limit to local species richness. In contrast, if islands behave as "targets" that are colonized independently by different species (Coleman et al. 1982), we would expect some variance about the expected species number in our null model. Empirically, a "target" model is consistent with the finding that island area typically explains only 50% of the variation in species number (Boecklen and Gotelli 1984). Although Gilpin and Diamond (1982) did not emphasize this point, their approach was an important first step toward incorporating this sort of variability into null models.

Unfortunately, there are several problems with the Gilpin and Diamond (1982) model. First, the formula for cell probabilities (R_iC_j/N) is actually the cell expectation (Connor and Simberloff 1983), and consequently some of the expected "probabilities" in a matrix can take on values > 1.0. Even when a corrected formula is used, the contingency table model is not strictly correct, because it allows for multiple occurrences in each cell of the matrix, whereas a presence-absence matrix only contains zeros and ones. This may not be a problem in practice, because Monte Carlo simulations of cell probabilities gave qualitatively similar results (appendix to Gilpin and Diamond 1982).

Second, the Gilpin and Diamond (1982) model implicitly allows for "degenerate" distributions: empty islands and missing species, which correspond to matrix columns or rows with all zero entries (Connor and Simberloff 1983). In the Gilpin and Diamond (1982) model, occasionally a given island would never be "hit" by any of the species. Unless the observed presence-absence matrix contained the full sampling universe of missing species and empty islands, the expected values from this model would be biased. On the other hand, Haefner (1988b) found that degenerate distributions introduced only a slight bias toward accepting the null hypothesis.

Finally, the Gilpin and Diamond (1982) model is susceptible to Type I error. Wilson (1987) constructed a random presence-absence matrix with a probability of occurrence of 0.33 for every cell. This matrix was significantly nonrandom by the Gilpin and Diamond (1982) model ($p < 0.001$), with a slight excess of positive species associations. Gilpin and Diamond (1987) objected that such randomly constructed matrices may contain biological structure. Nevertheless, Wilson's (1987) analysis suggests that the Gilpin and Diamond (1982) model is probably not appropriate for the analysis of co-occurrence data.

Summary of the Controversy and a New Approach

We think the controversy over R-mode analysis boils down to four issues:

1. Which species and which islands should be analyzed? It is surprising how little attention has been given to this point. The same data sets have been analyzed over and over with little discussion of source pools, colonization potential, and habitat availability of islands (Terborgh 1981; Graves and Gotelli 1983). Some of these factors have been discussed post hoc, but they must be considered in a systematic fashion *before* any analysis is attempted. Careful a priori selection of sites and species by explicit criteria is at least as important as the particular null model used for analysis.

2. Which metric should be used? In other words, how do we properly quantify nonrandomness and species associations in a presence-absence matrix? There are many different kinds of structure in a presence-absence matrix, but for the purposes of recognizing species associations, we think the following five metrics are most informative:

a. The number of species combinations. This is perhaps the most basic measure of community organization (Pielou and Pielou 1968). If assembly rules are operative, there should be fewer species combinations observed than expected under an appropriate null model.

b. The number of checkerboard distributions. The checkerboard distribution is the simplest and most clear-cut of Diamond's (1975) assembly rules. It represents the strongest possible pattern of species repulsion.

c. The "checkerboardedness" index of Stone and Roberts (1990). This statistic measures the overall tendency for species pairs in a matrix to co-occur. It may reveal species pairs that associate negatively but do not occur in a perfect checkerboard.

d. The "togetherness" index of Stone and Roberts (1992). Both positive and negative associations are possible in the same matrix, and this index measures the tendency for species to co-occur.

e. Schluter's (1984) variance ratio. Negative co-occurrence as measured by the variance ratio is not always equivalent to that measured by the "checkerboardedness" index. This difference arises because the variance ratio test does not constrain column totals. Different patterns of negative covariation may be revealed by comparing the variance ratio to null model predictions.

3. Which simulation procedure should be used? We accept the logic of Connor and Simberloff (1979) that neither islands nor species are equiprobable and that this should be reflected in the null model. However, their simultaneous constraint of row and column totals was simply too severe. We prefer an approach similar to Gilpin and Diamond's (1982), which treats the row and column totals as expectations; the actual row and column totals should be allowed to vary from one simulation to the next. Although both the Connor and Simberloff (1979) and the Gilpin and Diamond (1982) approaches are flawed, we think the following two simulation procedures are acceptable alternatives:

a. Row totals fixed, column totals probabilistic. This model takes the observed frequency of occurrence of each species as a constraint but treats each site as a "target"; the probability of occurrence of each species at each site is proportional to the total number of species at that site. Thus, species number in each site will vary somewhat from one simulation to the next, although the relative rankings of sites in their species richness will be maintained on average. Simberloff and Gotelli (1984) used this procedure to examine incidence functions, which will be described later. This protocol is the inverse of Connor and Simberloff's (1978) Null Hypothesis II and Patterson and Atmar's (1986) RANDOM1 algorithm, in which column totals were fixed and row totals were probabilistic.

b. Row and column totals probabilistic. A less constrained null model would allow both the row and column totals to vary randomly. In this case, what is simulated is not the placement of each individual species across the set of sites, but rather, the placement of the N species-occurrences across the entire matrix. For cell a_{ij} in the matrix, the initial probability of a "hit" in the simulation is the joint probability of selecting the species (R_i/N) *and* selecting the site (C_j/N). This cell probability is thus (R_iC_j/N^2), which corrects the error in Gilpin and Diamond (1982). In this simulation model, the most likely occurrence will be of the most common species on the most species-rich site, and the least likely occurrence will be of the rarest species on the most depauperate site.

One complication is that these estimated probabilities will apply only to the very first occurrence that is placed in the matrix. After the initial placement, the distribution of less probable combinations will be more "even" than predicted by these probabilities. Because sites can only be occupied once per species, the less probable sites are consecutively hit as the matrix fills up. If the marginal probabilities are squared and then rescaled, the resulting marginal distributions in the simulated matrix will more closely resemble the original column and row totals (Bruce D. Patterson, personal communication).

A second complication is that both protocols, and particularly protocol *(b)*, could occasionally lead to degenerate distributions (= empty rows or columns) in simulated matrices. As we noted earlier, degenerate matrices should not be compared to observed presence-absence matrices, unless the full sampling universe of sites and species is known. Simulated degenerate matrices should be either discarded from the analyses or have a single species occurrence randomly repositioned to fill the empty row or column. Because all occurrences can be easily placed by either algorithm *(a)* or *(b)*, difficulties in filling the matrix and simultaneously maintaining row and column totals (Connor and Simberloff 1979) are not present.

This simulation protocol may be expanded so that marginal probabilities do not depend on row and column totals but on independently measured attributes of species and islands. For example, site probabilities could be set proportional to island area (Coleman et al. 1982; Simberloff and Gotelli 1984) rather than total species richness. Species probabilities could be scaled proportional to density (Haila and Järvinen 1981) or geographic range size (Graves and Gotelli 1983) rather than to the total number of occurrences for each species. This sort of analysis requires a good deal of biological insight and information about sites and species, but it avoids the circularity (and convenience) of using marginal sums to estimate cell probabilities.

4. How should the observed and simulated distributions be compared? Both Connor and Simberloff (1979) and Gilpin and Diamond (1982) used a chi-squared test to decide statistical significance. This is problematic, because none of the frequency classes in their analyses were independent of one another. We recommend summarizing matrix patterns in a single metric (or five metrics!). In this way, statistical significance can be directly estimated by classical randomization procedures (Edgington 1987)—the metric for the observed matrix can be directly compared to the distribution of values from a large number of simulated matrices (usually ≥1000) to estimate the probability value. This is much more straightforward than trying to compare a simulated with an observed *distribution* when the frequency classes of that distribution are not independent of one another.

This approach also highlights an important difference in the strategy of analyzing presence-absence matrices. Connor and Simberloff (1978), Wright and Biehl (1982), and Gilpin and Diamond (1982) all advocated examining deviations of all possible pairs of islands or species and then attributing significance to those pairs that showed extreme values. We think there are statistical and conceptual difficulties in this. The statistical difficulty is that none of the pairs are independent of one another, so it is unclear which pairs are statistically and biologically significant. The conceptual difficulty is that this procedure comes perilously close to "data-dredging" (Selvin and Stewart 1966). There may be a temptation to infer the hypothesis from emergent patterns, rather than explicitly stating an a priori hypothesis and testing for it with the null model. Rather than examining the individual pairs to reveal potential interaction, we prefer to carefully select species and sites for this purpose ahead of time, and then test whether there are nonrandom patterns in the matrix. In this way, the patterns and the mechanisms that produce them are kept conceptually distinct from one another. We cannot overemphasize that the selection criteria must *not* include the distributional patterns being tested!

Other Tests of Assembly Rules

Diamond's (1975) approach to assembly rules emphasized the particular combination of species *within* a guild that coexist and the intermeshing resource utilizations that allow these species to persist. Other studies have expanded on Diamond's (1975) model and used null models to test for patterns of community assembly. For example, Pulliam (1975) used estimates of seed availability, bill sizes, and diets of wintering sparrow species to construct a "coexistence matrix" that predicted the bill sizes of species combinations that could coexist. The initial application of the model was successful, but additional data for three

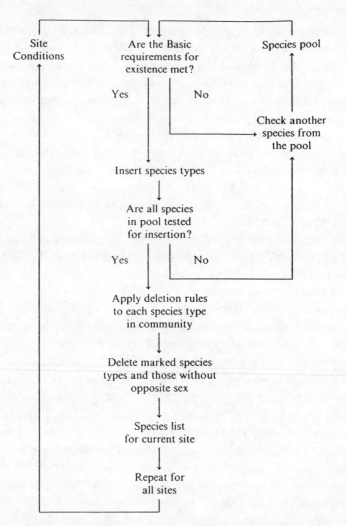

Figure 7.6. Flow chart for null models used to test assembly rules of Greater Antillean *Anolis* lizards. From Haefner, J. W. 1988b. Assembly rules for Greater Antillean *Anolis* lizards. Competition and random models compared. *Oecologia* 74:551–565, Figure 1. Copyright © 1988 by Springer-Verlag GmbH & Co. KG.

subsequent years fit the model very poorly (Pulliam 1983). A null model that incorporated habitat preferences of the species but did not include species interactions fit the data about as well as the assembly rules, although some patterns were still nonrandom with respect to this model.

Haefner's (1988b) analysis of *Anolis* lizard coexistence in the Greater Antilles represents the most ambitious attempt to test Diamond's (1975) assembly rules against an appropriate set of null models. Haefner (1988b) analyzed the occurrence of eight species of *Anolis* at 11 Puerto Rican sample sites and asked what percentage of the observed species-site occurrences could be successfully predicted by a suite of 20 (!) different assembly models (Figure 7.6). "Random insertion and deletion models" placed species on sites independently of one another, but with varying degrees of habitat affinity and niche requirements. These models constituted null hypotheses of varying complexity with respect to competitive interactions. In contrast, a set of "simple deletion models" removed species according to rules of body size and niche overlap. "Complex deletion models" removed species according to rules derived from Williams's (1972, 1983) ecomorph model.

Some of Haefner's (1988b) null models provided a good fit to the data, especially those that constrained row or column sums and incorporated habitat affinities. As expected, the best-fitting models were the complex deletion models, which were calibrated to maximize the fit to the Puerto Rican data set. Simple deletion models did not fit the data very well, suggesting that if competition structured this community, competitive asymmetries between species were probably common. When these same models were applied to co-occurrence of Jamaican *Anolis,* the data were best fit by a null model that maintained column sums, or that maintained row sums and habitat affinities of species. As with the Puerto Rican data, the fit of the complex deletion models was good and that of the simple deletion models was poor.

Although Haefner's (1988b) results enhance our understanding of community assembly, the interpretations are by no means clear-cut. On the one hand, the good fit of the data to several of the simple null models suggests that competition is unimportant in community assembly. On the other hand, the ability of the calibrated complex models to successfully predict community structure of Jamaican *Anolis* supports Williams's (1972, 1983) ecomorph model and implicates competitive interactions.

OTHER ASSEMBLY RULES

Although most of the controversy surrounding assembly rules has been over forbidden combinations of species and competitive interactions, there are other types of assembly rules that may dictate the organization of communities. These other assembly rules have also been addressed productively with null models, and here we review these approaches.

Incidence Functions

Diamond (1975) introduced the *incidence function* to describe the probability
of occurrence of a species with respect to ordered site characteristics, such as
species number. To calculate the incidence function, Diamond (1975) classified
the islands of an archipelago into discrete size classes, according to species
richness. He then plotted the proportion of islands occupied ($0.0 \leq f \leq 1.0$) in
each size class, ordered from species-poor to species-rich classes. The resulting
incidence curve has been viewed as a characteristic "fingerprint" of the distributional ecology of a species.

For most species, the incidence curve increases monotonically, though not
linearly (Figure 7.7). Diamond interpreted different incidence functions for
birds of the Bismarck Archipelago as reflecting different distributional strategies. "High-S" species occurred mostly on large, species-rich islands, whereas
the much less common "supertramp" species showed the opposite pattern and
were found only on species-poor islands. Diamond (1975) speculated that
high-S species competitively excluded supertramps from large, species-rich

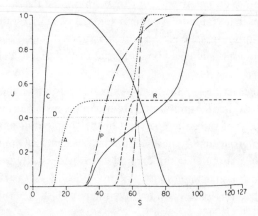

Figure 7.7. Incidence functions for gleaning flycatchers of the Bismarck Archipelago.
The *x* axis is the number of species on an island, and the *y* axis is the proportion of islands in a given size class that were occupied by the species. C = *Monarcha cineras-
cens;* D = *Pachycephala melanura dahli;* A = *Myiagra alecto;* P = *Pachycephala
pectoralis;* H = *Myiagra hebetior;* V = *Monarcha verticalis;* R = *Monarcha chryso-
mela.* From Diamond (1975). Reprinted by permission of the publisher from *Ecology
and Evolution of Communities.* M. L. Cody and J. M. Diamond (eds). Cambridge,
Mass.: The Belknap Press of Harvard University Press. Copyright © 1975 by the President and Fellows of Harvard College.

islands, and that shifts in incidence functions in different archipelagoes reflected different species pools and subsequent levels of competition.

In contrast, Gilpin and Diamond (1981) explored the connection between the incidence function and the equilibrium theory of island biogeography. They viewed an assemblage as having no competitive interactions, with each species at a dynamic equilibrium in which colonizations and extinctions were balanced. In this scenario, the incidence function represents the fraction of *time* that a species occupies islands of a particular size class. From these incidence functions, Gilpin and Diamond (1981) inferred species-specific colonization and extinction rates, and derived the community-level extinction and colonization curves of the MacArthur and Wilson (1967) equilibrium theory (see Chapter 8). Hanski (1992) successfully applied this model to the insular distribution of shrews in eastern Finland, where field data have corroborated the assumption of dynamic turnover (Peltonen and Hanski 1991).

Other interpretations of incidence functions are possible. The incidence function may reflect nothing more than the distribution of habitat types among islands. Thus, high-S species may simply be habitat specialists, such as birds that are restricted to lakes, marshes, and high-elevation forest found only on large islands (Wiens 1989). Even in the absence of habitat specialization, the incidence function will reflect sampling variability, both in terms of the number of islands censused and the number of islands "sampled" by the species (Taylor 1991). Common and widespread species will have their incidence functions shifted to the left because they will occur on a variety of different island sizes (Haila et al. 1983). Whatever the cause of the incidence function, environmental stochasticity should lead to a shallower curve as occurrences become more unpredictable with respect to ordered site characteristics (Schoener 1986b).

Null models clarify some of these differing interpretations by asking how an incidence function would appear in the absence of any structuring force. Whittam and Siegel-Causey (1981b) made the first attempt to analyze incidence functions statistically, for seabird colonies of Alaska. For an archipelago of islands that have been sorted into size classes, they constructed an $S \times C$ table, where each species is a row and each column is a size class (*not* an individual island). The entries in the table were the number of islands of a particular size class occupied by a species. Contingency table analysis was used to assess statistical significance, and standardized residuals pinpointed particular cells in the table that contributed positive or negative deviations.

For Alaskan seabird colonies, the distributions of 20 species were highly nonrandom with respect to colony richness. Each species showed one or more significant deviations, and the sign of the deviations showed only one change in direction, running from small to large colonies (Figure 7.8). The analysis

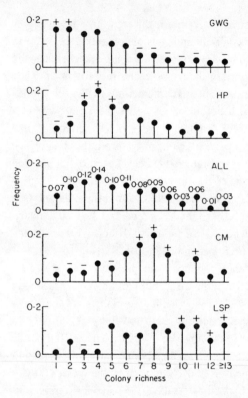

Figure 7.8. Statistical analysis of incidence functions for species in Alaskan seabird colonies. The x axis is the number of species per colony, and the y axis is the fraction of species occurrences in colonies of a given size. Plus and minus signs indicate significant deviations for a particular size class. Numbers indicate overall frequency of occurrence of species in colonies of different size. ALL = all species studied. Other species abbreviations as in Figure 7.3. From Whittam and Siegel-Causey (1981b), with permission.

identified supertramp species, such as the Glaucous-winged Gull (*Larus glaucescens*) and the Tufted Puffin (*Lunda cirrhata*), which occurred less often than expected in large colonies and more often than expected in small colonies. The more typical deviation was the high-S pattern, typified by several species of murres and auklets that were unusually present in large colonies and unusually absent from small colonies. Finally, some species showed no significant pattern of deviation, suggesting that occurrences were random with respect to colony size.

There are two points to note about Whittam and Siegel-Causey's (1981b) analysis of incidence functions. First, they defined incidence differently from Diamond (1975). Whereas Diamond (1975) defined incidence as the proportion of occupied islands in a size class, Whittam and Siegel-Causey (1981b) used the proportion of the total occurrences of a species that fell in a particular size class. Second, unusual deviations in the Whittam and Siegel-Causey (1981b) analysis were measured relative to the distribution of all other species in the assemblage. Thus, high-S species were those which occurred relatively more frequently on species-rich islands than did all other species. If all species showed an identical supertramp distribution, nonrandomness would not be revealed.

Incidence functions may have important implications for conservation biology. In particular, an incidence function analysis can be used to identify unusual minimum area requirements for particular species. Simply scanning a list of occupied sites may not be sufficient for this purpose, because even if a species were distributed randomly, it might be missing from some small sites by chance. Simberloff and Gotelli (1984) tested for unusually small minimum area occurrences of plant species in five archipelagoes of remnant prairie and forest patches in the North American prairie-forest ecotone. For each species, they ordered the patches on the basis of site area and then calculated the tail probability of finding the observed number of smaller, unoccupied sites. For three of the five archipelagoes, there were more species showing nonrandom patterns than expected by chance.

However, it might not be correct to conclude from this result that species have *unusual* minimum area requirements. In particular, this null model assumes that all sites are equivalent. But even if species have no special minimum area requirements, we expect large sites to be disproportionately occupied. A simulation model placed each species randomly in sites, with the probability of occurrence being proportional to the area of the patch. The simulation was repeated 10 times, and then the cumulative distribution functions for the observed and expected site occupancy were compared. The result was that far fewer of the species showed unusual deviations. In other words, nonrandomness in the occupancy of sites could be effectively accounted for by differences in the areas of the sites. Nevertheless, the distributions of seven plant species in one of the assemblages were significantly nonrandom by this test. Interestingly, none of these species showed an unusually large minimum area requirement. Instead, they followed the supertramp pattern and occurred too frequently in small prairie and forest patches (Simberloff and Gotelli 1984). Wilson (1988) tested for the occurrence of plant species with respect to island area and also found only a few species that exhibited supertramp distributions.

Finally, Schoener and Schoener (1983) expanded Diamond's (1975) idea of incidence functions beyond considerations of island area or species richness. They pointed out that sites can be ordered on any number of criteria, and then the occurrence of species tested against this ordering. "Haphazard" sequences of presence and absence would suggest that a variable does not play a direct role in determining the occurrence of a species. But if the sequence is highly ordered, the occurrence of the species is predictable with respect to that factor (Figure 7.9). The Mann-Whitney U test is a simple nonparametric analysis of the degree of this ordering for any particular variable. Within an archipelago, each species displays the same total number of presences and absences, so the

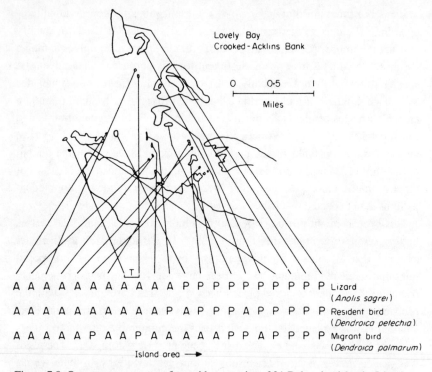

Figure 7.9. Occurrence sequence for resident species of 21 Bahamian islands. Islands are ordered on the basis of area. A = absent; P = present; T = islands of equal area. Note that the resident lizard *Anolis sagrei* has a perfectly ordered sequence, the resident bird *Dendroica petechia* has a highly ordered sequence, and the migrant bird *Dendroica palmarum* has a more haphazard sequence. From Schoener and Schoener (1983), with permission.

size of the Mann-Whitney statistic is a measure of the relative strength of the orderings (Simberloff and Levin 1985).

Schoener and Schoener (1983) used this test to analyze their extensive distributional data on 76 species of birds on 521 small islands in the Bahamas. Not only did they systematically census vertebrates on these islands, they also measured 54 variables that quantified area, isolation, habitat availability, and vegetation structure. The results indicated a very high degree of ordering. Species occurrences were quite predictable, although different groups of species seemed to follow different assembly rules. For example, the occurrence of lizards and resident birds was orderly with respect to island area, whereas the occurrence of migrant birds was more related to island isolation. The occurrence of both birds and lizards on islands could be predicted by vegetation and habitat structure, although the two taxa were ordered on slightly different vegetation characteristics.

Within each group, distributional complementarities were more clear-cut when habitat variables were controlled for with a logistic regression (Schoener and Adler 1991). Thus, some checkerboards will be detected only when habitat differences among sites are measured and incorporated into the analysis. The more orderly the distributions of species are with respect to site characteristics, the less the patterns will conform to a simple checkerboard in which two species never co-occur within a set of similar islands. Such ordering at the community level may lead to "nested" species distributions, which we discuss in the next section.

Assembly rules, as originally described by Diamond (1975), have been very difficult to discern in nature. The extent to which the occurrence of a species can be predicted by the distribution of other species is still open to debate. In contrast, the evidence seems quite compelling that site characteristics can be used to successfully predict the occurrence of most, if not all, species in an assemblage. We do not deny the potential importance of species interactions, but we do suggest that assembly rules might best be developed in an autecological framework. Such rules would emphasize the ecological requirements of each species and the characteristics of individual sites, rather than the presence of forbidden combinations of species (Graves and Gotelli 1983).

Nestedness

Suppose that each species in an assemblage showed a perfectly ordered occurrence sequence with respect to species richness. In this case, the incidence function would be a steep J-shaped curve, with an incidence of zero below a critical species richness class and 1.0 above that class. At the community level, this occurrence sequence would correspond to a "nested" distribution of species (Patterson and Atmar 1986). Like a collection of puzzle boxes that fit perfectly within one another, the species composition of each small assemblage would be a perfectly nested subset of all larger assemblages.

Many presence-absence matrices conform to this pattern (Patterson 1990; Wright and Reeves 1992). For example, the distribution of five fish taxa in 28 South Australian springs (Kodric-Brown and Brown 1993) showed only a single species occurrence that deviated from a pattern of perfect nestedness (Table 7.1). Patterns of nestedness have been shown for assemblages of mammals (Patterson and Brown 1991), birds (Bolger et al. 1991), insects (Patterson 1990), plants (Wright and Reeves 1992), and parasites (Dobson and Pacala 1992), for insular and oceanic islands (Patterson and Atmar 1986); for habitat fragments (Bolger et al. 1991); and for fossil assemblages and colonizing insect faunas (Patterson 1990). Nestedness has been noted before in the ecological (May 1978) and biogeographic (Darlington 1957) literature, but it has only received widespread attention since the 1980s.

How can nestedness be quantified, and what level of nestedness is expected in a randomly constructed biota? Indices of nestedness can be derived for entire communities or for individual species. Given that most assemblages exhibit a significant pattern of nestedness, the latter may be more informative (Simberloff and Martin 1991). Deviations from nestedness occur when species are found where they are not expected ("outliers") or are absent where they are expected ("holes"). For example, both montane mammals and birds of the Great Basin exhibit significant nestedness, but the bird distribution is outlier-rich, whereas the mammalian pattern is hole-rich (Cutler 1991). Atmar and Patterson (1993) measured "unexpectedness" as a diagonal deviation from a perfectly nested matrix, and Wright and Reeves (1992) introduced a scaled index that can be used to compare matrices of different dimension. Finally, Ryti and Gilpin (1987) used parameters from a logistic regression model to quantify the degree of nestedness in a matrix.

All of these metrics can be compared to values expected from randomly assembled matrices. Patterson and Atmar (1986) introduced two null models for randomizing matrices and comparing them with nestedness statistics. In the first model (RANDOM0), site richness was retained and species were drawn equiprobably from the source pool. In the second model (RANDOM1), species were drawn in proportion to their occurrences. These models are identical to Null Hypotheses 0 and 2, proposed for Q-mode analysis (Connor and Simberloff 1978). Because the observed number of species occurrences was not maintained in these simulations, species that occurred in every site artificially inflated the apparent degree of nestedness and should have been omitted from the analysis (Simberloff and Martin 1991). But even without such species, the pattern of nestedness in most archipelagoes is so strong that it is unlikely to have been caused by a simulation artifact.

What explanations have been offered for the nestedness pattern? The dominant interpretation, first offered by Patterson and Atmar (1986) for montane mammals, is that the nestedness reflects a contraction of insular area, followed by an orderly sequence of extinctions, so that the same subset of widespread species survives in small habitats. If this "selective extinction" hypothesis is true, it suggests that faunal collapse is a highly deterministic process. The implication for conservation biology is that the biotas of small habitat fragments converge by loss of species that are uncommon in the landscape (Wright and Reeves 1992). This interpretation of nestedness is also a restatement of the

Table 7.4
Relative nestedness of avifaunas of land-bridge and oceanic islands

Fauna	Observed N	Expected N	p
Oceanic	53	53.32	~0.50
Land-bridge	158	363.73	<0.00001

The nestedness index, N, indicates the degree to which a presence-absence matrix departs from perfect nestedness. The simulation procedure (RANDOM1) holds species number constant on islands; the probability of occurrence of each species is weighted by its frequency. Note that the faunas of land-bridge islands are more highly nested than the faunas of oceanic islands. From Patterson (1987).

SLOSS (single-large-or-several-small) debate in conservation biology (Simberloff and Martin 1991).

But this is by no means the only explanation for nestedness. Darlington (1957) first proposed that the pattern could be explained by "selective immigration"—nestedness arises because of differences among species in their ability to immigrate and successfully colonize islands. Finally, a nested pattern of species occurrences might be related to neither immigration nor extinction, but simply reflect a nesting of habitats on islands of different sizes. In the West Indian avifauna, for example, the proportion of single-island endemics is much higher on the four large Greater Antilles than on other smaller islands (Terborgh 1973a). The Greater Antilles also support a greater diversity of habitat types, and the nestedness of the avifauna may simply reflect this pattern of habitat diversity.

How can these mechanisms be distinguished? Support for the "selective extinction" hypothesis comes from the observation that the degree of nestedness is somewhat greater for faunas of land-bridge islands than oceanic islands (Table 7.4). However, land-bridge and oceanic islands may differ in many factors besides their previous mainland connection (Gotelli and Graves 1990), and the evidence for "faunal collapse" of land-bridge island faunas is not generally compelling (Faeth and Connor 1979; Boecklen and Simberloff 1986). Moreover, highly nested faunas have been discovered in archipelagoes that are dominated by stochastic colonization and extinction, such as defaunated mangrove islands and vacant city lots (Patterson 1990). These findings suggest that nestedness need not imply orderly extinction, and that the pattern of nestedness may be a general property of many communities, rather than a specific attribute of islands undergoing biotic relaxation (Patterson 1990).

Lomolino (in press) has shed light on the problem by measuring the degree of nestedness when islands are ordered first by area and then by the degree of isolation. If selective extinction is more important, the ordering by area should show the strongest pattern of nestedness. If immigration is more important, the pattern should be more nested when sites are ranked by isolation. Significance was assessed by randomly reordering the matrices and then examining the weighted deviations from perfect nestedness.

Lomolino (in press) applied this test to distributions of nonvolant mammals in three archipelagoes of the Great Lakes and the St. Lawrence River. For all three archipelagoes, faunas were nested with respect to both area and isolation. But for two of the three, patterns of nestedness were more orderly with respect to isolation than to area. This finding suggests that immigration dynamics may play an important role in determining the pattern of nestedness, even though isolation itself was not always significantly correlated with species richness. We need more tests of this sort on additional archipelagoes to evaluate the relative contributions of immigration and extinction to nestedness.

Finally, it is worth noting that nestedness will cause faunas of similar size to be similar in composition, whereas checkerboard distributions and other forbidden combinations of species will have the opposite effect and increase diversity of similar sites (Graves and Gotelli 1993). Consequently, the degree of nestedness in an archipelago is correlated with the average similarity in species composition among sites (Wright and Reeves 1992). Perhaps the frequent occurrence of nestedness is one reason that checkerboard patterns of distribution seem to be the exception, rather than the rule, for most assemblages.

Niche Limitation

Wilson et al. (1987) suggested that if niche limitation were generally important, then the number of species that coexist in a guild would be constrained by competition (Colwell 1979). This approach does not emphasize the identities of particular species combinations, but instead draws on the older literature of niche limitation initiated by studies of species/genus (S/G) ratios (see Chapter 1).

Wilson et al. (1987) measured niche limitation as the variance in species number among a set of similar sites. If competition limited the number of species that could coexist locally, then the *variance* in species number would be unusually small compared to the variance in an unstructured community. On the other hand, the variance in S will also be increased if sites differ in their suitability, or if the community is not in an ecological or evolutionary equilib-

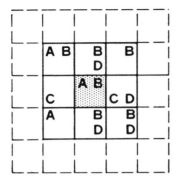

Figure 7.10. A patch model for small-scale niche limitation. The local source pool for colonization of a quadrat is the set of species occurring in the centered 3 × 3 grid. In this example, there are three local occurrences of species A, so it is placed with a simulation frequency of 3/9 = 0.333 for the central quadrat. Reprinted with permission from A. J. Watkins and J. B. Wilson. 1992. Fine-scale community structure of lawns. *Journal of Ecology* 80:15–24.

rium. The expected variance can be calculated analytically (Barton and David 1959) or generated by a null model simulation in which species occurrences are randomly allocated to quadrats. The test is very similar to the variance ratio (Schluter 1984), because strong negative associations between species pairs will reduce the variance in total S.

Wilson et al. (1987) applied their test to a number of floristic data sets. To control for differences in suitability of sites, they searched for niche limitation of coexisting plant species at small spatial scales (5 m × 5 m contiguous quadrats) that were presumed to be environmentally uniform. For 164 sites in a homogeneous agricultural field, the observed variance in S was significantly greater than expected. Results were similar when the quadrats were subdivided floristically or environmentally. A large variance in S was also found for the vegetation of a uniform dune slope, but not for Patrick's (1968) data on diatom colonization of glass microscope slides. Similar results were obtained by Wilson and Sykes (1988). Variance in species richness was reduced for plants of 12 "lawns" in New Zealand and Fiji, but only for tiny quadrat subdivisions (360 and 160 mm^2; Watkins and Wilson 1992). Palmer (1987) found reduced variance in plant species number of Minnesota old fields, although his sites were unlikely to have been in equilibrium. Collectively, these results provide little evidence for strong niche limitation in floristic assemblages.

The Wilson et al. (1987) test assumes that all sites are colonized from a common species pool. An alternative assumption is that subtle microhabitat variation generates spatial variation in the pool of species available to colonize plots. Watkins and Wilson (1992) tested this "patch" model by randomly selecting species for a quadrat from a set of adjacent quadrats (Figure 7.10). This null model is conservative, because the number of species that can be sampled from a few adjacent quadrats is usually much smaller than the total number from all quadrats. Nevertheless, there was still a variance deficit in species richness for most sites. The results suggest that niche limitation for plants may occur at an extremely small spatial scale, perhaps reflecting spacing constraints of individual plants in small quadrats.

Guild Structure

Whereas Wilson et al. (1987) emphasized the number of coexisting species within a particular guild, other studies have examined the relative frequency of different guilds. The null hypothesis, often implicit, is that the relative frequency of guilds in the assemblage represents a random sample of species from the colonizing source pool.

Two deviations from this null model are possible: the difference in guild frequencies between the source pool and the assemblage might be unusually large or unusually small. Biological significance has been attributed to both patterns of deviation. When the deviations are large, certain guilds are over- or underrepresented in local assemblages. In particular, many authors have noted the apparent "disharmony" of small island faunas compared to large mainland assemblages (Carlquist 1974). For example, MacArthur et al. (1972) attributed the consistent absence of some bird families from Neotropical land-bridge islands to interspecific competition. D. L. Lack (1976) also described examples of the limited coexistence of confamilial bird species in the West Indies and the role of reduced habitat and resource availability in producing these patterns. However, as in the analysis of species/genus (S/G) ratios (Chapter 1), we expect some deviations from the expected number of species in a guild because of sampling error. Drawing species randomly from an appropriate source pool is the correct procedure for evaluating the deviations of guild frequencies in small assemblages.

As described in Chapter 2, Gotelli and Abele (1982) used the hypergeometric distribution to test for deviations in species richness of West Indian land-bird families. For each island, the observed number of species in each family was compared to the expected number if species were drawn equiprobably from the archipelago list. Based on this test, the number of coexisting species of parrots (Psittacidae) was less than expected per island, whereas the number of pigeons and doves (Columbidae) and mockingbirds (Mimidae) was greater than expected. For a set of Neotropical land-bridge islands, the Columbidae were also overrepresented, as were species in all families with large geographic ranges (Figure 2.5) or large body sizes (Gotelli and Graves 1990). Neither study provided evidence that competition within avian families limited insular coexistence in the Neotropics, or that certain families were extinction-prone on islands (cf. Terborgh and Winter 1978; Faaborg 1979).

Trophic Ratios

In some assemblages, guild frequencies show unusually small deviations, and this pattern has also been accepted as evidence for community assembly rules. The explanation is that biotic interactions, such as competition between different functional groups or predation between different food web components, constrain community structure (see Chapter 10). For example, the ratio of prey species number to predator species number was relatively constant in a sample of 100 community food webs (Cohen 1978), suggesting a trophic constraint on community assembly. Assemblages that did not contain the "correct" proportions of different groups were presumably unstable and did not persist. The hypothesis here is that the observed assemblage shows an unusually *small* deviation in guild frequencies from a colonizing source pool. This "constraints" hypothesis says nothing about what shapes guild frequencies in the source pool, only that, whatever these forces are, they dictate the stability of observed communities. The correct null hypothesis is that small deviations between observed and expected guild frequencies represent sampling error. This is the same null hypothesis for related tests of body-size matching (Schluter 1990) and convergence of morphology between communities (see Chapter 6).

Heatwole and Levins (1972) searched for trophic constraints in Simberloff's (1969) mangrove insect recolonization data. They constructed a source pool list for six islands that were experimentally defaunated, assigned species to eight trophic classes (predators, parasites, detritivores, etc.), and calculated the expected frequencies in each trophic class. Using recolonization data, they calculated the summed deviation between observed and expected trophic class frequencies. This index decreased significantly with time since defaunation. In other words, as colonization proceeded, the observed fauna converged on the trophic structure of the source pool.

However, the Heatwole and Levins (1972) index was sensitive to sample size. Because species richness increased during colonization, it may not be surprising that the deviation index decreased with time. Simberloff (1976b, 1979b) showed with a null model simulation that the observed deviations from the source pool were no different than expected, given the number of species

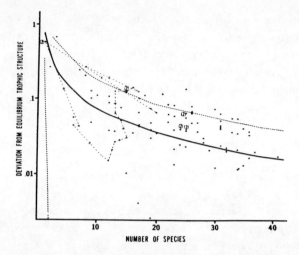

Figure 7.11. Sample-size dependency of the trophic deviation index. The solid line gives the expected deviation index for trophic classes of insects recolonizing six defaunated mangrove islands. The smooth dotted lines enclose two standard deviations. Each point represents a different recolonization sample, and the jagged line connects the observations for a single island. Note that although the trophic deviation index decreases with increasing species richness, most observations fall within the predictions of the null model. From Simberloff (1976b), with permission.

observed at that point in the recolonization sequence (Figure 7.11). Whether or not the trophic ratios were nonrandom in the source pool fauna, the mangrove insect assemblage did not exhibit unusual trophic constraints during recolonization.

Evans and Murdoch (1968) claimed that the ratio of herbivorous to entomophagous species number in a grassland insect community was unusually constant. In a reanalysis of Evans and Murdoch's (1968) data, Cole (1980) compared the observed and expected number of herbivorous species for each of 14 samples with the hypergeometric model. Cole (1980) found that all but one of the 14 samples were within two standard deviations of the expectation, and concluded that there was no evidence for unusual trophic structuring.

Finally, Wilson (1989) tested the guild proportionality of plants in a New Zealand rain forest by assigning species to one of eight stratification classes. He then measured the variance in the proportion of species in each stratum across 80 quadrats (each 100 m^2), and assigned species randomly to quadrats to generate the null expectation for this variance. Most strata did not deviate significantly, although the proportion of lianas was more variable than expected and inversely proportional to the number of epiphyte species in the quadrat. The observed proportion of canopy trees was unusually constant, perhaps reflecting space constraints in the number of trees per quadat.

Functional Groups

Fox (1987) introduced a related type of assembly rule that also predicted pattern in the proportional representation of different guilds in an assemblage. He argued that the species pool for small-mammal communities could be divided into a number of distinct "functional groups," and that these functional groups showed an unusual propensity to be equally represented in any local assemblage. The assembly rule specified that species are added from different groups until all groups are represented in the assemblage, and then the rule repeats. In other words, Fox (1987) hypothesized that the distribution of species among functional groups was not simply constant (as in the guild limitation tests) but was unusually *uniform.*

Functional groups do not reflect forbidden combinations of species per se, but only "favored" or "unfavored" states. Favored states have equal (or nearly equal) representation by each functional group and are predicted to occur more frequently than expected by chance. For example, if a species pool is composed of three functional groups, then a local three-species assemblage with all groups represented (1,1,1) would be a favored state. A four-species assemblage with (2,1,1) would also represent a favored state, because the mix of species is maximally even. In contrast, a three-species assemblage with a (0,1,2) mix would represent an unfavored state, because there are no species from the first functional group but two species from the third group.

As in Diamond's (1975) analysis, competition for food resources is thought to be responsible for the uniform frequencies of different functional groups. However, Fox's (1987) hypothesis is less restrictive than Diamond's (1975) original assembly rules. Whereas Diamond (1975) emphasized the identities of coexisting species, Fox (1987) considered only functional group identity. Diamond's (1975) analysis was restricted to taxonomic guilds of closely related species, but functional groups may be more phylogenetically diverse and could include unrelated species that are united by common morphology and foraging strategy. For example, Fox and Brown (1993) recognized one functional group of "quadrupedal non-heteromyids" that included four species of cricetids, three species of deer mice, one sciurid, and one ground squirrel. Other groups (e.g., "bipedal heteromyids") included only closely related congeners and were more similar to Diamond's (1975) taxonomic guilds. The species in different functional groups may differ in body size (Figure 7.12), which has been used as a

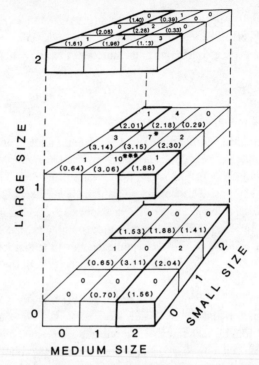

Figure 7.12. A three-dimensional model illustrating functional groups of soricid assemblages from mesic forests in the northeastern United States. Three functional groups based on body size were recognized. Each cell represents the number of occurrences of a different combination of zero to two species of small, medium, or large soricids. Expected values from the null model are indicated in parentheses, and unfavored cells are shown with heavy outline. Significant departures from randomness are indicated by asterisks (* $p < 0.05$; *** $p < 0.001$). From Fox and Kirkland (1992), courtesy of the American Society of Mammalogists.

convenient character to define functional groups (Fox and Kirkland 1992). Whatever criteria are used, the functional groups must be defined a priori and independently of the co-occurrence data (Fox and Brown 1993).

Once the functional groups are defined, observed assemblages are classified as favorable or unfavorable states. For example, suppose there are three functional groups in the source pool, each with two species. In any local assemblage, each functional group will be represented by zero, one, or two species. Thus, there are $3^3 = 27$ different combinations of species from the three functional groups. In this hypothetical example, there are 15 favored combinations (including the 0,0,0 state) in which the functional groups are uniformly represented, and 12 unfavored combinations. As in Pielou and Pielou's (1968) analysis of 2^k contingency tables, the different states are not equiprobable, and instead are conditional on the frequencies with which each species is represented in the source pool.

The expected number of favored and unfavored states was determined by a simulation in which species were drawn randomly and equiprobably from the source pool, without regard to their functional group. For a set of 52 mammal assemblages in temperate Australian heathlands, Fox (1989) divided the fauna into three functional groups (insectivore, herbivore, granivore-omnivore) of six, six, and three species each. Because no site contained more than two species in any functional group, the simulations were also constrained in this way to collapse the number of possible combinations. Fox (1989) found significantly more favored combinations and significantly fewer unfavored combinations than expected by chance. The same pattern held for mammals of Australian eucalypt forests (Fox 1987) and for North American soricid communities (Fox and Kirkland 1992).

However, these initial analyses used an algorithm of sampling with replacement that was not appropriate for small assemblages (Biehl and Matthews 1984). Fox and Brown (1993) constructed null models that sampled without replacement and extended the study of functional groups to North American desert rodent assemblages. For rodent assemblages in a small region of Nevada and at sites dispersed across the southwestern United States, there were again more favorable states represented than expected by chance (Figure 7.13).

Fox and Brown (1993) next examined the individual cells of the contingency table to pinpoint particular combinations that led to nonrandomness. Although favorable combinations were more probable than unfavorable ones, not all favorable combinations were equally likely. For example, the strongest deviation for the Nevada data set was a favored state of two quadrupedal heteromyid species, one bipedal heteromyid, and one generalist granivore. In contrast, the strongest deviations for the dispersed sites were two unfavored cells that had more assemblages than expected, even though the net result was that favored combinations were too frequent.

These results have been interpreted primarily in the context of interspecific competition: the different functional groups exploit food resources in different ways that are presumed to promote coexistence. The patterns reinforce experimental evidence for resource-based competition in both North American (Munger and Brown 1981) and Australian (Dickman 1986) rodent assemblages.

Two puzzles remain. First, why should the functional group rule repeat itself as more species are added to the system? In other words, if resource limitation is severe, how can two or more species from the same functional group coexist?

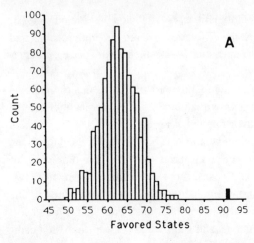

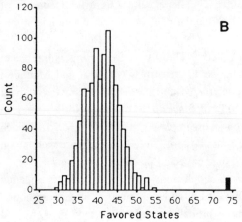

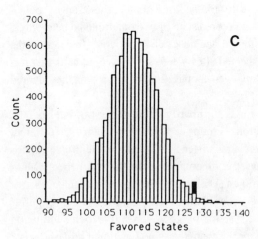

Figure 7.13. Observed and expected frequencies of favored states for North American desert rodent assemblages. The frequency histograms show the number of favored states when species are sampled equiprobably from the source pool. The observed number of favored states is shown with a solid bar. (**A**) 11 granivore species in three functional groups from 115 sites in Nevada; (**B**) 14 rodent species in five functional groups from 115 sites in Nevada; (**C**) 28 granivore species in three functional groups from 202 sites in southwestern deserts. From Fox and Brown (1993), with permission.

One might expect a superior competitor to exclude all other species within a functional group. Competition is not the only force leading to favorable states. Schluter (1990) showed that the same pattern will arise if source pools are small and if there is variation in colonization probabilities within a functional group. Wilson (1995) reanalyzed the Nevada data of Fox and Brown (1993) and showed that the statistical evidence for the functional group rule disappears if the assumption of equiprobable colonization is relaxed.

Second, what role does phylogeny play in producing functional group assembly rules? Because many of the functional groups are composed of closely related species, historical processes such as allopatric speciation may be responsible for the orderly composition of local assemblages. Whatever the role of interspecific interaction, phylogeny and history determine the mix of local species available for colonization (Cornell and Lawton 1992). Fox and Brown (1993; see also Brown 1988) argued that these phylogenetic effects are only present at a regional scale and that even at this scale, geographic range boundaries (and hence source pool composition) may be shaped primarily by ecological forces (Bowers and Brown 1982). However, phylogenetic correlates of geographic range boundaries may be strong, even within groups of closely related species (Taylor and Gotelli 1994; see Chapter 9). Unraveling these historical and ecological correlations is a major goal of the comparative method (Harvey and Pagel 1991), and the functional group assembly rules could be profitably analyzed from this perspective.

RECOMMENDATIONS

For Q-mode analyses of shared species, we suggest Simberloff's (1978a) weighted colonization models. For R-mode analyses of species combinations, there are several useful tests. The variance ratio (Schluter 1984) is a simple test for patterns of covariation that does not require Monte Carlo simulations. For detecting checkerboard distributions and unusual species combinations, we recommend a simulation in which row and/or column totals act as probabilistic constraints (Graves and Gotelli 1993). Other assembly rules and community patterns can also be addressed profitably with null model simulations, including incidence functions (Whittam and Siegel-Causey 1981b; Simberloff and Gotelli 1984), nestedness (Simberloff and Martin 1991; Atmar and Patterson 1993), niche limitation (Wilson et al. 1987), guild structure (Cole 1980; Wilson 1989), trophic ratios (Simberloff 1976b), and functional groups (Fox and Brown 1993). In all cases, analyses will be greatly strengthened by independent estimates of colonization potential, resource availability, source pool composition, and phylogenetic effects.

8
SPECIES-AREA RELATIONSHIPS

SPECIES-AREA RELATIONSHIPS

In Chapter 7, we pointed out that a major difficulty in assessing co-occurrence patterns was variation in site quality. If some sites are more favorable than others for all species, patterns of species aggregation will emerge that do not reflect interspecific interactions (Pielou and Pielou 1968). Variation in site quality is often manifest in total species richness, which should be controlled for in null models of species co-occurrence (Connor and Simberloff 1979).

But why is species richness greater in some sites than in others? This question is an important one that has been studied independently of factors that determine co-occurrence. Area is the most basic correlate of species richness. Large areas support more species than small areas, although the relationship is rarely linear. For oceanic archipelagoes, species number roughly doubles for every tenfold increase in island area (Darlington 1957). The species-area relationship is most obvious when the "sites" are true islands (Figure 8.1). For example, mammalian species richness is well correlated with area in archipelagoes of oceanic, land-bridge, coastal, and river islands (Wright 1981; Lomolino 1984).

Species richness also correlates with the area of most insular patches of habitat. Familiar examples include mammals of forested mountaintops (Brown 1971), decapod crustaceans of pocilloporid coral heads (Abele 1976), and insects of thistleheads (Brown and Kodric-Brown 1977). "Areas" need not even be insular. Species number is related to area for vascular plants of different-sized quadrats (Connor and McCoy 1979), lumbricid earthworms of European sites (Judas 1988), and parasitic fungi of British trees, where area was defined as the geographic range of the host plant species (Strong and Levin 1975). Species-area relationships hold for tropical and temperate archipelagoes (Schoener 1976b) and for fossil and extant assemblages of entire continents (Flessa 1975).

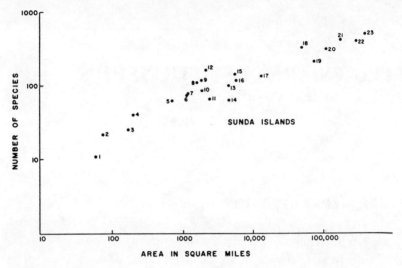

Figure 8.1. Species-area relationship for land and water birds of the Sunda Islands. Numbers indicate different islands (1 = Christmas Island, 23 = New Guinea). Note the logarithmic transformation of both axes. Data such as these were used to support the equilibrium model, although other models may account for the species-area relationship as well. From MacArthur and Wilson (1963), with permission.

"One of ecology's few genuine laws" (Schoener 1976b), the species-area relationship has been described and interpreted for over 120 years (McGuinness 1984a), but there is little agreement on its cause. Some authors have viewed it as a dynamic balance between immigration and emigration (MacArthur and Wilson 1963, 1967) that may ultimately reflect energetic constraints on community development (Wright 1983). Because of their insularity, nature reserves have been likened to islands, and species-area curves have formed the basis for conservation strategy (Wilson and Willis 1975). Others have suggested that the species-area relationship embodies little more than a passive sampling effect and may have no biological significance (Connor and McCoy 1979). A null model that treats islands as targets and individuals as passive propagules incorporates minimal biological forces, but may account for the species-area relationship (Arrhenius 1921; Coleman 1981; Coleman et al. 1982). In this chapter, we review four hypotheses that have been put forth to explain the species-area relationship, discuss other patterns that are predicted by these mechanisms, and describe the use of null models in understanding species-area curves.

WHAT MECHANISMS ACCOUNT
FOR SPECIES-AREA CURVES?

In spite of the generality of the species-area relationship, it is likely to result from a variety of forces that reflect the sampling properties of islands, habitat variability, population processes, and the underlying species abundance distribution (Figure 8.2). To date, four distinct mechanisms have been proposed to account for the species-area relationship. These mechanisms are not mutually exclusive, but they do emphasize different processes that can cause a correlation between species richness and area:

1. *The disturbance hypothesis.* Disturbances that reduce species diversity are more common on small islands than on large islands (McGuinness 1984a).
2. *The habitat diversity hypothesis.* Large areas contain more habitats and hence more species (Williams 1943).
3. *The passive sampling hypothesis.* Large areas function as "targets" that sample more individuals, and hence more species (Arrhenius 1921; Coleman 1981; Coleman et al. 1982).
4. *The equilibrium hypothesis.* Large areas support larger population sizes of all resident species than do small islands. Consequently, the probability of stochastic extinction is reduced on large islands (Munroe 1948; Preston 1962; MacArthur and Wilson 1963, 1967).

Figure 8.2. Mechanisms controlling the relationship between area and species number. Several mechanisms may contribute to the apparently straightforward correlation between *S* and *A*. From Haila (1983), with permission.

ISLAND AREA
(traditional independent variable)

↓

Ecological space

↕

Amount & heterogeneity
of ecological resources

↕

Number of individuals

↕

Species-abundance distribution

↓

SPECIES NUMBER
(traditional dependent variable)

Table 8.1
Predicted patterns for hypotheses that explain the species-area relationship

Pattern	Equilibrium hypothesis	Habitat diversity hypothesis	Passive sampling hypothesis	Disturbance hypothesis
Substantial turnover	Yes	Yes or no	No	Yes (small islands)
S-A correlation for equal-sized quadrats	Yes	No	No	No
Fit with passive sampling model	Yes or no	Yes or no	Yes	Yes or no
Fit with habitat-unit model	No	Yes	No	No

These hypotheses have not received equal attention in the literature. The disturbance hypothesis, for example, was offered as an explanation for species-area relationships only in the 1980s (McGuinness 1984a). And although the passive sampling hypothesis was first introduced more than 70 years ago (Arrhenius 1921), it has only recently been employed as a null model for the species-area relationship. The equilibrium hypothesis, as popularized by MacArthur and Wilson (1967), dominated the literature in the 1960s and 1970s, and was often accepted without adequate proof (Williamson 1989). Gilbert (1980) reviewed the uncritical acceptance of the theory during this period, and Boecklen and Simberloff (1986) discussed its premature application to the design of nature reserves, through "faunal collapse" and "relaxation" models.

The essential problem was that many authors viewed the species-area relationship as sufficient evidence for the equilibrium theory, without a critical evaluation of the alternatives. Although the four hypotheses all predict a species-area relationship, each has a different set of assumptions and a unique set of additional predictions (Table 8.1). In the following sections, we review the assumptions, predictions, and critical tests of each hypothesis. Next, we explain how null models have been used to examine two particular species-area patterns: (1) the slope of the species-area regression, which has been interpreted as a measure of isolation, and (2) the constancy of species number (*S*) through time, which has been taken as an indicator of equilibrium status.

THE DISTURBANCE HYPOTHESIS

If small islands are disproportionately subject to chronic disturbances that remove species, then a species-area relationship will result (McGuinness 1984a). This hypothesis assumes that small islands are more vulnerable to disturbance, and that species richness increases as disturbance frequency decreases. Like the MacArthur and Wilson (1967) model, the disturbance hypothesis predicts that turnover on small islands should be substantial. However, the MacArthur and Wilson (1967) model predicts continuous turnover, whereas the disturbance model predicts synchronous extinctions. A more fundamental difference is that the MacArthur and Wilson (1967) model envisions all communities as being in an ecological equilibrium, whereas the disturbance hypothesis describes small-island communities in a state of disequilibrium.

Evidence for the disturbance hypothesis comes from sessile marine communities, where fouling panels (Osman 1977) or intertidal boulders (McGuinness 1984b) function as islands. Wave action and predation often control diversity in these space-limited systems (Sousa 1984), although the perturbations may not always lead to a species-area relationship. For example, in intertidal boulder fields of California, species richness was greatest on intermediate-sized boulders. Small boulders had low species richness because they were chronically disturbed by wave action. But large boulders also had low species richness because they were rarely overturned and became dominated by a few species of competitively superior algae (Sousa 1979). Thus, even if disturbance frequency is correlated with island area, it may not always lead to a species-area relationship. Biotic "disturbances" may also lead to species-area relationships. In forest bird assemblages, for example, species-area slopes were steeper for guilds that were susceptible to nest predation (Martin 1988), suggesting that this disturbance may be more important in small forest patches. The increased perimeter/area ratio ensures that any "edge effects" will be relatively more severe on small islands.

THE HABITAT DIVERSITY HYPOTHESIS

The habitat diversity hypothesis assumes that species diversity is controlled by the availability of different habitat types. This model predicts that habitat diversity increases with area, and that species richness increases with habitat diversity. Area per se has a minor effect on species richness, and instead serves as a surrogate variable for underlying habitat diversity (Williams 1943).

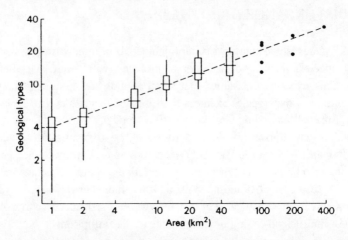

Figure 8.3. Relationship between area and habitat diversity. The *x* axis is the plot area for regions of England and Wales, and the *y* axis is the number of geological types recorded in those areas. The box-and-whisker plots illustrate the extremes (vertical lines), quartiles (box ends), and medians (horizontal lines) for multiple observations. The sloping line connects the medians with the total number of geological types observed for the entire area. Note the logarithmic transformation of both axes. The close relationship between area and habitat diversity may be responsible for many species-area relationships. From Williamson (1981), with permission of Oxford University Press.

The habitat diversity hypothesis implies that habitat specialization is important. This explanation fits the naturalist's perspective that many species can be reliably located by paying close attention to their habitat affinities. If unique habitat types are found only on large islands or areas, then species richness will inevitably increase with area. In the West Indian avifauna, for example, single-island endemics such as the Zapata Wren of Cuba (*Ferminia cerverai*) and the Elfin Woods Warbler of Puerto Rico (*Dendroica angelae*) are habitat specialists whose exclusive occurrence on large islands contributes to the species-area relationship.

Several studies have confirmed the basic relationship between habitat diversity and species richness, in both terrestrial (e.g., MacArthur and MacArthur 1961) and marine (e.g., Abele 1974) communities. Much less common are studies of the direct relationship between habitat diversity and area itself. For example the number of geological formations in the Lake District of England was well-correlated with plot area, and the slope of the relationship varied between 0.20 and 0.35 on a log-log scale (Figure 8.3; Williamson 1981). Many species-area relationships may reflect this underlying pattern of habitat variation and area (Scheuring 1991).

On the other hand, many species are not strict habitat specialists, and species-area relationships are found in very homogeneous habitats, such as mangrove or *Spartina* islands (Wilson and Simberloff 1969; Rey 1981). But even in apparently homogeneous habitats, the perimeter/area ratio will change with island size, and this "edge effect" may represent an important element of habitat diversity (Schoener and Schoener 1981; Janzen 1983). However, without an experimental manipulation, it may be impossible to distinguish the contributions of area and perimeter to species richness (Blouin and Connor 1985).

Multiple Regression Models

How has the habitat diversity hypothesis usually been tested? Historically, habitat and area effects were partitioned with multiple regression analyses (Hamilton et al. 1963; Simpson 1974; Connor and Simberloff 1978). If habitat diversity is important, it should make a statistical contribution to species richness above and beyond the variation explained by area. Although the test is conceptually valid, the tight correlation between area and habitat diversity compromises the statistical analysis. Consequently, the biological interpretation of multiple regressions is problematic, and it has been difficult to tease apart the contributions of area and habitat diversity to species richness (Connor and Simberloff 1978).

For example, bird species richness in isolated woodlots was well correlated with area and vegetation structure (Blake and Karr 1987), but in a multiple regression analysis, only the area effect was statistically significant. However, species richness of interior forest birds was correlated with both area and habitat diversity, whereas richness of edge species was influenced by only area and perimeter. Moreover, habitat diversity was correlated with the abundances of particular species, suggesting that habitat diversity influenced species occurrence and hence total species richness.

Multiple regression analyses can be very sensitive to statistical outliers. For plants of the British Isles, number of soil types contributed significantly to species richness (Johnson and Simberloff 1974), but only if the island of Great Britain was excluded from the analysis (McCoy and Connor 1976). Thus, the measured effects of habitat diversity on species richness may hinge on which groups of species and which groups of islands are considered.

None of these "whole-island" tests is very satisfying. By emphasizing the habitat diversity of an entire island, multiple regression analyses neglect the

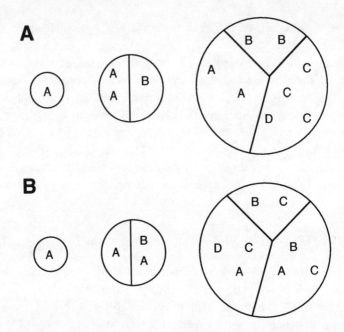

Figure 8.4. Effects of habitat diversity on within-island distributions of species. Each circle is an island, and the divisions within the circle represent different habitat types. The letters represent individuals of different species. In (**A**), the species-area relationship arises because each species is a specialist on a single habitat type. In (**B**), habitat diversity does not contribute to the species-area relationship because individuals of the different species occur randomly with respect to habitat type within an island.

spatial patterns of species occurrence *within* islands. If the habitat diversity hypothesis is correct, species will be distributed nonrandomly with respect to different habitats within a single island. In contrast, species may occur randomly within habitats if any of the other three hypotheses is correct (Figure 8.4).

The Habitat Unit Model

This suggests a promising avenue for testing the habitat diversity hypothesis. First, map the habitats of each island, and then record the occurrence of each species within those habitats. If the habitat diversity hypothesis is correct, the relative areas of different habitats should be a better predictor of species richness than total island area.

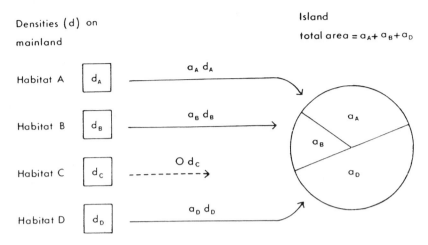

Figure 8.5. Construction of a prevalence function. The density (d) of species in different habitats on the mainland and the relative area (a) of those habitats on the island generate the expected density of each species on an island. From Haila et al. (1983), with permission.

Buckley (1982) took exactly this approach in a study of plant species richness of the Lowendal Islands of Western Australia. For each of 22 islands, Buckley (1982) recorded the distribution of vascular plants in three habitat types: white sand, limestone, and red sand. He next categorized the plant species according to the habitat types in which they occurred. There were three groups of habitat "specialists" that occurred in only one habitat, three groups of species that occurred in exactly two of the habitats, and one group of ubiquitous species that occurred in all three habitats. For a set of n habitats in an archipelago, there will be $2^n - 1$ such groupings or "habitat units."

For each habitat unit, Buckley (1982) then constructed a species-area curve, using the combined area of the component habitats of each island. Summing the predicted values across all the habitat units gave the expected number of species for an island. This expectation was compared to the predictions from a simple species-area regression that ignored habitats. For 17 of the 22 islands, the predictions of the habitat unit model were superior to those of the simple regression. It is important to note that Buckley's (1982) result was not a trivial consequence of extreme habitat specialization, because most of the species occurred in two or more habitats.

Haila and Järvinen (1983) took this approach one step further and measured not only the occurrence, but also the abundance, of individual species. Similar

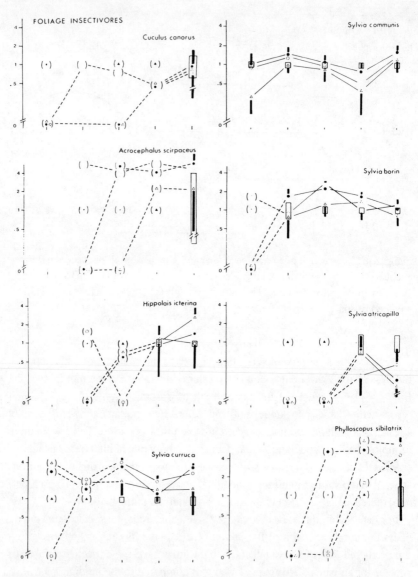

Figure 8.6. Prevalence functions for 8 species of insectivorous birds of the Äland Islands of Finland. Five island size-classes are represented on the *x* axis. The *y* axis gives the logarithm of the prevalence function, that is, the ratio of the observed to the expected island density. Symbols indicate data from different yearly censuses. For expectations greater than 5 breeding pairs, the vertical solid line indicates the range and the vertical open bar indicates the standard deviation. Note that for some species the expected density on small islands is effectively zero. From Haila et al. (1983), with permission.

to Diamond's (1975) incidence function (see Chapter 7), the *prevalence function* is the ratio of observed to expected density of a given species on islands of different size (Figure 8.5). For bird species of the Åland Islands of Finland, Haila et al. (1983) constructed the prevalence function by estimating mainland densities of species in different habitats (Figure 8.6). This model accurately predicted species richness, and the authors concluded that a sampling metaphor was appropriate to explain avian species occurrence in this archipelago. Note that the model of Haila et al. (1983) is actually a hybrid of the habitat diversity hypothesis and the passive sampling hypothesis, explained later in this chapter.

In sum, the habitat unit model and the prevalence function are useful tools for evaluating the role of habitat diversity in producing species-area correlations. Because they emphasize the occurrence of species within particular habitats on islands, they are more powerful tests of the habitat diversity hypothesis than conventional regression analyses.

THE EQUILIBRIUM HYPOTHESIS

Popularized by MacArthur and Wilson (1963, 1967) and independently developed by Munroe (1948; see Brown and Lomolino 1989), the equilibrium theory envisions island species richness as a balance between rates of colonization from a mainland source pool of P species and island extinctions of established populations. The theory has two sets of assumptions, one concerning the demography of island populations and the other concerning community-level rates of immigration and extinction. The theory is usually presented in terms of the rate assumptions, but ultimately these are derived from processes at the population level. The population-level assumptions are as follows:

1. The species-abundance distribution of the mainland source pool is a canonical log normal (see Chapter 3). This assumption is not absolutely necessary for the model, but it does generate quantitative predictions about the form and slope of the species-area relationship.
2. The summed abundance of all species is proportional to island area.
3. The probability of population extinction is inversely proportional to island population size.
4. The probability of colonization is inversely proportional to island isolation or distance from the source pool.

The community-level assumptions are:

1. The immigration rate (number of new species/time) decreases with increasing species number on the island and decreases with increasing isolation of the island.
2. The extinction rate (number of species disappearing/time) increases with increasing species number on the island and decreases with increasing island size.

Finally, the predictions that arise from the equilibrium model are:

1. There should be substantial turnover in species composition through time.
2. The species-area curve should be best fit by a power function ($S = CA^z$), where S is species richness, A is island area, and C and z are fitted constants.
3. The slope of the curve on a log-log plot (z) should approximate 0.26 for isolated archipelagoes, and should be shallower with decreasing isolation.
4. Species number on an island should be relatively constant through time, although some variability in S is expected because extinctions and recolonizations are stochastic (Diamond and May 1977).
5. In a comparison of equal-sized quadrats, species density should be higher on the mainland or on large islands than on small islands.

TESTS OF THE ASSUMPTIONS

In the following sections, we review the evidence supporting the important assumptions and predictions of the equilibrium theory. Some, but not all, of these patterns have been tested with null models.

Do Extinction and Immigration Rates Vary with Species Number?

Graphs of extinction and immigration rates as a function of species number are the most famous summary of the MacArthur and Wilson (1967) model. The precise shape of these curves depends on species interactions and immigration dynamics. If species extinctions are independent (a noninteractive community)

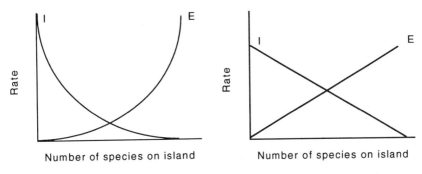

Figure 8.7. Concave and linear immigration (*I*) and extinction (*E*) curves. The original MacArthur and Wilson (1963) model presented concave immigration and extinction curves, whereas a Markovian model generates linear curves.

and species immigrations are equiprobable, the curves are strictly linear. In contrast, an interactive or heterogeneous assemblage will give concave immigration and extinction curves (MacArthur 1972), which is how the theory was originally presented (Figure 8.7). This distinction is important for null model tests of species constancy, which we describe later in this chapter. However, for a qualitative test of the MacArthur and Wilson (1967) model, it is sufficient to show that the immigration rate falls and the extinction rate rises with increasing island species richness.

In spite of the obvious importance of the immigration and extinction curves to the equilibrium theory, long-term sampling data are necessary to construct them, and there are few examples from the literature. Strong and Rey (1982) demonstrated a significant increase in extinction rate and a significant decrease in immigration rate for insect recolonization of fumigated *Spartina* islands (Rey 1981). Williamson (1981) assembled three other examples from long-term census data in insular assemblages. For an established bird community in Eastern Wood, Williamson (1981) plotted extinction and immigration rates as a function of species number for 26 yearly censuses. Immigration rates declined significantly with *S*, but extinction rates did not increase significantly (Figure 8.8). For birds of Skokholm Island, only the extinction rate was significantly correlated with island species richness. The correlation for the immigration curve was nonsignificant and had a positive, not a negative, slope.

Williamson's (1981) final example was plant colonization data for the volcanic island of Surtsey. In this study, the highest immigration rates occurred not at the start of colonization, but after some initial pioneer species became established, perhaps indicating successional changes in the hospitality of the island. In all of these examples, the variance about the curves was substantial,

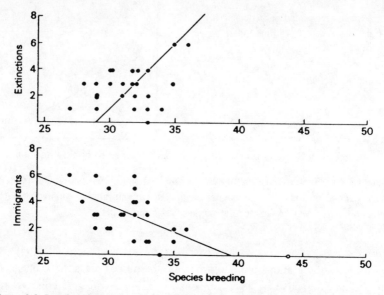

Figure 8.8. Immigration and extinction curves for breeding birds of Eastern Wood. The immigration curve decreases significantly with increasing S, as predicted by the MacArthur and Wilson (1967) model, but the increase in the extinction rate is not significant. Compare with Figure 8.7. From Williamson (1981), with permission of Oxford University Press.

suggesting that species number had only a very minor effect on local immigration and extinction rates.

Do Population Sizes Vary with Island Area?

In spite of the critical importance of population size and stochastic extinction to the MacArthur and Wilson (1967) theory, relatively few studies have examined how total population size of an individual species changes as a function of island area (Haila and Järvinen 1981). One problem is that MacArthur and Wilson (1967) were not entirely explicit about what the predicted patterns were. As developed by Schoener (1976b), there are two possibilities. The first is that the fauna is noninteractive and population size is proportional to area. In the second model, competition is proportional to species number, so that average population size is a function of both island area and species richness. Whether or not the fauna is interactive, it would seem that a basic prediction of the MacArthur and Wilson (1967) model is that equilibrium population sizes increase with island area (Preston 1962).

Figure 8.9. Average population densities of *Drosophila* species as a function of island area. (**A**) *D. affinis* subgroup species. (**B**) Mushroom-feeding species. Curves are fit to data collected in three different years. Mainland densities are shown on the far right. From Jaenike, J. 1978. Effect of island area on *Drosophila* population densities. *Oecologia* 36:327–332, Figure 1. Copyright © 1978 by Springer-Verlag GmbH & Co. KG.

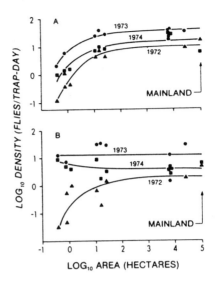

Jaenike (1978) measured *Drosophila* densities on islands off the coast of Maine (Figure 8.9). For the *D. affinis* subgroup, density was constant for large islands and mainland areas, but dropped off sharply for small islands. Thus, populations on small islands were even smaller than would be predicted on the basis of area alone. On small islands, exposure to wind and violent storms may have depressed population densities, which were correlated with the ratio of island circumference to area. For mushroom-feeding *Drosophila,* the relationship between island area and density was less clear-cut and varied among years, perhaps because these populations tracked fluctuations in mushroom density. Jaenike's (1978) results suggest that the relationship between population size and island area may not be linear, and that the factors that regulate species richness may be fundamentally different on large than on small islands.

Also working in the Deer Island Archipelago in Maine, Crowell (1973, 1983) introduced deer mice and voles onto rodent-free islands. These island populations grew to greatly exceed mainland population densities, which were probably limited by predation and dispersal. For islands in the Gulf of California, the highest densities of the lizards *Uta* and *Cnemidophorus* were found on small islands (Case 1975). Contrary to the assumptions of the MacArthur and Wilson (1967) model, lizard density declined with increasing species richness and island area.

These examples cast doubt on one of the basic premises of the equilibrium model—that population size is proportional to island area. Although the idea that *N* increases with area is intuitively reasonable, the frequent occurrence of density compensation (MacArthur et al. 1972; Wright 1980), habitat shifts (Ricklefs and Cox 1978; Crowell 1983), and ecological release from predators and competitors (Toft and Schoener 1983) suggests that island area is not always the overriding factor that determines insular population size.

TESTS OF THE PREDICTIONS

Is There Substantial Turnover in Species Composition?

Turnover is one of the most salient features of MacArthur and Wilson (1967) equilibrium communities. It distinguishes the MacArthur and Wilson (1967) model from other scenarios of insular community assembly, including co-evolutionary models of species interaction (see Chapters 6 and 7) and non-interactive colonization models with little or no turnover (Case and Cody 1987). Unfortunately, turnover in island populations may be difficult to establish. Measures of turnover are affected by the thoroughness of sampling effort at different times (Lynch and Johnson 1974), the length of the census interval (Diamond and May 1977), sampling error (Nilsson and Nilsson 1983), the establishment of a species equilibrium (McCoy 1982), the occurrence of habitat change between censuses (D.L. Lack 1976), and the use of relative versus absolute turnover rates (Schoener 1988b).

More importantly, the measurement of turnover depends critically on how an investigator defines colonization, extinction, and residency status. If vagrant or nonresident species are included in the calculations, estimates of turnover can be greatly inflated. For example, Simberloff and Wilson (1969) initially estimated turnover rates of insect species colonizing mangrove islands at 0.67 species per island per day. Simberloff (1976a) reanalyzed the data and eliminated probable transients and widely dispersing species. The revised turnover estimate was only 1.5 species per island per year! Similarly, Whitcomb et al. (1977) computed turnover rates for forest birds of 15–25% over 30 years. But if edge species and wide-ranging raptors were excluded, the turnover was close to 0 (McCoy 1982). Williamson (1989) concluded that the MacArthur and Wilson (1967) model is thus "true, but trivial." In other words, many communities do display substantial turnover, but this inevitably occurs among transient, peripheral species that may not be typical residents of the community.

However, not all "transient" turnover is biologically uninteresting. It is important to distinguish between turnover of populations and turnover of individuals through movement among sites. In some cases, community assembly occurs through individual movement. For example, breeding birds of coniferous forest seasonally colonize habitat fragments and establish breeding territories (Haila et al. 1993), so that turnover does not reflect true population extinction. Haila et al. (1993) suggested that seasonal movement of individuals is likely to be very important in the structure of many boreal animal communities.

Is the Species-Area Curve Best Fit by a Power Function?

The log normal distribution provided a theoretical justification for using the power function in species-area studies (Preston 1962). But if the species abundance distribution is not log normal, other transformations may be more appropriate. For example, if a log series describes abundances, an exponential (semi-log) transformation will linearize the species-area relationship (Fisher et al. 1943; Williams 1943, 1947b). McGuinness (1984a) reviewed the extensive history of efforts by plant ecologists to infer the correct functional form of the species-area relationship. For animal ecologists, the power function quickly became synonymous with the log normal distribution (Preston 1960, 1962) and the equilibrium model (MacArthur and Wilson 1967). However, Coleman et al. (1982) warned that inferring the species abundance distribution from the species-area transformation requires that the same distribution hold for all islands in an archipelago, which is a tenuous assumption.

What is the empirical evidence that the power function or the exponential provides the best fit to species-area data? Connor and McCoy (1979) fit regression models to a heterogeneous collection of 100 species-area curves from the literature. Using logarithmic and untransformed data, they chose the best-fitting model as the one that linearized the curve and minimized least-squares deviations (high r^2). In some cases, more than one model fit the data equally well (r^2 values differed by less than 5%). These criteria were somewhat arbitrary (Sugihara 1981), but without repeated measurements of species richness on islands of identical size, there seems to be no other reasonable way to assess the fit of a regression model (Connor et al. 1983).

Although the power function (log-log model) fit three-quarters of the data sets, it was the best-fitting model in only 43 of 119 cases. The exponential model did not fare any better, and in many cases, the untransformed data gave the best fit. Unless the assumptions of the MacArthur and Wilson (1967) model can be confirmed independently, there seems to be little biological significance to the transformation that best linearizes a species-area curve.

What Is the Observed Value of *z*, and What Is Its Significance?

Although the log-log transformation may have little biological significance, there is a long tradition of interpreting the slope of this regression in the context of equilibrium theory. The impetus came from Preston (1962), who derived a slope of 0.26 for an archipelago of "isolates" sampled from a log normal distribution. He felt that sampling errors and other factors would lead to slope values in the range of 0.17 to 0.33, whereas MacArthur and Wilson (1967) accepted a range of 0.20 to 0.35. May (1975a) derived slopes in the range of 0.15 to 0.39 for a variety of log normal distributions, and Schoener (1976b) predicted slopes between 0 and 0.5 for an equilibrium model with species interactions.

Within the equilibrium framework, species-area slopes were thought to reflect the degree of isolation of an archipelago. In the original MacArthur and Wilson (1967) model, isolation affected only the immigration curve, so that distant islands had lower species richness and distant archipelagoes had steeper slopes. Lomolino (1984) confirmed this pattern for mammals in island archipelagoes: the slope of the species-area relationship was correlated with the relative isolation of an archipelago (Figure 8.10).

However, isolation may affect the extinction rate as well (Brown and Kodric-Brown 1977), making it unclear what slope ought to be expected. Schoener (1976b) thought that distant archipelagoes would be colonized primarily via a

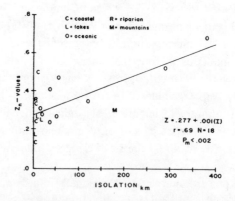

Figure 8.10. Effects of isolation (average distance to the nearest mainland or large island) on the slope of the species-area regression. Each symbol represents a different archipelago. As the original MacArthur and Wilson (1967) model predicted, slopes were steeper for more isolated archipelagoes. From Lomolino, M. V. 1984. Mammalian island biogeography: effects of area, isolation and vagility. *Oecologia* 61:376–382, Figure 2. Copyright © 1984 by Springer-Verlag GmbH & Co. KG.

"stepping stone" effect from other occupied islands, rather than from a distant source pool. In addition, the pool of species for a distant archipelago may be smaller than for a close archipelago. In Schoener's (1976b) models, these effects generated shallower slopes for distant archipelagoes, a pattern that holds for some avian species-area data. These extensions of the MacArthur and Wilson (1967) model suggest that a wide range of slopes are possible for equilibrium communities.

Slopes of species-area curves have also been used to compare taxa within an archipelago. A shallow species-area slope for a taxonomic group has often been interpreted as an indicator of good colonization potential (Terborgh 1973a; Faaborg 1979): because successful colonizers can reach many islands in an archipelago, the increase in species richness due to area is much weaker than for a group of poor dispersers.

But before species-area slopes can be interpreted in the context of equilibrium theory, other forces that affect z must be considered. First, there are a number of statistical decisions that affect the slope of the species-area curve (Loehle 1990b). For example, the estimate of the slope will depend on whether the power function or the linear log-log model is fit. The two models are not equivalent; they treat the error term differently and may give different slope estimates (Wright 1981). The slope of the curve may also be affected by the range of island sizes considered. If the range of areas sampled is too narrow, the area effect may not be statistically significant (Dunn and Loehle 1988). Slopes also tend to be much steeper for archipelagoes of small islands than large islands (Martin 1981). Finally, slope estimates may be sensitive to the particular islands included in the sample. For example, the estimated species-area slope for butterflies of woodland lots (Shreeve and Mason 1980) is 0.28 ($n = 22$ lots), but z ranges from 0.23 to 0.35, following the deletion of a single island from the sample (Boecklen and Gotelli 1984). This sort of statistical variation suggests that differences in slope will have to be substantial to reflect any biological meaning.

For these reasons, comparisons of slope among different taxonomic groups are problematic. For Neotropical birds, species-area slopes varied markedly among different families (Terborgh 1973a; Faaborg 1979). However, most of this variation in slope could be attributed to variation in species richness within families (Gotelli and Abele 1982). Regardless of dispersal potential, families with very few species will have shallow species-area slopes (Figure 8.11). The estimated slope in a regression is also proportional to the correlation coefficient. Grafen (1984) showed similar effects of species richness on the comparison of r^2 values among guilds of insects associated with British trees (Kennedy and Southwood 1984).

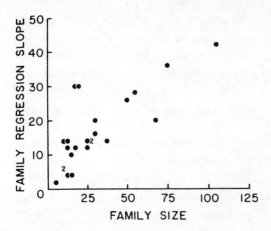

Figure 8.11. Effects of species richness on the slope of the species-area regression. Each point is a different family of West Indian land birds. From Gotelli and Abele (1982), with permission.

In addition to these important statistical considerations, slopes of species-area curves will be influenced by biological forces that are not explicitly considered in the equilibrium model. For example, habitat diversity will affect the slope as different species sets are added with new habitat types on large islands (Williams 1943). From published studies of forest plots in the eastern United States, Boecklen (1986) quantified habitat diversity with a principal components analysis of vegetation measures, and then randomly combined plots of differing size and habitat diversity. Species-area curves for breeding birds were steeper for "archipelagoes" with strong habitat heterogeneity.

Incidence functions and minimal area requirements of particular species can also generate a range of slope values that span the interval suggested by the equilibrium hypothesis (Abbott 1983). Disturbance (McGuinness 1984a) and predation (Martin 1988) may also change the slope of the curve. Finally, species-area curves may change during the course of colonization (Schoener and Schoener 1981), although for vascular plants on lake islands in Sweden, the slope did not change during a century of primary succession (Rydin and Borgegård 1988).

Given all these factors, it is not surprising that Connor and McCoy's (1979) literature survey yielded a wide range of slope values, of which only 55% fell within the liberal range suggested by MacArthur and Wilson (Abbott 1983). Connor and McCoy (1979) suggested that any tendency for slope values to cluster between 0.2 and 0.4 was an artifact. They argued that the pattern was generated by the small variance in species number relative to variance in island area, and by the fact that small or nonsignificant correlation coefficients would be underrepresented in the literature. Because the estimated slope in a regression is the product of the correlation coefficient and the ratio of variances of y to x, it follows that slopes in this range are often expected by chance.

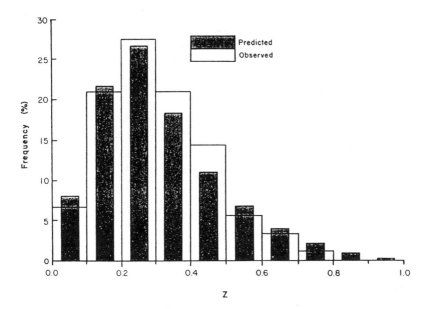

Figure 8.12. Distribution of 100 species-area slopes. Although most observed values fall between 0.20 and 0.30, this pattern is predicted by the observed variances in area and species richness and by the observed distribution of correlation coefficients. Reprinted by permission of the publisher from Connor, E. F., E. D. McCoy, and B. J. Cosby. 1983. Model discrimination and expected slope values in species-area studies. *American Naturalist* 122:789–796. Copyright © 1983 by The University of Chicago.

Sugihara (1981) argued that this analysis was incorrect and that observed slopes were significantly clustered in a narrow range. However, a reanalysis using observed variances and marginal distributions of r confirmed that there was no tendency for slopes to cluster (Figure 8.12). For carefully selected archipelagoes, it may be possible to interpret relative values of z (Martin 1981). But the most sensible view is that slopes of species-area curves are simply fitted constants, with little or no biological significance (Connor and McCoy 1979; Gilbert 1980; Abbott 1983).

Less attention has been given to the intercept of the species-area relationship (Gould 1979), although the statistical problems will be similar to those of slope analyses. Nevertheless, if the slopes of two species-area curves are identical, the intercept represents the expected species richness after controlling for differences in area. For example, Abele (1976) compared species richness of decapod crustaceans inhabiting coral heads in constant and fluctuating environments. Although there was a significant species-area relationship, the intercept was higher for coral heads in the fluctuating environment, indicating greater local species richness. Note that a comparison of intercepts statistically removes the effect of area from the comparison of species richness.

The initial appeal of the equilibrium theory motivated much research in biogeography (Brown 1981), but the interpretation of species-area slopes has been a largely unproductive avenue. There are some communities that seem to fit the MacArthur and Wilson (1967) model (e.g., Rey 1981), but the critical tests come from observations of turnover and population extinctions on islands, not from statistical curve fitting. Like the Hutchinsonian size ratio of 1.3 (see Chapter 6), the z value of 0.26 is another of ecology's "magic numbers" that has not withstood detailed scrutiny.

Is Species Number Constant Through Time?

Although the MacArthur and Wilson (1967) model describes a steady-state balance between immigration and extinction, it does not predict a strict constancy in S through time, because immigration and extinction curves reflect underlying probabilities of discrete events (Diamond and Gilpin 1980). The intersection of the immigration and extinction curves yields the expected species number with an associated variance.

But how much variability is acceptable? In other words, how much change is expected in species number at equilibrium for the MacArthur and Wilson (1967) model? Keough and Butler (1983) noted that many ad hoc limits have been invoked in the literature; authors have claimed a species equilibrium for temporal coefficients of variation (CV) between 5 and 75%. Using literature data and computer simulations of different sampling distributions, Keough and Butler (1983) suggested a rough empirical limit of approximately 10%. Comparison with any cutpoint is dependent on sample size, and Keough and Butler (1983) provided statistical tests for deciding whether the CV is greater or less than some hypothesized value. Applying the "10% rule" to their own data on marine epifauna of mollusc shells, they rejected the null hypothesis—temporal fluctuations in S were too large to be considered in equilibrium. Much of the variability in S was due to chance colonization of shells by colonial ascidians, which were superior space competitors. Predation by monomanthid fishes removed these ascidians and greatly reduced the variability.

Even with such an empirical guide, documentation of equilibrium is tricky. Species number on real or virtual islands is always bounded between 0 and P, the species pool size, so the fact that a mean and a variance can be calculated for a series of census data need not imply an underlying equilibrium (Boecklen and Nocedal 1991). Instead, an explicit null model for temporal change in species richness should be used. If a real community is in equilibrium, temporal fluctuations in S should be substantially smaller than predicted by the null model.

Simberloff (1983c) used a Markov model of species colonization and extinction to contrast with the MacArthur and Wilson (1967) equilibrium model. For each species k in the source pool, the Markov model assumes a constant probability of successful immigration during a given time period (i_k) and a constant probability of extinction (e_k). The corresponding probabilities of not immigrating and not going extinct are ($1 - i_k$) and ($1 - e_k$), respectively. These probabilities need not be equivalent for all species. If species immigrations and extinctions are independent of one another, an equilibrium will be reached at

$$\hat{S} = \sum_{k=1}^{p} \frac{i_k}{i_k + e_k} \qquad (8.1)$$

This noninteractive Markov model has been derived many times, for both island biogeography models (Bossert 1968; Simberloff 1969; Gilpin and Diamond 1981) and analogous single-species metapopulation models (Gotelli 1991). The Markov model generates linear immigration and extinction curves, in contrast to the concave curves of the MacArthur and Wilson (1967) model. Both models predict an equilibrium determined by the balance between immigration and extinction, and both models predict that species number will decline if it is above that equilibrium.

However, the forces leading to this decline are somewhat different for the two models. In the Markov model, species richness declines above equilibrium, because it is improbable that such a large number of species will persist through time. Extinctions will outnumber colonizations and S will decline. Demographic factors are not invoked in these extinctions. In the MacArthur and Wilson (1967) model, an increase in S implies a decline in the population size of each component species, because of an assumed limit on summed population densities. With smaller population sizes, the probability of extinction increases and species number declines. In the MacArthur and Wilson (1967) model, the immigration and extinction curves are more divergent than in the Markov model, so that species number will return more rapidly if it is displaced either above or below equilibrium. The steeper the curves and the greater their concavity, the faster the return to equilibrium (Figure 8.13; Diamond and Gilpin 1980).

Thus, in a regulated MacArthur and Wilson (1967) equilibrium, variance or change in S should be smaller than under the null hypothesis of the Markov model. Simberloff (1983c) fit the Markov model to bird census data from

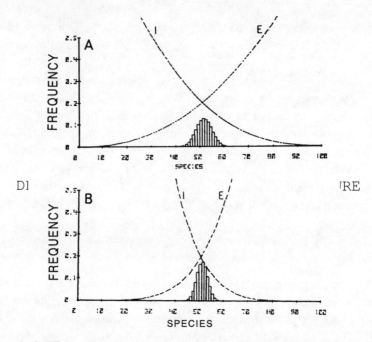

DI   IRE

Figure 8.13. Effects of immigration (*I*) and extinction (*E*) curves on frequency distribution of species number (*S*) at equilibrium. The steeper and more concave the immigration and extinction curves, the less variability in *S* at equilibrium. Reprinted by permission of the publisher from Diamond, J. M., and M. E. Gilpin. 1980. Turnover noise: contribution to variance in species number and prediction from immigration and extinction curves. *American Naturalist* 115:884–889. Copyright © 1980 by The University of Chicago.

Skokholm Island and the Farne Islands, and the forested plot of Eastern Wood (Figure 8.14). Because independent estimates of extinction and immigration probabilities were not available, Simberloff (1983c) estimated them from the sequential census data. Using the Markov transition probabilities, Simberloff (1983c) generated a null distribution by simulating each species trajectory, starting with the island composition observed in the initial census.

The null hypothesis was never rejected in the direction of the regulated equilibrium, and observed measures of variance in *S* were usually in the wrong tail of the distribution. For the Skokholm data, the variance was significantly greater than even that predicted by the Markov model. This result is consistent with Williamson's (1981) finding that the immigration curve for these data showed a nonsignificant increase with species richness. With the immigration and extinction curves both increasing with *S*, fluctuations in species number

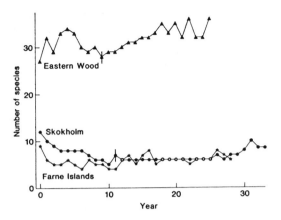

Figure 8.14. Species trajectories for birds of Skokholm Island and Farne Islands and Eastern Wood. Vertical lines indicate years in which more than one census was conducted. These trajectories could not usually be distinguished from those generated by a noninteractive Markovian model (see Figure 8.7). Reprinted with permission from Simberloff, D. 1983. When is an island community in equilibrium? *Science* 220:1275–1277. Copyright © 1983 American Association for the Advancement of Science.

will be especially large. Simberloff (1983c) concluded there was little evidence from these analyses to support a model of regulated species equilibrium.

Simberloff's (1983c) analysis was predicated on the idea that the observed sequence of presences and absences provided a reasonable empirical estimate of extinction and immigration probabilities. Boecklen and Nocedal (1991) explored this problem with seven species trajectories drawn from the literature. They assumed that the estimated transition probabilities were true and simulated 30 new presence-absence matrices for each set of trajectories. Transition probabilities were again estimated from each new matrix, and 1000 additional species trajectories were generated. Finally, the 30 estimates of cumulative probabilities were compared to the probability value estimated from the original presence-absence matrix. If estimates of transition probabilities from the original matrix were valid, they should have been equivalent to those that were secondarily estimated from the new presence-absence matrices.

However, the original and derived probability estimates usually did not agree. Sometimes the observed probability values were too conservative, and sometimes they were overly liberal; results varied unpredictably among data sets. This analysis also showed that coefficients of variation, even if tested statistically by the Keough and Butler (1983) method, were unreliable indicators of equilibrium status. Boecklen and Nocedal (1991) concluded that although the Markov model was probably valid for testing equilibrium status, transition probabilities should not be estimated from the same data set to be tested. A reanalysis using maximum likelihood estimates (Clark and Rosenzweig 1994) would be informative, because the transition probabilities estimated by Simberloff (1983c) and by Boecklen and Nocedal (1991) may be biased in some cases.

Does Species Richness Increase in Equal-Sized Quadrats?

An important prediction from Preston's (1962) work has been relatively neglected in the species-area literature: in an equilibrium community, not only will total species richness be greater on the mainland than on islands, but so will species richness in *equal-sized* quadrats. This is because the mainland supports many rare species from the tail of the log normal distribution that would not occur on islands. A similar logic can be applied to a comparison of large and small islands. If the MacArthur and Wilson (1967) model is correct, there should be a significant correlation between S and island area for equal-sized quadrats sampled *within* islands.

Westman (1983) first tested this hypothesis in xeric shrublands of the California Channel Islands. Although there was a significant overall species-area relationship, the number of plant species per quadrat showed no relationship with island area. Kelly et al. (1989) found only a weak positive correlation between island area and local richness of plants for islands in Lake Manapouri, New Zealand. Island area accounted for no more than 17% of the variance in species number in equal-sized quadrats, whereas area accounted for 92% of the variation in whole-island species richness (Quinn et al. 1987).

For animal communities, Stevens (1986) examined the species-area relationship for wood-boring insects and their host plants by sampling insect communities at different sites within the geographic range of the host. Although species richness of insects was correlated with the size of the geographic range of the host species (the measurement of "area"), richness within sites did not show a significant host-area effect. All these studies point to the fact that species were not uniformly distributed within an island. The results suggest that total island area (or host geographic range size) did not have a direct effect on local population size and hence on total species richness.

THE PASSIVE SAMPLING HYPOTHESIS

Biological processes such as local extinction, chronic disturbance, and habitat specialization have provided competing explanations for the species-area relationship. But the correlation could also arise as purely a sampling phenomenon. The passive sampling hypothesis (Connor and McCoy 1979) envisions individuals as "darts" and islands as "targets" of different area. Continuing this analogy, different colors of darts represent the different species, and the darts are tossed randomly at the array of targets. It follows that large islands will accumulate more darts, and hence more species, than will small islands.

Arrhenius (1921) introduced this model and found good agreement between observed and predicted species richness for plants in quadrats of different size. However, the passive sampling hypothesis was largely ignored in the species-area literature until Coleman (1981; Coleman et al. 1982) developed the theory mathematically.

The passive sampling hypothesis has only two assumptions:

1. The probability that an individual or a species occurs on an island is proportional to island area.
2. Islands sample individuals randomly and independently. In other words, inter- or intraspecific forces do not modify the probability of individual occurrence.

Given these assumptions, the passive sampling hypothesis predicts the expected species richness for an island as

$$E(S_j) = \sum_{i=1}^{S} 1 - \left(1 - \frac{a_j}{A_T}\right)^{n_i} \tag{8.2}$$

where a_j is the area of the jth island, A_T is the summed area of all islands, and n_i is the abundance of species i summed over all islands. The term inside the summation sign is the probability that species i occurs on the island, given n_i dart tosses at the target. When summed across all species, this gives the expected species number.

Coleman (1981) also derived the variance of species richness and the expected slope of the species-area curve, which could be compared to values derived from equilibrium theory or other hypotheses. However, Coleman's (1981) slope test may not always discriminate among different hypotheses (McGuinness 1984a). Because the expected slope is ultimately determined by the species abundance distribution, a range of curves is possible. The extremes are a linear species-area relationship for an inequitable species abundance distribution and a steep, monotonic curve for a perfectly equitable assemblage (Figure 8.15). Exponential or power function curves may lie between these two extremes (McGuinness 1984a). These curves are identical in shape to those

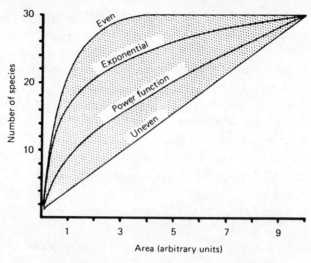

Figure 8.15. Effect of the underlying species abundance distribution on species richness in the passive sampling model. The exponential and power functions will often lie between the extremes generated by a maximally even or uneven species abundance distribution. Compare with Figure 2.7. From McGuinness (1984a). Reprinted with the permission of Cambridge University Press.

generated by rarefaction (see Figure 2.7 in Chapter 2) because each island effectively rarefies the collection to a small sample determined by relative island area.

The passive sampling hypothesis is appealing as a null model because of its simplicity—the observed collection of individuals in the archipelago is taken as the possible universe from which samples (island communities) are randomly drawn. As in the MacArthur and Wilson (1967) model, species richness in the passive sampling model depends on the species abundance distribution. However, the MacArthur and Wilson (1967) model envisions extinctions due to small population size as the ultimate cause of the species-area relationship, whereas the passive sampling hypothesis makes no demographic assumptions. Instead, areas function only as targets that randomly accumulate individuals and species. The idea that island immigration is proportional to island area seems biologically reasonable. In contrast, the equilibrium theory assumes that area controls only the extinction process (Brown and Kodric-Brown 1977). The best independent evidence for the "target-area" effect on immigration is that migration of mammals across ice onto islands in the St. Lawrence River was correlated with island area (Lomolino 1990).

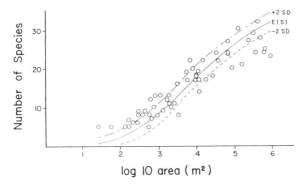

Figure 8.16. Observed and expected plant species richness (legumes, milkweeds, and goldenrods) for prairie remnants. The solid line is the expected value based on a passive sampling model adapted for presence-absence data. Reprinted from Simberloff, D., and N. Gotelli. 1984. Effects of insularisation on plant species richness in the prairie-forest ecotone. *Biological Conservation* 29:27–46, p. 35. Copyright © 1984, with kind permission from Elsevier Science Ltd, The Boulevard, Langford Lane, Kidlington OX5 1GB, UK.

One disadvantage of the passive sampling hypothesis is that it requires measurements of island population sizes. Because these data are difficult to obtain, there have been relatively few tests of the passive sampling hypothesis. If abundance data are not available, an analogous test can be conducted with presence-absence data. Observed species occurrences are reshuffled randomly among islands, with probabilities of occurrence proportional to island areas. Simberloff and Gotelli (1984) used this method to predict plant species richness in prairie and forest remnants. The observed and expected species richness showed reasonable agreement, although richness was somewhat higher than expected for very small patches and lower than expected for large patches (Figure 8.16).

When data are available on the distribution of individuals, the passive sampling hypothesis has proven useful as a baseline for examining species-area curves. The hypothesis adequately explained over half of the species-area curves for sessile organisms of rocky intertidal boulders in Australia (McGuinness 1984b). For breeding birds on islands in a Pennsylvania reservoir, the passive sampling hypothesis provided a better fit to species-area data than did a power or exponential function (Figure 8.17). At a larger spatial scale, passive sampling characterized most species-area relationships for vascular plants of the Appalachian Mountains and provided a method for estimating the number of rare species to be found in a region (Miller and Wiegert 1989).

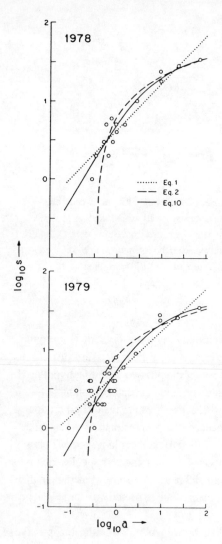

Figure 8.17. Fit of the exponential function, power function, and passive sampling model to species-area data. The x axis is the logarithm of island area, expressed as a proportion of the total area of the archipelago. The y axis is the logarithm of island species number. Each point is the observed number of breeding bird species on forest islands in Pymatuning Lake for census data in two consecutive years. The straight line is the power function, the dashed curve is the exponential function, and the solid curve is the expectation from the passive sampling model. Exponential and power functions were fit by standard linear regression. Note the superior fit of the passive sampling model to observed data. From Coleman et al. (1982), with permission.

In other communities, however, the passive sampling model overestimates species richness. For example, Gotelli et al. (1987) tested the model for an amphipod-mollusc assemblage that colonized artificial substrates in the Gulf of Mexico. Observed species richness was less than expected, and the deviations became more severe as colonization proceeded, perhaps due to crowding in a space-limited habitat. For natural rock islands, Ryti (1984) also found that the species richness of perennial plants was less than predicted by the passive sampling model. He suggested that multiple source pools and dispersal constraints might account for the discrepancy.

If the assumption of independent placement of individuals is violated, then the summed abundance of a species (n_i) will not provide an accurate estimate of the probability of occurrence (Abele and Patton 1976). For example, if density compensation leads to large population sizes on a few islands, the passive sampling hypothesis will simulate the random placement of those individuals across many islands and therefore lead to an overestimate of species richness for most islands. In the analysis of species co-occurrence patterns (Chapter 7), it was necessary to control for differences in species richness among islands. Conversely, in the analysis of species richness, it may be necessary to control for species interactions and demographic limits on island population sizes.

A more subtle problem is that the passive sampling model provides only a "snapshot" explanation for the species-area curve. For habitats that are recolonized seasonally (Osman 1977; Haila 1983), the system is periodically reset and the passive sampling model can be applied to colonization within a single season. But suppose there is a stable mainland pool of species, such that immigrants are continuously available for island colonization. In other words, there is an unlimited supply of "darts" that can be tossed at the target. If passive sampling continues over a long period of time, we would expect small islands to eventually accumulate the same set of species as large islands. The passive sampling hypothesis does not address the accumulation of species on small islands through time. In contrast, the other three hypotheses for the species-area relationship invoke some mechanism that ultimately limits S on small islands— habitat specificity, stochastic extinctions of small populations, or chronic disturbances. This temporal aspect of the passive sampling hypothesis has not been addressed in the literature and deserves further attention.

RECOMMENDATIONS

We recommend the passive sampling model as a simple null model for studying species-area relationships. If abundance data are available, Coleman's (1981) analytic solutions can be used. If only presence-absence data are available, the Monte Carlo simulations of Simberloff and Gotelli (1984) can be used to estimate expected species richness. The passive sampling model can be refined by incorporating prevalence functions (Haila et al. 1983) and habitat availability (Buckley 1982) on islands. Temporal change in species richness can be tested with a Markov model (Simberloff 1983c), although estimation of transition probabilities may be problematic (Boecklen and Nocedal 1991; Clark and Rosenzweig 1994). Critical tests of the MacArthur and Wilson (1967) equilibrium model include evidence of population turnover (Simberloff 1976a), measurement of immigration and extinction rates as a function of species richness (Williamson 1981; Strong and Rey 1982), and documentation of a species-area relationship within equal-sized quadrats (Kelly et al. 1989). Further studies of the species-area slope or the best-fitting transformation will not allow for critical tests. Instead, researchers should concentrate on unique predictions associated with hypotheses for the species-area relationship (Table 8.1).

9
BIOGEOGRAPHY

Chapters 7 and 8 emphasized assemblage patterns on islands or in discrete habitat patches. This chapter considers community patterns measured against a more continuous spatial background. For this problem, we need to consider not only the occurrence of a species, but its spatial distribution. The spatial distribution of individuals or populations can be mapped as a line segment in one dimension or as a polygon in two dimensions. Null models have been applied to the pattern of species occurrences in one and two dimensions across a spectrum of spatial scales. At small scales, one-dimensional analyses are appropriate for species occurrences along environmental gradients such as mountainsides (McCoy 1990) or intertidal transects (Colman 1933). At large scales, one-dimensional patterns include geographic gradients, such as the distributional ranges of species along coastlines (Pielou 1977) or narrow peninsulas (Brown and Opler 1990). Two-dimensional patterns include the small-scale occurrence of species in quadrats of fixed size (Hurlbert 1990) or the large-scale spatial overlap of the geographic ranges of species (Lynch 1989).

ASSUMPTIONS

The occurrence of a species or a set of populations can be represented as a line segment in one dimension, or as a closed polygon in two dimensions. This representation requires the following two assumptions:

1. Spatial patterns do not change through time. As in analyses of island assemblages, the mapped distribution of a species is treated as a static "snapshot" (Diamond 1986). It is difficult to evaluate patterns in the distributional maps of species if their ranges are constantly changing size and shape. If we wait long enough, all distributional maps will change, if only because all species have finite lifetimes. However, spatial patterns may be stable on time scales that are relevant to ecological or evolutionary mechanisms. In general,

239

the smaller the spatial scale, the shorter the time until the distribution pattern changes. For example, the vertical distribution of an intertidal barnacle may change on a seasonal basis (Wethey 1983), whereas its geographic range may remain stable for decades or centuries (Wethey 1985).

2. *Distributions of species are continuous throughout their mapped ranges.* In other words, we assume there are no "gaps" in the spatial occurrence of a species. Null model analyses become exceedingly complex if rules must be specified for the origin and placement of disjunct populations or individuals. In the extreme, if there are many gaps and relatively few areas of continuous distribution, it may be more appropriate to represent the occupied sites as insular populations in an archipelago of habitat patches.

If gaps are present, they may represent true biological disjunctions or gaps in sampling of sparsely inhabited areas (Lawton and Woodroffe 1991). No species has a truly continuous distribution. Representing spatial pattern as a line segment or a closed polygon is a simplification, but this in itself does not invalidate the analysis. For example, occupied sites within the geographic range of a species may be organized as a metapopulation (Levins 1969), in which local extinctions and recolonizations are common. Nevertheless, drawing a closed polygon around the metapopulation delineates a somewhat arbitrary "area of occurrence" (Gaston 1991), which may reflect important climatic boundaries that limit distribution (Brown 1988).

The danger arises when we attempt to make inferences between different spatial scales. For example, patterns of co-occurrence of Australian reef fishes in small coral heads are highly unpredictable in time and space (Sale 1979; Sale and Steel 1989). Persistent species combinations and strong local organization seem absent (Sale 1984), suggesting a lottery for species coexistence (Sale 1982). In contrast, species combinations at the regional or biogeographic scale exhibit apparent stability and consistency. Competitive interactions have been invoked to explain community organization at this level (Anderson et al. 1981), but similar patterns can be generated with null models that do not incorporate competition (Sale and Williams 1982). Long-term studies of shrubsteppe bird assemblages (Wiens and Rotenberry 1980, 1981b) have also shown that community patterns depend on the spatial scale of sampling (Wiens et al. 1987) and that a hierarchical analysis may be necessary (Kotliar and Wiens 1990). Unfortunately, most ecological data sets do not offer the luxury of exploring assemblage patterns at different hierarchical scales, making it especially important to restrict the analysis and interpretation of mechanisms to an appropriate spatial scale.

Range gaps may represent sampling error and bias. At regional geographic scales, in particular, it may be difficult to obtain an accurate spatial map of species occurrence. For example, in elevational surveys of bird communities in the Andes (Terborgh 1971, 1977), species sightings can be influenced by topography, habitat patchiness, trail location, weather, observer experience, and sampling intensity (Graves 1985). Even intensive field efforts may sample only a small fraction of available sites during a limited time of year. In many cases, distributional maps derived from such surveys are crude approximations, at best.

Sampling at small spatial scales also presents challenges. Although small quadrats may be thoroughly searched, many life history stages, such as eggs, seeds, or larvae, cannot be accurately censused. As Hurlbert (1990) has demonstrated in a simulation study of the "montane unicorn" (*Monoceros montanus della Roba*), statistical analyses of quadrat data are sensitive to both the spatial distribution of organisms and the size, number, and placement of quadrats (Williams 1964; Anderson and Marcus 1993). No two species will have identical spatial patterns, but if quadrats are too large or too widely separated, many species may show concordant distributions. These apparent "ties" will affect the power of null model tests of spatial pattern. Quadrat sampling is dealt with in many ecological texts (Greig-Smith 1964; Pielou 1974) and will not be discussed extensively here.

In spite of these limitations, distribution maps at all spatial scales can be studied profitably with null models. In this chapter, we discuss the analysis of both one- and two-dimensional spatial maps. Such maps are relevant to problems of ecological zonation along small-scale environmental gradients, as well as the origin and maintenance of range boundaries on large-scale geographic gradients. Next, we consider the relationship between regional distribution and local abundance. Finally, we discuss correlations at large biogeographic scales among population size, body size, and geographic range, including recent studies of "macroecology" (Brown and Maurer 1989), plus older analyses of the "taxon cycle" (Wilson 1961; Ricklefs and Cox 1972).

PATTERNS IN ONE DIMENSION

The distribution of organisms along one-dimensional environmental gradients provides some of the best examples of the organization of natural communities. The striking patterns of zonation of plants and animals in the rocky intertidal (Colman 1933; Paine and Levin 1981) and the orderly appearance of vegetation associations along altitudinal gradients (Whittaker 1967) suggest that strong nonrandom forces determine the position of each species within the gradient. These forces include (1) biotic interactions, such as competition (MacArthur 1972), predation (Paine 1966), or mutualism (Bertness and Hacker 1994) with

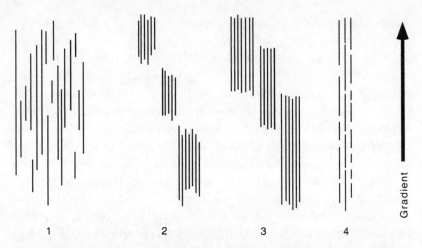

Figure 9.1. Four models of community organization in gradients. Each vertical line represents the range of a different species. Model 1: Random arrangements of range boundaries and species overlap. Species distributions are completely independent of one another. Model 2: Abutting range boundaries and high overlap. The species are organized into well-defined communities, with sharp ecotonal boundaries between communities. Model 3: Nonabutting range boundaries and high overlap. The species are still organized into well-defined communities, but there is more overlap between assemblages and a lack of sharp ecotonal boundaries. Model 4: Abutting range boundaries and low overlap. The species are organized into several guilds, with abutting ranges within a guild but no pattern of overlap between guilds. Adapted from Dale (1986).

syntopic species; (2) abiotic limits, which represent physiological tolerance boundaries (Connell 1961); (3) ecotones, or sharp discontinuities in habitat or vegetation (Terborgh 1977); (4) dispersal constraints, which prevent species from colonizing some habitable regions of the gradient (Rabinowitz 1978; Grosberg 1982).

At the community level, Whittaker (1967) described four models of organization that provide a useful framework for understanding assemblage patterns along gradients. The four models are distinguished on the basis of whether species form discernable groupings and the extent to which boundaries between species are exclusive (Figure 9.1). At one extreme, ranges of species might occur independently of one another along the gradient. The resulting assemblage would show no natural groupings and no unusual exclusions, although the ranges of some species might abut by chance. This assemblage could be taken as a reasonable null model for community organization on an environmental gradient. At the other extreme, species might co-occur in well-defined exclusive groups, with nonoverlapping sets of species replacing one another along the gradient. This pattern reflects Clements's (1904) "super-organism" view of tightly integrated communities separated by sharp ecotonal boundaries. A third model also results in species groups, but with a good deal of overlap in ranges, so there are not well-defined boundaries between communities. In such an assemblage, apparent community structure arises because species share similar preferences along the gradient, as envisioned by Gleason (1926). Some might argue that Model 1 also describes a Gleasonian community, because species are distributed independently of one another. A final model is that the assemblage is organized into guilds of competing species (Root 1967), and that species within a guild replace one another sequentially along the gradient. If the guild structure is ignored, the entire assemblage might fit the pattern of Models 1 or 3. As we will explain, null models developed by Pielou (1977, 1978) and Dale (1984, 1986, 1988) allow one to distinguish among the spatial patterns predicted by these four models.

At the outset, we note that any null model for community structure in one dimension will involve the random placement of species ranges or their range limits within a bounded number line. For this reason, some of the statistical tests and biological interpretations are identical to those used to recognize niche segregation (Chapters 4 and 5), nonrandom dispersion patterns of body sizes in a community (Chapter 6), or the distribution of relative abundances from the broken-stick model (MacArthur 1957) or some of its variants (Chapter 3).

The Statistics of Overlapping Sheaves

Suppose that an assemblage of species occurs along a well-defined spatial gradient in one dimension, such as an intertidal transect. The gradient can be represented as a number line of length one, and the species distributions can be portrayed as line segments that occur within this number line. The species distributions are analogous to a sheaf of overlapping line segments (Pielou 1977). Qualitative patterns of co-occurrence (segregated, overlapping, or nested occurrences) and quantitative patterns, (the degree of overlap and the size of the gaps in species distributions) can be analyzed with null models.

Pielou (1977, 1978) developed the first models for analyzing the overlap of species ranges. For a set of n species, there are $n(n-1)/2$ pairwise overlaps that can be measured. For each pair of species, she assigned a score of 0, 1, or 2, depending on whether the ranges are nonoverlapping, partially overlapping, or nested (Figure 9.2). This index, summed over all species pairs, characterizes

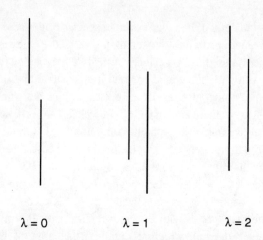

$\lambda = 0$ $\lambda = 1$ $\lambda = 2$

Figure 9.2. A qualitative index of range overlap in one dimension. For each species pair, $\lambda = 0$, no overlap; $\lambda = 1$, partial overlap; $\lambda = 2$, complete overlap. Adapted from Pielou (1977).

the average amount of overlap between any randomly chosen pair of species in the assemblage. Because it relies on the qualitative pattern of overlap, the index is insensitive to minor sampling errors in range estimates.

If the species are distributed independently of one another, how much overlap is expected? Pielou (1977, 1978) suggested two null hypotheses. The first was that the upper and lower range boundaries for each species were randomly placed on the gradient. The only restriction on randomization was that the lower bound of a species fell below its upper bound. Under this model, the expectation for the index is

$$E(\text{overlap}) = n(n-1)\,/\,2 \qquad\qquad (9.1)$$

which is simply the number of unique species pairs. The distribution is symmetric with variance

$$\sigma^2 = n(n^2 - 1)\,/\,9 \qquad\qquad (9.2)$$

One can compute from this expectation and variance whether a single set of species is unusually nested or nonoverlapping. Alternatively, if many sets of species are available, one can tally the number of sets for which the observed overlap is above or below the expectation. For 684 species of benthic marine algae on the western shores of the Atlantic, latitudinal ranges within a genus overlapped significantly more often than expected by chance (Pielou 1977).

Table 9.1

The observed fraction of Atlantic algal genera for which observed overlaps exceeded null expectations

	Rhodophyta	Chlorophyta	Phaeophyta
Null Hypothesis 1	51/69	22/26	17/23
Null Hypothesis 2	29/63	13/27	8/21

Null Hypothesis 1 is that the north and south range boundaries are located randomly and independently. Null Hypothesis 2 is that species ranges are placed randomly, but observed range lengths are retained. For Null Hypothesis 1, there were too many genera with high overlap, whereas approximately half of the genera had high overlaps under Null Hypothesis 2. Adapted from Pielou (1977).

The overlap statistic can be divided into components due to overlapping and nested ranges. Atlantic coast algae were more often nested than overlapping, and the overlap within a genus was consistently higher than the overlap between genera (Pielou 1978). This result parallels studies of the species/genus (*S/G*) ratio (Chapter 1), which have often revealed that insular coexistence of congeners is greater than expected (Simberloff 1970). Based on the high frequency of nested congeners, Pielou (1978) suggested that Atlantic coast algae may frequently undergo "quasi-sympatric" speciation, in which sister species diverge and become isolated within a single geographic region.

In contrast, the latitudinal spans of Pacific coast algae overlapped one another significantly less than those of Atlantic seaweeds. Because the location of range boundaries was randomized, this null hypothesis did not take into account the length of the range of each species. Thus, part of the difference between Atlantic and Pacific algal distributions could be attributed to the fact that geographic ranges were much smaller on the Pacific coast than on the Atlantic coast. However, because Pielou (1978) compared each species with its congeners, differences in range size cannot entirely explain different overlap patterns on the two coasts.

A second, more realistic null hypothesis retained the range lengths for each species but randomized their position within the range. For a pair of species with range lengths x and y ($x \geq y$) and a total space of length W, the expected overlap between any pair of species is

$$E(\text{overlap}) = \frac{2x(W-x) - y^2}{(W-x)(W-y)} \quad \text{if } W \geq x + y \tag{9.3}$$

$$E(\text{overlap}) = \frac{W + x - 2y}{W - y} \quad \text{if } W < x + y \tag{9.4}$$

Summing these terms over all possible species pairs gives the expected overlap for the entire assemblage; the variance does not have a simple derivation. For the Atlantic coast genera of algae, overlaps were greater than expected for about half of the species pairs. Thus, at least some of the nonrandomness in range distributions of Atlantic coast algae could be attributed to the length of the geographic spans of the species (Table 9.1).

Null Models for Quadrat Data

Pielou's (1977, 1978) null hypotheses are appropriate if the species ranges have been estimated on a continuous scale. If the data have been collected in discrete quadrats sampled along a transect, other methods of analysis are required. Pielou and Routledge (1976) used Bose-Einstein statistics to distinguish between random, clustered, and regular boundaries of species. This test considers the distribution of upper (or lower) boundaries of k species among a set of Q quadrats. Let U equal the number of quadrats cut by at least one upper boundary. If the boundaries are assigned randomly to quadrats, the probability that U is unusually large or small can be calculated. If U is large, the range boundaries are regularly dispersed, whereas if U is small, range boundaries are clustered.

Using these methods, Pielou and Routledge (1976) showed that the landward boundaries of marsh plant species tended to be more clustered than the seaward boundaries, which, in some cases, were distributed more evenly than expected. The tendency toward clustering of both landward and seaward boundaries was more pronounced at high latitudes.

The use of Bose-Einstein statistics implies that each species combination is equiprobable (Feller 1968). The Pielou and Routledge (1976) method is valid for the null hypothesis that species boundaries and quadrat boundaries are randomly interspersed (Pielou 1979b). However, these two kinds of boundaries have completely different meanings and should probably not be equated in the same test. It is more appropriate to treat the quadrats as fixed "boxes" and the assignment of each species boundary to a quadrat as an independent event. For this model, Maxwell-Boltzman statistics should be used to calculate the probability of observed arrangements (Underwood 1978a).

Unfortunately, the exact calculation of these probabilities is difficult. Gardiner and Haedrich (1978) used a Poisson approximation and detected a clustering of species boundaries for deep megafauna living between 200 and 3,000 m

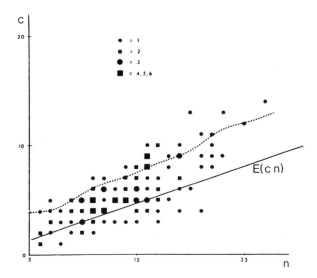

Figure 9.3. Observed and expected number of range contiguities of marine intertidal algae. The x axis is the number of species (n) in the transect, and the y axis is the number of range contiguities (c) for that transect. Each point is a transect, and the different symbols represent different numbers of observations. The solid line is the null expectation, and the dotted line is the 5% significance level. Note that most transects contained more range contiguities than expected. From Dale (1984), with permission.

depth. Underwood (1978a) used a similar binomial approximation and found no evidence for a clustering of vertical boundaries of intertidal organisms in Britain. Null model analyses of these and other data (Underwood 1978b) do not support the hypothesis that intertidal distributions are clustered at certain critical tidal levels (Doty 1946; Doty and Archer 1950).

The preceding tests treat upper and lower boundaries in separate analyses. However, competitively structured communities are best identified by the intermingling of upper and lower boundaries. Specifically, the "contiguity hypothesis" predicts that the upper boundary of one species tends to be followed by the lower boundary of a second species (Chapman 1973). If the boundaries are placed randomly with respect to one another, the expected number of contiguities for n species boundaries is

$$E(\text{contiguities}) = (n-1)/3 \qquad (9.5)$$

Dale (1984) applied the test to zoned communities of marine algae in transects and found that, in the majority of transects, the number of contiguities was greater than expected (Figure 9.3).

Null Models for Quantitative Overlap Patterns

One drawback of the previous null models is that they only consider the qualitative pattern of overlap. They do not test for the degree of overlap in species ranges or the size of gaps between nonoverlapping spans. For example, Dale's (1984) contiguity test considered only the sequence of upper and lower boundaries, and not the spacing between them. A pattern in which ranges of species abut closely suggests strong species interactions at the boundary. In contrast, a pattern in which ranges of species are separated by wide gaps (with no intervening range boundaries) suggests ecotonal boundaries, habitat patchiness, or sampling error.

To address this problem, Dale (1986) expanded Pielou's (1978) analyses of the expected number of species pairs that were nonoverlapping, lapped, and nested. He derived expressions for the expected gap length (g) and the expected overlap length (y) for any pair of species given their observed range lengths. The derivation is similar to Cole's (1981) calculation of phenological overlap for a pair of plant species with fixed flowering times (see Chapter 5).

Using the idealized communities in Figure 9.1, Dale (1986) showed that it is possible to distinguish among the four models of community organization. For intertidal algae, the patterns were consistent with the guild model of organization (Model 4): there was little evidence of natural groupings of species, but pairwise overlaps with narrow zones of intermingling were common.

Finally, Dale (1988) derived tests for the clustering of range boundaries at particular locations in the gradient, again retaining the observed range lengths as a constraint and randomly placing species ranges within the gradient. The test statistic is the sum of the product of pairwise distances between adjacent boundaries. This number should be unusually small if boundaries are clustered and unusually large if boundaries are evenly spaced throughout the gradient. Using this test, Dale (1988) detected only weak evidence for a critical clustering of species boundaries, a result that was consistent with Underwood's (1978b) tests of the critical tidal-level hypothesis.

In summary, the null model machinery for analyzing community patterns of overlap in one dimension is well-developed. We now need tests of communities other than intertidal algae to gain an understanding of community structure in gradients. Reanalysis of disputed avian distributions on elevational gradients (Terborgh 1971, 1977; Graves 1985) might be especially informative.

PATTERNS IN TWO DIMENSIONS

Once the analysis is expanded to two dimensions, simple statistical tests are no longer practical. Instead, the placement and possibly the size of each species range must be determined by simulation. We begin by considering null models that have been applied to the general problem of global diversity gradients. Next, we discuss relatively simple examples, in which investigators have considered only the placement of one range boundary, before turning to studies of the placement of entire geographic ranges.

Global Diversity Gradients

On a global scale, three major diversity gradients have been described: latitudinal gradients in species richness, which usually increases at low latitudes (Dobzhansky 1950; Pianka 1966); (2) elevational gradients in species richness, which often peaks at mid-elevation (Terborgh 1971; Olson 1994); and (3) gradients in the latitudinal spans of geographic ranges, which sometimes decrease at low latitudes (Stevens 1989). Stevens (1989) designated this third pattern Rapoport's rule (Rapoport 1982), and it seems to hold for many, but not all (Rohde et al. 1993), taxa. Stevens (1989) suggested that Rapoport's rule might be the cause of latitudinal gradients in species richness. If low-latitude species have low tolerance for environmental variability, then most of the populations at any particular site in the tropics might be "marginal populations" that are poorly adapted for the site but maintained by immigration.

A great deal of effort has gone into understanding the causes of diversity gradients, but few studies have asked what diversity gradients would arise with minimal biological assumptions. Osman and Whitlach (1978) warned that diversity gradients can be artifacts of open and dynamic systems. They suggested that an equilibrium patch model (Terborgh 1973b) might account for diversity gradients without invoking factors such as global environmental gradients, niche characteristics, trophic complexity, or temporal stability. However, because their null model invokes dynamic turnover, there must ultimately be spatial gradients in the frequency of disturbance or the probability of local colonization and extinction to produce observed species richness gradients.

More recently, Colwell and Hurtt (1994) developed a much simpler null model to account for global diversity patterns that does not invoke dynamic turnover. The model begins with a globe that is covered with randomly located circles, which represent the geographic ranges of species. A point is randomly chosen to represent the "pole," and diversity gradients and species ranges are mapped from pole to equator. The poles represent a "soft boundary," because

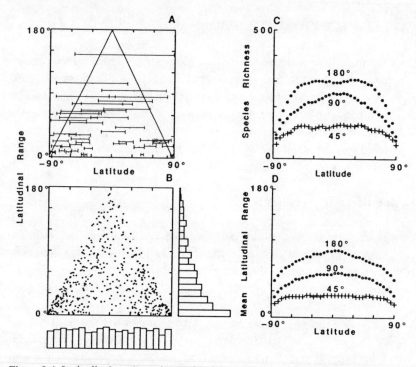

Figure 9.4. Latitudinal gradients in species richness and range distributions from a simple null model. (**A**) A latitudinal range midpoint is randomly chosen from a uniform distribution for each species, and then a permissible latitudinal range is chosen. (**B**) The resulting distribution of ranges and midpoints falls within the triangle of acceptable values. Ranges are limited above and below the equator by a "hard boundary" at a specified latitude. (**C**) The null model generates a latitudinal gradient of species richness and a "reverse Rapoport effect," in which the latitudinal span of species near the hard boundary is less than the span of species near the equator (**D**). Reprinted by permission of the publisher from Colwell, R. K., and G. C. Hurtt. 1994. Nonbiological gradients in species richness and a spurious Rapoport effect. *American Naturalist* 144:570–595. Copyright © 1994 by The University of Chicago.

ranges that cross over one of the poles are measured only in one focal hemisphere. This baseline model shows no latitudinal gradient in species richness.

Next, Colwell and Hurtt (1994) imposed a symmetric "hard boundary" in both hemispheres, beyond which no species range could extend. Such a boundary might represent a major barrier or climatic limit, or a continental boundary for all species in the assemblage. For each species, a midpoint was randomly selected within the hard boundary limits, and then a feasible latitudinal range was chosen. The simulation results (Figure 9.4) show that species richness decreases as a hard boundary is approached, even though there is no biological or physical gradient between the boundaries. Thus, the model might account for both latitudinal gradients and mid-elevational peaks in species richness. However, the model did not produce a Rapoport effect. In fact, species ranges actually decreased in size as the hard boundary was approached. Thus, a Rapoport effect need not be the cause of species richness gradients, as Stevens (1989) suggested.

These results are based on perfect knowledge of range distributions. Colwell and Hurtt (1994) next used a sampling model to understand the effects of sampling biases on diversity gradients. They began by imposing a species richness gradient above and beyond that produced by the null model. Next, they assumed that within a species, the distribution of individuals across its geographic range was either uniform or normal. Finally, they sampled a finite number of individuals at each point in a latitudinal transect. The model mimics diversity gradients that would be expected when sampling is less than complete.

The estimated geographic ranges for this model often led to a Rapoport effect. The problem was that individual species in the diverse tropics were often poorly sampled compared to species at high latitudes. Consequently, the geographic ranges of tropical species were underestimated, leading to a spurious Rapoport effect. This sampling bias arises from equal sampling effort at all locations, because fewer individuals per species are collected at species-rich sites. For well-studied North American taxa, there is no question that diversity gradients are real and do not represent sampling artifacts. But the distributions of many tropical taxa are poorly known, and this form of sampling bias may be important. Colwell and Hurtt's (1994) study suggests that even "obvious" diversity patterns may have a sampling component to them that reflects the geometry of the continents rather than underlying biological or physical gradients.

The Location of Range Boundaries

Just as the range limit of a species can be represented as a point on a one-dimensional number line, the range boundary can be represented as a line segment on a two-dimensional map. One of the simplest cases for analysis is the placement of range boundaries along a large-scale geographic gradient. For example, species richness often decreases from the base to the tip of geographic peninsulas (Simpson 1964). This "peninsular effect" can be investigated by examining the placement of the range boundaries of species that drop out along a peninsula. Three hypotheses have been proposed for the peninsular effect:

1. An equilibrium hypothesis, which posits that immigration rates decrease and extinction rates increase from the base to the tip of a peninsula (MacArthur and Wilson 1967).
2. A time hypothesis, which posits that peninsulas are geologically young and have not had enough time for recolonization, or are historically depauperate because of small source pools (Orr 1960).
3. A habitat diversity hypothesis, which posits that low habitat diversity in peninsulas is responsible for the progressive dropout of species (Taylor and Regal 1978).

Means and Simberloff (1987) tested the habitat diversity hypothesis in an analysis of range boundaries along the Florida peninsula for 48 species of amphibians and reptiles. As a null model, they generated species range distributions that were independent of one another and independent of habitat features of the peninsula. The simulation retained the size and general range features for each species but allowed the position of the range boundary to vary randomly.

Compared to this simulation, herpetofauna range boundaries were highly clustered in a few counties along the mid-peninsular axis of Florida (Figure 9.5). These counties have the highest elevations and greatest habitat diversity in the state, both of which decline rapidly to the south. Historical and island biogeographic explanations seem relatively unimportant in this case, and the results suggest that habitat reduction alone could account for the peninsular effect in Florida herpetofauna.

When expanded to a continental scale, the analysis of range boundaries is often more challenging. Root (1988a) analyzed distributional boundaries of 148 wintering land bird species in North America. She compared range boundaries to gradient maps of six environmental factors: average minimum January temperature, mean length of frost-free period, potential vegetation, mean annual precipitation, average general humidity, and elevation. The first three factors were frequently associated with northern range boundaries (60%, 50%, 64%), whereas vegetation (63%) and precipitation (40%) were most frequently associated with eastern boundaries. Associations with western boundaries were less clear-cut, and southern boundaries were not studied because most species occurred throughout the southern United States.

With six intercorrelated environmental variables and 148 species, some associations are expected to occur by chance alone. Root (1988a) used a simple null model to place species range boundaries and evaluate this effect. She first selected 51 species randomly from the list of 148. For each species, she used a

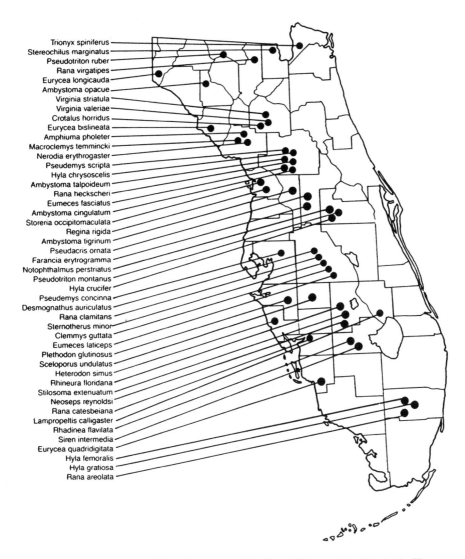

Figure 9.5. Distribution of tipward range termini of amphibians and reptiles in the Florida peninsula. Compared to null model simulations, these range boundaries are clustered in counties with the highest elevations and greatest habitat diversity in the state. From Means and Simberloff (1987), with permission.

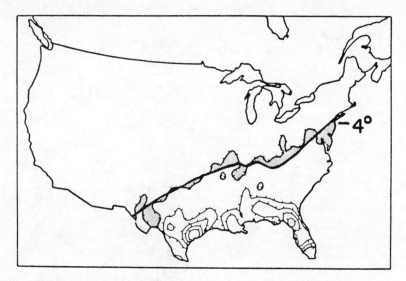

Figure 9.6. Distribution and abundance of the Eastern Phoebe (*Sayornis phoebe*) with respect to winter isotherms. The tick-marked lines represent four contour intervals of 20%, 40%, 60%, and 80% of maximum abundance, which is highest in the southern United States. The thick black line is the –4° C average minimum January temperature isotherm. The stippled area highlights the difference between this isotherm and the northern range limit. Compared to randomly placed range boundaries, most species range boundaries showed unusual concordance with temperature isotherms or other environmental measures. From Root (1988b), with permission.

random number table to move the distribution *x* degrees latitude north or south, and *y* degrees longitude east or west, and to rotate it *z* number of octants clockwise or counterclockwise. Thus, the simulation retained the shape of each range boundary but randomized its location and orientation (Figure 9.6). In these simulated ranges, only two of the 51 species range boundaries coincided with environmental factors, compared to over 50% of the real boundaries. Range boundaries of wintering birds coincided with environmental factors more often than expected, and the patterns may reflect energetic constraints associated with cold temperatures (Root 1988b). However, the strong intercorrelation among the variables makes it difficult to pin down the mechanisms (Castro 1989; Root 1989).

The Size of the Geographic Range

A primary question in any simulation of geographic ranges is whether the size of the range ought to be strictly retained or possibly allowed to vary. Indeed,

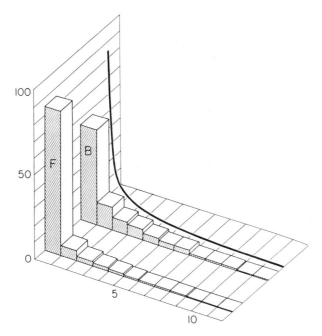

Figure 9.7. Range size distributions of North American fishes (F) and birds (B). The x axis is the area of the geographic range (1×10^6 km^2), and the y axis is the percentage of species. These distributions contain more species with intermediate-sized ranges than predicted by a logarithmic series (solid line), which results from a simple Markovian model of range expansion and contraction. From Anderson (1985), courtesy of the American Museum of Natural History.

before considering the placement of geographic ranges, it is worthwhile to ask what factors determine range size.

The frequency distributions of range sizes of related species tend to follow a log normal distribution (Anderson 1984), with most species having relatively small geographic ranges. Anderson (1985) constructed a number of Markovian null models in which transition probabilities between cells in a gridded map dictated random increases or decreases in range size. The equilibrium distribution of range sizes in this model qualitatively fit the observed range sizes for North American vertebrate taxa, although there were usually more intermediate-sized ranges than predicted (Figure 9.7).

An important consideration in the analysis of geographic ranges is the extent to which historical versus ecological mechanisms are invoked (Endler 1982). Anderson's (1985) null models did not specify the biological factors that influenced range size. However, the mechanisms are clearly ecological and operate on relatively short time scales, because the model predicts that ranges are continuously expanding and contracting in size. Carter and Prince (1981) used epidemic models of invasion that also invoke short-term changes in site occupancy to explain biogeographic range limits.

An alternative perspective is that range limits are relatively static and largely reflect the historical legacy of speciation (Lynch 1989). This perspective can also be incorporated into simple null models. For example, Rapoport (1982) showed that the distribution of range sizes of mammalian subspecies (and the relative areas of land held by rich and poor landowners) could be approximated by taking random partitions of x and y coordinates in a square. If these random partitions represented the emergence of dispersal barriers, and each isolated taxon speciated allopatrically, the resulting range areas would reflect historical speciation events with no current change in range size. Similarly, the species composition in local assemblages may be a reflection of biogeographic constraints on source pools rather than ecologically driven assembly rules (Cornell and Lawton 1992).

Geographic ranges reflect both ecological and historical processes, so neither scenario is entirely correct (Taylor and Gotelli 1994). Historical processes are difficult to incorporate into null models, so most analyses have either taken the range sizes as a constraint (Beven et al. 1984) or constructed them with simple accretion algorithms (Means and Simberloff 1987) that do not resemble explicit speciation or dispersal processes.

Randomization of Geographic Ranges

The random placement of geographic ranges can be simulated in two ways. First, the map of the range can be randomly relocated on the continental map. Alternatively, an algorithm can be used to specify the "growth" of the range in a grid of cells superimposed on the map. Problems arise at the edge of maps with either approach. If the species range maps were distributed at random across a map surface, one could discard those placements that spilled over the map boundary. However, as Ashton et al. (1988) showed for one-dimensional simulations of flowering phenology (Chapter 5), this procedure inevitably biases the model toward "interior" distributions with high overlap among species.

If the ranges are created by filling a grid, growth rules must be specified at boundaries. Haefner et al. (1991) examined the performance of several edge algorithms used in simulation models of spatial competition. The best procedure was to simply embed the grid in a larger area, but this does not solve the problem for continental maps with natural coastal boundaries. Mapping the area onto a torus is also inappropriate for geographic maps, because it would introduce extreme range disjunctions. We think the best solution for geographic range maps is to choose the starting cell randomly and then use an algorithm to accumulate contiguous cells until the desired area is filled.

Pleistocene Forest Refugia

The analysis of gridded maps is well illustrated by a study of Pleistocene refugia (Beven et al. 1984). The "biological model for diversification in the tropics" proposes that range fragmentation during Pleistocene glaciations led to increased rates of allopatric speciation and high species richness (Haffer 1969; Simpson and Haffer 1978; Haffer 1982). Several authors have used biogeographic data to delineate the locations of hypothesized Pleistocene refugia. If the refugia hypothesis is correct, then the occurrence of species distributional boundaries should be concentrated between refugia, with few or no boundaries occurring within refugia. Similarly, refugia should correspond to centers of high endemism for particular taxa. Finally, there should be an unusual concordance between refugia delineated for different taxa if they were influenced by the same vicariant events.

Beven et al. (1984) used null models to test for these patterns in proposed refugia and centers of endemism for Amazonian birds (Haffer 1978). Distributional maps for Amazonian birds were digitized and converted to a 100 × 77 rectangular grid covering Amazonia. Next, centers of endemism and Haffer's (1969) refugia were superimposed on the maps (Figure 9.8). Finally, the number of species boundary segments in each square was tabulated and compared to those generated by a null model.

Rather than randomize species ranges, Beven et al. (1984) randomized the position of the proposed refugia while maintaining their observed areas. Two randomization algorithms were used. In the first, grid squares were chosen completely at random. In the second, grid squares were chosen randomly but constrained so that the refugia remained contiguous. The analyses were repeated excluding squares that had major rivers, which might act as current ecological barriers to dispersal (Salo et al. 1986). Finally, they measured the overlap between sets of refugia proposed independently for plants (Prance 1973), birds (Haffer 1969), and lizards (Vanzolini and Williams 1973). To test whether such refugia were unusually concordant, Beven et al. (1984) cast scale cutouts of the proposed refugia by hand onto a map of South America and then measured the overlap between refugia proposed for different taxa. The only restriction was that the randomly thrown refugia lie entirely on land and not overlap within a given set of proposed refugia.

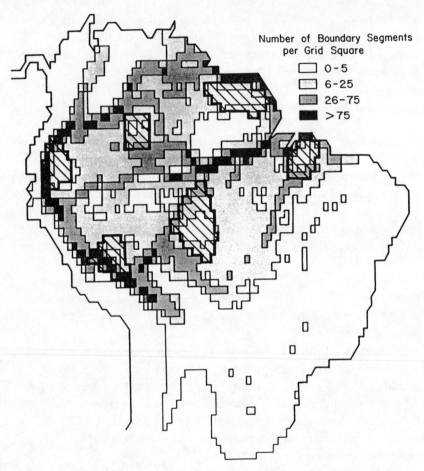

Figure 9.8. Digitized map illustrating the density of species range boundaries and the centers of endemism proposed by Haffer (1978) for birds of Amazonia. Centers of endemism are indicated by thick boundaries and diagonal hatching. From Beven et al. (1984), with permission.

The results of these analyses were mixed. Some refugia and centers of endemism included substantially fewer range boundaries than expected, as predicted by the refugia hypothesis. Others did not differ from the simulation results, and in a few cases, refugia had significantly more distributional boundaries than expected by chance. Most proposed refugia had fewer boundaries than expected, although the pattern was not striking (Figure 9.9; 14 of 21 refugia; $p = 0.094$, rivers excluded). Overlap among refugia proposed for different taxa also was not significantly large. However, the simulation was

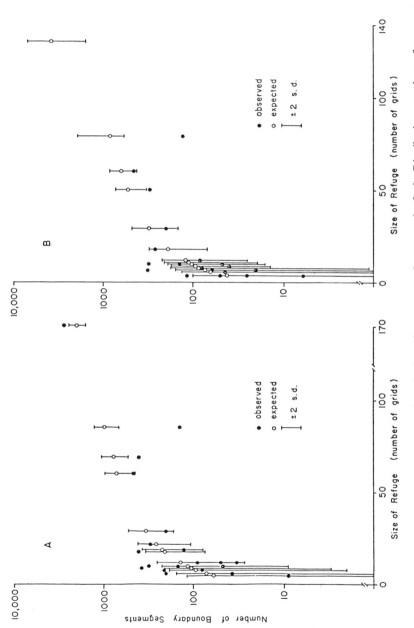

Figure 9.9. Observed and expected number of species boundary segments in proposed refugia. Distributions are shown for simulations with (**A**) and without (**B**) river squares excluded. If the refugium hypothesis were correct, the proposed refuges would have significantly fewer range boundaries than predicted by the simulations. Note that most proposed refuges have about the number of range boundaries predicted by the null model. From Beven et al. (1984), with permission.

biased toward finding this result, because the hand-thrown ranges were restricted by map edges (Ashton et al. 1988). Given that the refugia and centers of endemism were delineated primarily on the basis of the range maps themselves (Nelson et al. 1990), the evidence in support of such refugia is hardly overwhelming. These null model results seem to confirm detailed geological (Räsänen et al. 1987) and palynological studies (Salo 1987; Bush et al. 1990) that also find little evidence for the refugia hypothesis.

DISTRIBUTION AND ABUNDANCE

Although biogeography and ecology have developed as distinct fields of study, patterns of distribution and abundance are intimately related to one another (Andrewartha and Birch 1954). *Distribution* refers to the geographic range or number of occupied sites, whereas *abundance* refers to the density of organisms within an occupied site. The two measures are closely related, because as abundance decreases across a spatial gradient, the frequency of occupied sites also tends to decrease. Finally, the edge of the range can be recognized as those sites for which abundance always equals zero (Caughley et al. 1988). Within a species, abundance usually decreases from the center to the edge of the geographic range (Hengeveld and Haeck 1981, 1982), probably because of correlated two-dimensional environmental gradients (Brown 1984). Between species, those that are widespread or have a large geographic range tend to be more locally abundant than geographically restricted species (Bock and Ricklefs 1983).

Much of the recent interest in distribution-abundance relationships can be traced to the publication of an important metapopulation model by Hanski (1982a). His model predicted the fraction of homogeneous population sites occupied by a species, following the framework established by Levins (1969, 1970). Hanski's model incorporated a "rescue effect" (Brown and Kodric-Brown 1977), because it assumed that the probability of local extinction decreased as more population sites were occupied (Gotelli 1991). It also assumed that the probabilities of local extinction and local colonization were stochastic, with large variances.

Two major predictions emerged from Hanski's (1982a) model. First, there should be a correlation between distribution and abundance. When a species occupies many population sites, its average local abundance should be high, reflecting the assumption of a rescue effect. Second, the distribution of occupied sites should be bimodal: a species will usually occupy either few or many sites, and will infrequently occupy an intermediate number of sites. Hanski (1982a) has termed this bimodal pattern "the core-satellite hypothesis."

The data needed to rigorously test this and other metapopulation models (Gyllenberg and Hanski 1992; Hanski and Gyllenberg 1993) would consist of single-species records of population occurrences among a set of patches for many different time periods. Then it should be possible to determine whether the fraction of sites occupied is correlated with local extinction or colonization, and whether the distribution of occupied sites is bimodal or not (Gotelli and Kelley 1993). Unfortunately, data of this type are very difficult to come by (Harrison et al. 1988), so that most of the "tests" of Hanski's model have been at the community level (e.g., Gotelli and Simberloff 1987; Gaston and Lawton 1989; Collins and Glenn 1990). These tests are burdened by an additional and unrealistic assumption: species in an assemblage are "similar" to one another and exhibit comparable metapopulation dynamics. If this assumption holds, then it is possible to test for bimodality and the correlation between distribution and abundance by using species as replicates and examining a snapshot of the assemblage at one time, rather than replicating through time and examining the distribution and abundance of a single species.

Although the relationship between distribution and abundance is sensitive to habitat persistence (Novotný 1991) and scale (Gaston and Lawton 1990), the pattern seems to be ubiquitous. A positive correlation is found in many assemblages that probably are not influenced by metapopulation dynamics. Brown (1984) argued that widespread species have broader niches, so that the same factors that allow a species to occur in many sites also allow it to achieve greater abundance within those sites. Nee et al. (1991) modeled species-specific carrying capacities and their effect on regional dynamics, describing Brown's (1984) idea in mathematical terms (Hanski 1991).

However, independent evidence for this niche hypothesis has not been universally established (Hanski et al. 1993). Bowers (1988) showed with computer simulation that local population size was more variable for mammalian species with small geographic ranges than for those with large, geographic ranges, which is consistent with Brown's (1984) argument. However, because Bowers's (1988) analysis appears to have included "empty" sites, local population variability was confounded with small-scale distribution patterns.

It is important to determine whether correlations between distribution and abundance are sampling artifacts or inherent properties of species (Ricklefs 1972). Bock and Ricklefs (1983) pointed out that a correlation between distribution and abundance may be an artifact of limited sampling area. That is, the abundances of species may depend upon which part of their geographic range occurs in the sample space. Species that are sampled near the edge of their range will occur with low abundance in few local sites. In contrast, species that

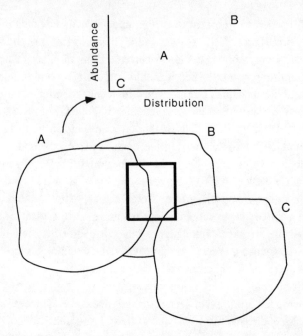

Figure 9.10. Correlations between distribution and abundance can arise from limited sampling. A, B, and C represent the geographic ranges of 3 hypothetical species, which are identical in all respects except for the placement of their ranges. The thick square represents a limited sampling area, within which distribution and abundance relationships are measured. Because the square is centered on the range of species B, this species will occur in most samples and have a high abundance. In contrast, species A and C are sampled near the edges of their ranges, so they will appear to be sparsely distributed and relatively rare in the places they do occur.

are sampled near the center of their range will appear to be more widespread and abundant (Figure 9.10). Null model analyses show that similar artifacts may confound relationships between geographic range and geologic duration of taxa in the fossil record (Russell and Lindberg 1988).

Because most species show an abundance peak at least somewhere within their biogeographic ranges (Brown 1984; Rabinowitz et al. 1986), this explanation certainly can account for some, but not all, correlations between distribution and abundance. However, the correlation between distribution and abundance holds for North American birds when abundances are measured over their entire geographic ranges (Bock and Ricklefs 1983), so this pattern cannot be attributed to a sampling artifact.

Finally, Wright (1991) argued that correlations between distribution and abundance are expected entirely by chance. If individuals are distributed by a Poisson process across a landscape, and then sampled with quadrats, rare species will be less likely to occur in samples and will have a low abundance, even in the absence of other processes controlling spatial pattern. If the Poisson null model is correct, then a plot of the natural logarithm of the frequency of absences (ln $(1 - p)$) against the average abundance in occupied sites should have a slope of -1.0 and an intercept of 0.0. Most data sets that Wright (1991) examined did not fit the quantitative predictions of the Poisson model, in part because intraspecific clumping of individuals affected the shape of the curve.

Thus, four hypotheses have been proposed to account for the relationship between distribution and abundance: (1) metapopulation dynamics (Hanski 1982a); (2) niche relationships (Brown 1984); (3) limited sampling (Bock and Ricklefs 1983); and (4) chance correlations (Wright 1991). Because they operate at distinctly different spatial scales, the four hypotheses cannot be considered mutually exclusive or even complementary. Brown's (1984) explanation is appropriate for distribution-abundance relationships measured over the entire geographic range of a species, whereas Wright's (1991) null model operates within populations because it describes the random placement of individuals. Between these extremes, the models of Hanski (1982a) and of Bock and Ricklefs (1983) operate at an intermediate regional scale, above the level of the population but below the level of the entire biogeographic range.

The two regional-scale models make very different assumptions about population structure and patch homogeneity. In Hanski's (1982a) model, the patches are homogeneous and equivalent for the different species, and the population structure is highly dynamic. Because of stochastic variation in probabilities of extinction and colonization, there is no biological distinction between widespread "core" species and patchy "satellite" species, even though they are often discussed in this fashion. Instead, core and satellite status is expected to change unpredictably through time, so that species that are widespread and abundant at one time may be sparse and rare at another.

In Bock and Ricklefs's (1983) model, the suitability of a patch varies among species, depending on which portion of their biogeographic range has been sampled. Distribution and abundance relationships would be relatively static through time—widespread species would remain consistently abundant because the sample area occurs near the center of the biogeographic range, whereas sparse species would usually be in low abundance because they are sampled at the periphery of their ranges.

In summary, the correlation between distribution and abundance in nature is ubiquitous, and at least four hypotheses have now been proposed to account for it. The sampling models of Wright (1991) and of Bock and Ricklefs (1983) are appropriate null hypotheses at local and regional spatial scales, respectively. We now need additional data on niche and dietary relationships, geographic ranges, metapopulation structure, and temporal constancy of community structure in order to test these hypotheses.

Bimodality

The second community-level prediction to emerge from Hanski's (1982a) metapopulation model was that the frequency distribution of site occupancy by species in a community should be bimodal, with modal peaks of widespread "core" species and sparse "satellite" species. As in the analysis of distribution and abundance, there are many alternatives to the metapopulation explanation for bimodality.

The occurrence of bimodality in quadrat data has a long history in plant ecology. In particular, Raunkiaer's (1934) "law of frequencies" described a pattern of bimodality in the fraction of quadrat occurrences of plant species. Specifically, if the occurrence of species is partitioned into five frequency classes ($A = 1$–20%, $B = 21$–40 %, $C = 41$–60%, $D = 61$–80%, $E = 81$–100%), the law states that the A ("satellite") and E ("core") classes will form peaks in the histogram. Raunkiaer's (1934) explanation for this pattern was one of habitat specificity: species constituting the core (E) mode were those best adapted to the local habitat, so they occurred in most quadrats, whereas the rare species in the (A) mode were poorly adapted and occurred infrequently. His model predicted that the occurrence of species in the A and E modes would shift in different habitats. Note that Raunkiaer's (1934) explanation accounted for the identity of species in the rare and common classes, but it did not actually explain why the distribution was bimodal.

Raunkiaer's (1934) law has been repeatedly criticized as a sampling artifact that is sensitive to the size, placement, and number of quadrats examined (Gleason 1929; Williams 1950; McIntosh 1962; Greig-Smith 1964). In his characteristic fashion, Williams (1950, 1964) developed an appropriate null model and showed that the fraction of species in the core mode was sensitive to both the number and size of quadrats sampled: the E mode decreased in size as more quadrats were sampled or as quadrat size was decreased (Figure 9.11). The reason is that many species will occur in nearly every sample if the quadrats are large or if few samples are taken. As sampling intensity increases or the size of the quadrat is reduced, species shift into less common abundance classes and the E mode shrinks in size.

However, the fact that bimodality is sensitive to sample size does not mean that all bimodal patterns are artifacts. Using Williams's (1964) approach,

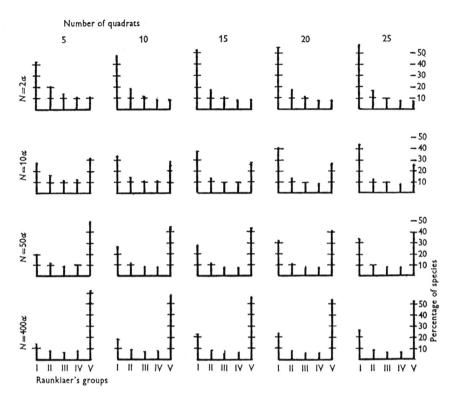

Figure 9.11. Effects of quadrat size and number on the occurrence of species. In each histogram, groups I–V represent the fraction of quadrats occupied, in 20% intervals. The *y* axis is the number of species that falls in each frequency class. The sizes of the histogram bars are based on random samples from a log series species abundance distribution. The columns are arranged in order of increasing quadrat number, and the rows are arranged in order of increasing quadrat size. Note that the fraction of species in the right-hand tail increases with quadrat size and decreases with sample size. From Williams (1964), with permission.

Gotelli and Simberloff (1987) randomized the placement of prairie plant quadrat data among different soil types and found that the size of the core mode was still greater than expected by chance (Figure 9.12). Alternatively, Collins and Glenn (1990) distributed species randomly among sites and showed that the bimodality of prairie grasses persisted at several sampling scales. However, because their null model did not control for quadrat number, it did not specifically address Williams's (1964) sampling hypothesis.

Finally, Brown (1984) argued that the bimodal patterns predicted by Hanski's (1982a) model are an artifact of sampling at a small spatial scale: when

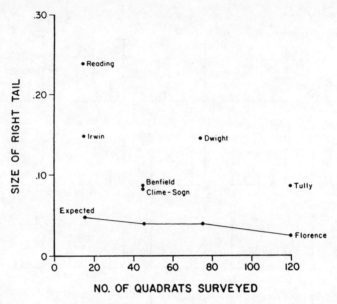

Figure 9.12. Effects of quadrat number on the fraction of widespread plant species in tallgrass prairie. Each point represents a set of quadrats sampled on a different soil series. The solid line gives the expected size of the right-hand tail of the distribution if quadrats were assigned randomly to soil series. Note that six of the seven series fall significantly above the expectation. Reprinted by permission of the publishers from Gotelli, N. J., and D. Simberloff. 1987. The distribution and abundance of tallgrass prairie plants: a test of the core-satellite hypothesis. *American Naturalist* 130:18–35. Copyright © 1987 by The University of Chicago.

species are sampled over their entire geographic ranges, bimodal distributions disappear. Brown (1984) was correct in asserting that bimodal patterns are less likely at the continental scale, but this is not a valid criticism of Hanski's (1982a) model. Hanski's (1982a) model was formulated at a regional scale, and we expect patterns to change at large spatial scales because sites are no longer homogeneous when sampling occurs across the entire geographic range of a species.

Macroecology

The field of macroecology seeks to understand the partitioning of physical space and ecological resources by species (Brown and Maurer 1989). In these analyses, individual species function as replicates and may exhibit correlated patterns of geographic range size, body size, and population density (Damuth

1981; Gaston and Lawton 1988a,b; Lawton 1990). Brown and Maurer (1989) have argued that both absolute and probabilistic boundaries determine the shape of the polygon when these variables are projected in two dimensions. These boundaries, in turn, are thought to reflect energetic constraints, and correlations with dispersal and extinction probabilities.

To explain these patterns, macroecology emphasizes ecological factors and deemphasizes historical or evolutionary mechanisms. But in many assemblages, the history of speciation affects species geographic range sizes (Taylor and Gotelli 1994), and phylogeny has an equally strong influence on body sizes (Elgar and Harvey 1987), so that ecological correlates may ultimately reflect historical or phylogenetic processes.

Even ignoring historical or evolutionary mechanisms, it is difficult to tease apart statistically the highly intercorrelated set of macroecological variables. For example, in some assemblages, body size and geographic range size are positively correlated (Brown and Maurer 1987; Gaston 1990). One interpretation of this correlation is that large-bodied species have large home range requirements and low population densities (Brown 1981). Consequently, a large-bodied species with a small geographic range would have a small total population size and a high probability of extinction (Brown and Maurer 1987). Alternatively, small-bodied species might be more vulnerable to density-independent fluctuations. In this scenario, differential extinction (or range contraction) of small-bodied species leads to the positive correlation between range size and body size (Gaston 1990).

But neither scenario takes account of latitudinal variation in body size and geographic range size. Body sizes tend to increase away from the tropics (Bergmann's rule), as does the north-south span of geographic range in many taxa (Rapoport's rule). Consequently, the correlation between body size and range size may be spurious and reflect underlying latitudinal gradients in both variables (Pagel et al. 1991b). When latitude and longitude are incorporated as covariates in macroecological analyses, correlations between body size and geographic range size may disappear (Taylor and Gotelli 1994).

The relationship between body size and population density may be more complex and nonlinear (Lawton 1989). For North American bird species, Brown and Maurer (1987) showed that maximum population density peaked at an intermediate body size (Figure 9.13). Morse et al. (1988) reported a similar result for rain forest coleoptera. These results contrast with broad taxonomic comparisons, which have shown that population density increases as body weight decreases (Peters and Wasenberg 1983; Damuth 1987). However, in both the bird and the beetle data sets, there were more intermediate-sized species than large- or small-bodied species. Therefore, it is not surprising that

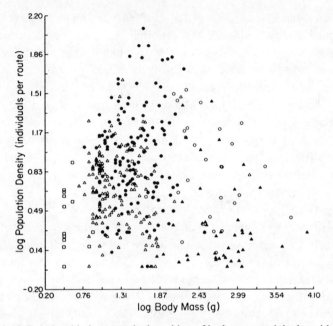

Figure 9.13. Relationship between the logarithm of body mass and the logarithm of average population density for North American terrestrial bird species. Each point in the graph represents a different species. □ = nectarivores; Δ = insectivores; O = herbivores; ● = omnivores-insectivores; ▲ = carnivores. Note the peak in population density for intermediate-sized species. Reprinted by permission of the publisher from Brown, J. H., and B. A. Maurer. 1987. Evolution of species assemblages: effects of energetic constraints and species dynamics on the diversification of the North American avifauna. *American Naturalist* 130:1–17. Copyright © 1987 by The University of Chicago.

the *maximum* population densities were greater for intermediate body size—the more species "sampled," the more likely it is that an extreme value for population density will be found.

Blackburn et al. (1990) explored this idea in a null model reanalysis of these data sets. By fitting a second-order polynomial to the data, they tested the hypothesis that the average population density peaked at an intermediate body size. Of the four beetle and two bird guilds, only one second-order regression was significant. In fact, the remaining guilds did not even show a significant first-order term, suggesting that population density within a guild was essentially constant across the observed range of body sizes.

Next, Blackburn et al. (1990) randomly reallocated species within guilds to break up any association between body size and population density. The

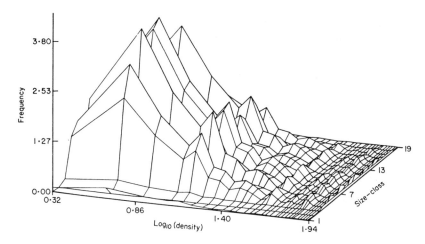

Figure 9.14. Relationship between distribution and abundance for a simulated avian guild of omnivores-insectivores. Sampling effects can lead to a peak of population abundances at intermediate body sizes. Compare with Figure 9.13, although note that the y axis is not log transformed. From Blackburn et al. (1990), with permission.

simulated "null guilds" also showed a pronounced peak in population density at intermediate sizes, and provided an independent check on the polynomial regressions (Figure 9.14). In sum, there seems to be little evidence that either the average or the maximum population density peaks at intermediate body size within guilds of related species. Of course, it is still interesting to consider why there are more intermediate-sized species than very large species within a guild (Van Valen 1973), but this pattern by itself seems sufficient to account for observed relationships between population density and body size.

Taxon Cycles

The taxon cycle (Wilson 1961) and taxon pulse (Erwin 1981) hypotheses predict cycles of expansion and contraction in the geographic distribution of species (Darlington 1957). The cycles are thought to be driven by community-wide competition. In the early stages of the cycle, a species is widespread and undifferentiated. As the cycle progresses, populations becomes more genetically differentiated and ecologically specialized, and the range of the species (or, more commonly, its occurrence on islands) become more fragmented.

The evidence for the taxon cycle is equivocal. On the positive side, the taxon cycle has been a useful framework for interpreting geographic distributions of Melanesian ants (Wilson 1959, 1961), insects (Greenslade 1968a, 1969), and birds (Greenslade 1968b). Narrative accounts of habitat affinities of selected taxa conform to a taxon cycle. For example, Ricklefs (1970) and Ricklefs and Cox (1972, 1978) looked for ecological correlates with stage of the taxon cycle for West Indian birds. On Jamaica, Stage IV species (single-island endemics) occurred in fewer localities and were less widespread than Stage I species (widespread and undifferentiated; Ricklefs 1970). Across the entire archipelago, Stage I species were more likely to flock and migrate than were species in other stages (Ricklefs and Cox 1972).

However, most analyses of habitat affinity and abundance have not revealed statistically significant differences between early and late stage species (Ricklefs and Cox 1978). Pregill and Olson (1981) argued that there is no evidence that West Indian bird species actually passed through the cycle in a temporal sequence. Instead, they suggested that apparent species replacement on islands could be attributed to extensive Pleistocene climatic change in the West Indies. Studies of the Cayman Island avifauna (Johnston 1975) and the birds and butterflies of Madeira and La Gomera (Jones et al. 1987) also failed to provide evidence for progressive shifts in habitat preference and abundance that are related to geographic distribution.

One element that has been lacking in most discussions of the taxon cycle is the phylogenetic pattern of habitat association that is predicted by the hypothesis. If the taxon cycle is real, there should be an orderly progression of habitat shifts that can be superimposed on the cladogram of a monophyletic group. Liebherr and Hajek (1990) took exactly this approach in a test of the taxon cycle and taxon pulse hypotheses for eight clades of tropical carabids. In this case, the null hypothesis was that the number of evolutionary habitat shifts necessary to account for habitat distributions of extant taxa was no more than expected by chance. If the taxon cycle hypothesis is correct, then an unusually small number of such habitat shifts should occur, because these shifts will be concordant with cladogenic divergence.

To test this hypothesis, Liebherr and Hajek (1990) treated habitat affinity as a cladistic character. They randomized observed habitat affinities among taxa and counted the number of evolutionary steps necessary to fit the habitat data to the observed species cladogram. Two different scenarios of habitat change were used. One scenario implicitly assumed that the progress of a species through habitats from the presumed primitive state was linear and irreversible (Camin-Sokal coding). In a less stringent model, the primitive habitat state was inferred by parsimony and evolutionary reversals in habitat affinity were permitted (Farris optimization).

Only one of the eight carabid clades showed a significant pattern consistent with the Camin-Sokal coding and the taxon cycle hypothesis (Figure 9.15).

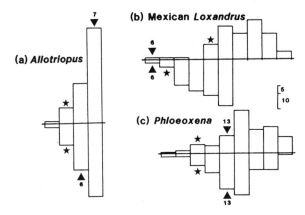

Figure 9.15. Distribution of transformation series lengths based on 100 randomizations of habitat affinity data for three groups of carabid beetles. Above the axis is the distribution of simulated series lengths using Camin-Sokal coding, and below the axis using Farris optimization. The triangle gives the observed transformation series length, and the star is the 5% tail of the distribution. If habitat affinities matched the predictions of the taxon cycle hypothesis, transformation series should be unusually short, a pattern realized only for the Mexican *Loxandrus* clade. From Liebherr and Hajek (1990), with permission.

Two clades were significant under the Farris optimization, suggesting that vicariant splitting of areas of similar habitat may have been responsible for speciation within these groups. Although habitat affinities undoubtedly change during evolution and biogeographic radiation, there do not appear to be simplified "rules" for predicting these changes, and there is little evidence (at this time) for the historical sequence of habitat shifts predicted by the taxon cycle and taxon pulse models.

RECOMMENDATIONS

For the analysis of qualitative overlap patterns in one-dimensional gradients, we recommend Pielou's (1977, 1978) tests for overlapping distributions. For tests of quantitative overlap, boundary contiguities, and simple models of community organization, we recommend Dale's (1984, 1986, 1988) tests. The location of range boundaries can be tested by the methods of Means and Simberloff (1987) or Root (1988a), depending on the type of data available. Analyses of two-dimensional patterns are more challenging. Although entire geographic ranges can be placed randomly on maps (Beven et al. 1984), we recommend simulation algorithms that maintain the size, though not necessarily the shape, of geographic ranges. A realistic algorithm for the placement of geographic ranges would have to take account of the short-term ecological changes (Anderson 1985), long-term evolutionary processes (Lynch 1989), and limits at continental or climatic boundaries (Haefner et al. 1991). A modification of Colwell and Hurtt's (1994) null models might also be used to study diversity gradients within continents. For studies of macroecology and distribution-abundance relationships, we recommend simple sampling models by Blackburn et al. (1990), Williams (1964), Bock and Ricklefs (1983), and Wright (1991) to account for apparent patterns. For studies of the taxon cycle, Liebherr and Hajek's (1990) "phylogenetic null hypothesis" is promising.

10
FOOD WEBS

Most of this book has been concerned with horizontal linkages in plant and animal assemblages. In other words, patterns of species richness (Chapter 8), diversity (Chapters 2 and 3), co-occurrence (Chapters 7 and 9), resource utilization (Chapters 4 and 5), and morphology (Chapter 6) of taxonomic or ecological guilds of species that potentially compete for resources and are thus at the same trophic level. Null models are an essential tool for delineating expected patterns in noninteractive assemblages of potential competitors.

A different perspective on community structure emphasizes the vertical linkages, that is, the identities and interactions of predators and their prey in an assemblage. Food web diagrams that depict binary interactions of "who eats whom" (Figure 10.1) have a long history in ecology, dating back to Shelford (1913). These diagrams have prompted a number of interesting ecological questions. What determines the number of links in a food web, and how is this related to the number of species in the web? Are certain web topologies more mathematically or biologically stable than others? What determines the maximum food chain length within a web? Does web structure vary systematically between terrestrial and aquatic habitats, or those with two- and three-dimensional structure?

Although the literature on food webs and on the ecological niche has developed somewhat independently, they are conceptually linked, because energetic constraints and prey availability are often the ultimate causes of niche divergence among competitors. For example, Hutchinson's (1959) seminal paper that suggested a constant size ratio between coexisting competitors (see Chapter 6) was primarily concerned with the way that energy flow ultimately constrains the total number of species in an assemblage. Assemblage patterns of qualitative niche overlap in diet can be directly equated with food web links. From food web diagrams, Cohen (1978) derived measures of niche overlap (and tested them against null models) that depicted the qualitative similarity in diet among a set of consumers at the same trophic level. Some of the detailed null models of food webs and biogeography are also similar. As an example,

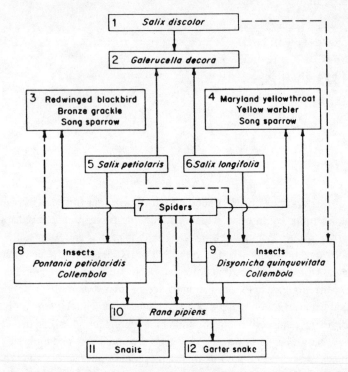

Figure 10.1. A simple food web for a willow forest (Bird 1930). Arrows are directed from prey to predator. Dashed lines are tentative linkages. Numbers indicate "kinds" of organisms used in food web analyses. Simplified food webs such as this have formed the basis for many analyses of web structure. From Cohen, J. E. *Food Webs and Niche Space*. Copyright © 1978 by Princeton University Press. Reprinted by permission of Princeton University Press.

Cohen's (1978) six randomization algorithms for food web matrices are very similar to some of Simberloff's (1978a) null model protocols for presence-absence matrices of co-occurring species.

In spite of these similarities, the influence of null models on niche and food web studies has differed. In niche analyses, null models arrived relatively late in the picture. By the time null models were used in niche overlap studies, theoretical principles were well established and explanations for assemblage patterns had often been uncritically accepted. Because null model tests often contradicted accepted interpretations of niche overlap patterns, they were highly controversial (see Chapters 4–7).

Null models also challenged conventional wisdom in food web studies, although their use has been less contentious, perhaps because they appeared so early in the food web literature (Stuart L. Pimm, personal communication). In particular, early null models (Gardner and Ashby 1970; May 1972) failed to garner support for the popular contention that complexity of food webs leads to stability.

Null models were also essential to the early analyses of empirical patterns in the food web literature (Cohen 1978; Pimm 1980a, 1982). For example, many published food webs have only two or three trophic links. In contrast, webs of the same size that are randomly connected typically have more than three links (Pimm 1980a). Null model analyses led to a catalog of food web patterns that did not seem to be a simple consequence of the number of species in the sample. Several recent studies have called these patterns into question (Sprules and Bowerman 1988; Martinez 1991; Polis 1991). However, this controversy surrounds the quality of the original data (Paine 1988), not the null models that were used to establish the patterns.

This chapter provides a brief overview of the food web and stability literature, as it relates to null models. For more extensive coverage, see Pimm (1982) and Pimm et al. (1991). We first describe the use of null models in the development of food web theory. Next, we describe analyses of published food web data, and the empirical generalizations that emerged from these studies. We then consider null model analyses of community stability, as measured by the community matrix, and by temporal data on the rank abundances of species. Finally, we summarize some recent empirical controversies in the literature and suggest how null models might be applied in future food web studies.

STABILITY ANALYSES OF MODEL FOOD WEBS

Both Elton (1958) and MacArthur (1955) popularized the notion that complex ecological systems are more stable than simple systems. Elton (1958) summarized a diverse set of observations from mathematical, laboratory, and field studies to establish this idea. He noted that simple predator-prey models predicted fluctuating populations and concluded that more complex models would lead to stable populations. He also pointed to laboratory experiments, such as Gause's (1934), which demonstrated how difficult it was to achieve stable coexistence of predators and prey. Turning to field systems, Elton (1958) argued that invasions and outbreaks of pest species were much more common in agricultural systems that had been modified and simplified by human activity. He also suggested that insect outbreaks were characteristic of simple temperate forests but not of complex tropical forests (but see Wolda 1978).

Elton (1958) described several measures of "stability": (1) a tendency for populations to return to an equilibrium value when perturbed; (2) a small variance in population size; (3) the ability of an assemblage to resist invasion; and (4) the change in populations of an assemblage following an invasion. By "complexity," Elton (1958) meant both the number of species in the web and the number of links in the web (connectance). Much of the confusion over the relationship between stability and complexity arose because there are many ways that ecological and mathematical stability can be defined, and because the relationship between stability and complexity depends critically on how these definitions are constructed (Pimm 1984b).

MacArthur's (1955) approach was more mathematical and formal than Elton's (1958). By stability, MacArthur (1955) meant the degree to which species abundances changed when the abundance of one species in the web was greatly perturbed. His argument was that complex systems with many different pathways for energy flow were more stable than systems with few pathways. For example, if the population of a single prey species is reduced, a polyphagous predator can shift to alternative prey. Therefore, webs with polyphagous predators should be relatively stable. In contrast, webs with monophagous predators should be less stable, because perturbations in prey abundance will cause more violent fluctuations in predator abundance.

MacArthur (1955) proposed two hypotheses for community stability. First, biotic interactions among the species in the web can impart stability. This hypothesis underlies mathematical analyses of food web structure and provides a justification for the use of the Lotka-Volterra equations and the corresponding community matrix (Levins 1968). The Lotka-Volterra equations are the simplest first-order differential equations that describe pairwise interspecific interactions. Interactions such as predation, competition, and mutualism among species pairs can be modeled by setting interaction coefficients to positive or negative values. The community matrix contains all these interaction terms, plus terms for self-limitation of each species along the diagonal of the matrix.

MacArthur's (1955) second hypothesis was that stability of the food web "can be intrinsic to the individual species." An assessment of this hypothesis ultimately requires knowledge of abiotic factors and physiological limitations to population growth of each species. MacArthur's (1955) second hypothesis acknowledges that food web stability may not be a biological property of interactions among species, but of the interaction of species with their physical environment.

In this view, food web patterns are an epiphenomenon, a secondary reflection of the habitat and abiotic factors that allow sets of species to persist together. Although this hypothesis does not deny the interaction of predators and their prey, it does imply that trophic and competitive interactions do not determine the stability of the system. In fact, food webs for some real communities do seem to be mathematically unstable (Auerbach 1979). MacArthur (1955) did not develop his second hypothesis any further, but it stands as an excellent null hypothesis for the study of food webs.

Random Connectance: An Early Food Web Null Model

The hypothesis that stability begets complexity corresponds to the naturalist's intuition about the "balance of nature" (Pimm 1991). Perhaps for this reason, the stability-complexity hypothesis was accepted uncritically until the early 1970s, beginning with the publication of a brief, but important, paper by Gardner and Ashby (1970). They were concerned with the stability and organization of large, complex systems, such as airports, human brains, and urban slums. They began with a matrix of pairwise interaction coefficients for systems of four, seven, and 10 variables. For a noninteractive system, they first set all off-diagonal elements to zero, and then assigned a random negative number to the diagonals of the matrix. If the diagonal elements are negative, the system is locally stable to small perturbations because each component is self-limiting. This would correspond in a food web to a set of species that do not interact with one another but have stable, self-limiting populations.

Next, Gardner and Ashby (1970) defined connectance as the percentage of nonzero off-diagonal elements. For a given connectance, they filled the matrix with random numbers drawn uniformly from the range -1.0 to 1.0, constructing a system with arbitrary positive and negative linkages. For each such randomly constructed matrix, Gardner and Ashby (1970) calculated local stability, the tendency for populations to return to equilibrium values following a small perturbation in numbers. The proportion of randomly constructed matrices that were stable for a given matrix size was then plotted against connectance.

For all the matrix dimensions they investigated, stability decreased with increasing connectance, a direct contradiction of MacArthur (1955) and Elton (1958). Not only did stability decrease with connectance, but the larger the matrix, the steeper the decrease (Figure 10.2). For very large matrices, Gardner and Ashby (1970) suggested there may be some critical threshold of connectance, above which complex systems will be unstable.

May (1972, 1973) generalized their results and applied them specifically to ecological systems. He showed that as the number of species becomes large, there is indeed a critical limit to connectance, although that limit depends in part on α, the average interaction strength in the community matrix. The assemblage will usually be stable if

$$\alpha\sqrt{SC} < 1 \qquad\qquad (10.1)$$

where α is the average interaction strength, S is the number of species, and C is the connectance.

These early food web simulations do not conform strictly to the null model definition given in Chapter 1. For one thing, these were not stochastic food web models. Although the coefficients for the community matrix were assigned randomly, the criterion of stability was entirely deterministic. Moreover, the simulation results were never compared with empirical data. Nevertheless, the stability-complexity hypothesis was so thoroughly engrained in the ecological literature (Goodman 1975) that these simulations served as an important null hypothesis that described the behavior of systems with arbitrary linkages.

Constraints and Biological Realism

What was the response to the finding that model stability decreased with complexity? The common criticism was that the models were "too null." In other words, the simulations included communities that were not biologically

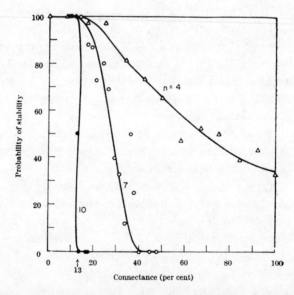

Figure 10.2. Relationship between the probability of stability and the connectance of a web of size 4, 7, or 10. Note that as connectance is randomly increased, stability decreases. This early null model contradicted conventional wisdom about stability-complexity relationships. From Gardner and Ashby (1970). Reprinted with permission from *Nature* 228:784, Figure 1. Copyright © 1970, Macmillan Magazines Limited.

reasonable. For example, if the community matrix is to represent a real community, the equilibrium population sizes must not only be stable, they must also be greater than zero. Gardner and Ashby (1970) did not impose this constraint of "feasibility" on their simulations. Roberts (1974) imposed the constraint, and his results suggest that feasible matrices tend to be stable, although his simulations did not directly vary connectance. However, Roberts's (1974) choice of parameters was restricted, and his results may not be general (Gilpin 1975; Goh and Jennings 1977).

A second criterion for a "biologically reasonable" simulation is that it obey basic principles of thermodynamics and energy transfer, which dictate that energy transfer from prey to predator is never 100% efficient. This restriction means that the magnitude of losses to the prey population must be greater than the corresponding gains to the predator population. DeAngelis (1975) built model food webs that incorporated energy transfer, imposed a hierarchical food web structure, and assumed that higher trophic levels were strongly self-damping. He also incorporated donor control, in which predators have only a limited ability to control their prey. These restrictions correspond to only a small subset of possible food web structures. When these constraints were imposed and coefficients were randomly assigned, stability sometimes increased with complexity.

Still another biologically reasonable constraint was that trophic loops not be allowed. In such a loop, species A eats species B, B eats C, and C eats A. The stability of models that forbid loops can increase with increasing species richness (Lawlor 1978). Although the early food web literature characterized these trophic loops as biologically unreasonable (Lawlor 1978; Pimm 1982), in fact they are quite common (Martinez 1991; Polis 1991), particularly for predators with size-structured populations or complex life histories (Polis et al. 1989). Thus, to some extent, modeling efforts were guided by preconceived ideas about the structure of food webs in nature.

Monte Carlo Modeling Strategies

Even in a simple food web, it is impossible to evaluate systematically all combinations of interaction coefficients. The Gardner and Ashby (1970) method has been used effectively to examine the general properties of other food web models. A common strategy has been to define the model and restrict either the sign or the range of values possible for the interaction coefficients. Within these constraints, the interaction coefficients are then chosen randomly and the mathematical stability of the resulting model is assessed. This process is repeated for a large set of community matrices. The result is an estimate of the proportion of models that are stable for a small, but random, subset of possible coefficients.

These analyses have revealed a bewildering array of possible answers to the stability-complexity question, although a few generalizations are apparent (Pimm 1982). The key elements determining stability in community matrices are often the diagonal or self-limiting elements. Donor-control equations, which characterize many real food webs (Hawkins 1992), tend to be more stable than Lotka-Volterra equations (Pimm 1982). Different answers to the stability-complexity question also arise if one uses the criterion of global stability, local stability, or species deletion and addition stability (Pimm 1984b).

The early simulation work on food web structure also prompted a search for empirical patterns. In particular, May's (1972) simple equation (10.1) was seized upon as a new empirical rule for community structure. If interaction strength is constant, then the product of S and C should be constant in stable assemblages. Thus, if mathematical stability is important in determining food web structure in the real world, a graph of connectance versus species richness should form a hyperbola. However, the search for this pattern seems premature unless the relationship between S and C in assemblages that are not dynamically constrained has been studied. Later in this chapter, we examine null models of the relationship between connectance and species richness that do not impose dynamical constraints but nevertheless predict a hyperbolic relationship.

NULL MODEL ANALYSES OF THE COMMUNITY MATRIX

The mathematical definition of local stability has been difficult to test in nature; small, controlled perturbations are difficult to achieve in field experiments and hard to recognize in time series of fluctuating populations. A more indirect approach is to take empirical community matrices and compare their properties with randomized matrices that are not subject to any dynamical constraints. The community matrix requires estimates of α_{ij}, the per capita effect on the growth rate of the population of species j caused by a small increase in the population of species i. In the absence of direct experimental manipulation, these coefficients can be estimated from resource utilization data (Levins 1968) or from multiple regression analyses in which the abundances of the component species are measured at different times (Schoener 1974d; Crowell and Pimm 1976).

Both methods have problems. As discussed in Chapter 4, overlap in resource use may or may not reflect competition (Sale 1974), and the estimates may be biased if the true niche overlaps are multidimensional (May 1975b). Regression estimates may also be biased and confounded by the presence of habitat heterogeneity (Rosenzweig et al. 1984; Rosenzweig and Abramsky 1985; Abramsky et al. 1986). Still, in the absence of experimental manipulation, these measures do provide some information about the nature of species interactions. Although the theory behind these concepts has been developed for predator-prey food webs, most of the data have come from studies of competitive interactions within a single trophic level, perhaps because overlaps within a single trophic level are easier to estimate quantitatively.

Lawlor (1980b) presented an ambitious null model analysis of the community matrix. His study asked two questions: first, is local (Lyapunov) stability important in real communities? If so, then the observed community matrix should be more stable than a corresponding set of randomized matrices. This is a different issue from that of simply establishing whether or not the observed matrix is stable. Second, if local stability is relevant to community structure, what makes observed communities more stable than analogous random communities?

Lawlor (1980b) analyzed 11 overlap matrices calculated by Cody (1974) for bird communities. The symmetric overlap matrices were based on observations of habitat, vertical foraging range, and feeding pattern. The stability of each matrix was measured as the minimum eigenvalue, which must be greater than zero for persistence. By this criterion, 9 of the 11 communities were stable. However, relative stability, as measured by the size of the eigenvalue, decreased with increasing species richness, in accord with May's (1972) result. Nevertheless, observed eigenvalues were always larger than eigenvalues for randomized communities (Figure 10.3). The interpretation of this result is a bit ambiguous, because some of the observed stability was a mathematical consequence of using a symmetric overlap index (May 1975b). On the other hand, this property was present in the randomized matrices as well.

A more powerful method is to directly randomize the resource utilization data, rather than rearrange the resulting competition coefficients. For this analysis, Lawlor (1980b) used the lizard resource utilization data of Pianka et al. (1979). He reshuffled the data with four randomization algorithms, all of which are discussed in Chapter 4. As in Cody's (1974) bird communities, observed stability decreased with increasing species richness, but was greater than expected stability generated by the null model. Average α (interaction terms) was also significantly lower than expected, and relative stability decreased with increasing average α and with increasing variance of α.

These patterns are important because Levins (1968) had suggested that coevolution should lead to a decrease in α variance. However, the observed α variances did not differ from expected except under RA1, the most liberal

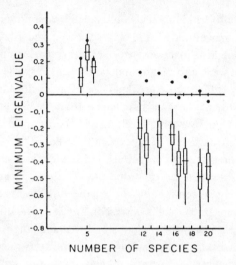

NUMBER OF SPECIES

Figure 10.3. Relationship between species number and minimum eigenvalue of the community matrix, a measure of local stability. Solid circles indicate observed bird communities (Cody 1974). The mean, standard deviation, and range of the eigenvalue are also shown based on 100 randomizations of the observed community matrix. Communities with more species had lower stability, in accord with Gardner and Ashby's (1970) results. However, the observed community matrix was always more stable than randomized matrices of the same size. Reprinted by permission of the publisher from Lawlor, L. R. 1980. Structure and stability in natural and randomly constructed competitive communities. *American Naturalist* 116:394–408. Copyright © 1980 by The University of Chicago.

simulation routine. Lawlor (1980b) concluded that neighborhood stability was important in local community structure, and that competition had shaped communities by reducing the average overlap (though not the variance) between competitors.

Hallett (1991) used a similar analysis of community matrices for six small mammal communities for which interaction coefficients had been estimated by the regression method. He considered not only local stability, but also global stability (the tendency to return to equilibrium following a large perturbation) and resilience (the return time to equilibrium). He also measured the community covariance (Vandermeer 1972) and the presence of indirect pathways (Lawlor 1979). These pathways represent higher-order interactions that cannot be predicted on the basis of pairwise coefficients (Lawlor 1979; Holt 1984). For each matrix, he randomly interchanged two of the coefficients, recalculated the community metrics, and then repeated this procedure until all possible distinct arrangements of the original matrix were produced. These matrices contained only three, four, or nine species, so it was not prohibitive to generate all of the matrix permutations. A second, more general set of randomizations filled the community matrix with elements chosen from segments of a random uniform distribution, representing strong or weak competitive effects. These simulations revealed the likelihood of finding indirect competitive pathways as a function of the number of species, the magnitude of competitive effects, and the structure of the matrix.

How did the observed mammal communities compare to these simulated assemblages? Both local and global stability were always significantly greater than expected, and return times were also unusually short compared to randomized matrices. Although total species number varied among the different assemblages, each community had only three or four competing species. Consequently, connectance fell as S was increased. However, the average interaction strength did not differ with S. This result implies that reduced connectance was a major factor that ensured stability of larger assemblages.

Community covariance was minimized for only one of Hallett's (1991) six assemblages. However, covariance seemed to be attributable to competitive structure: five of the six community covariances were negative and associated with asymmetrical competitive hierarchies. Finally, the observed matrices differed greatly from the simulated in the frequency of indirect pathways. The simulated and the randomized matrices had a high percentage of indirect pathways, and this percentage increased if the average interaction strength was higher. These pathways were relatively uncommon in two of the six real matrices and completely absent in the other four. Thus, observed assemblages tended to be relatively stable and resilient. They were also simple, with few or no indirect pathways, relatively few directly interacting species, and competitive hierarchies that usually were linear and asymmetrical (Figure 10.4).

The patterns revealed by the null model tests of Lawlor (1980b) and Hallett (1991) are intriguing, but it may be too great a leap of faith to assess community stability in terms of interaction coefficients, particularly when these are calculated from resource utilization data. Abrams (1981) questioned the use of resource utilization and the narrow criterion of neighborhood stability for analysis of the community matrix, although Hallet's (1991) results seem to be robust to the definition of stability. Abrams (1981) also suggested that the matrix rearrangements were biased toward revealing stability, and that some competitive structure would not be revealed by this method. We agree that in the absence of experimental manipulations of density, it may be difficult to say much about community stability. On the other hand, even nonexperimental overlap matrices contain a great deal of biological information, and the null

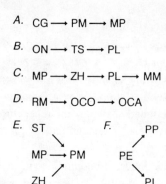

Figure 10.4. Competitive hierarchies in mammal communities. These linear (A–D) and branched (E–F) hierarchies are significantly smaller and more linear than predicted by null models. (**A**) Maine coastal island; (**B**) Tennessee temperate forest; (**C**) Maryland barrier island; (**D**) Venezuelan premontane humid forest; (**E**) North Dakota grassland; (**F**) Chihuahuan Desert. CG = *Clethrionomys gapperi;* PM = *Peromyscus maniculatus;* MP = *Microtus pennsylvanicus;* ON = *Ochrotomys nuttalli;* TS = *Tamias striatus;* PL = *Peromyscus leucopus;* ZH = *Zapus hudsonius;* MM = *Mus musculus;* RM = *Rhipidomys mastacalis;* OCO = *Oryzomys concolor;* OCA = *Oryzomys capito;* ST = *Spermophilus tridecemlineatus;* PE = *Peromyscus eremicus;* PP = *Perognathus penicillatus;* PI = *Perognathus intermedius.* From Hallett, J. G. 1988. The structure and stability of small mammal faunas. *Oecologia* 88:383–393, Figure 1. Copyright © 1988 by Springer-Verlag GmbH & Co. KG.

model tests can at least establish emergent patterns in the data that are relevant to discussions of stability.

Plant ecologists have been able to make more progress in experimentally measuring species effects on one another. The classic tool for studying species interactions in plant assemblages is the de Wit (1960) replacement series. In these experiments, seeds from a pair of species are planted in different ratios at constant density. Short-term measurements of output (growth, biomass, or seed production) are compared for species grown at a constant total density in monoculture and in various proportions in a two-species mixture. The ratio of growth in a mixed-species planting to growth in a monoculture has been interpreted as a measure of the Lotka-Volterra competition coefficients (Harper 1977).

There are some problems with this approach. The ratio diagrams address frequency, not density of competitors (Inouye and Schaffer 1980). They do not indicate the temporal dynamics of species interactions (Connolly et al. 1990), and they may exaggerate the competitive abilities of large plants, particularly in short-term experiments (Grace et al. 1992). Nevertheless, pairwise studies of competitive interactions are the most powerful approach to the study of community structure and stability, particularly when all the species in an assemblage have been experimentally tested in pairs.

Shipley (1993) used a simple null model to examine structure in competitive matrices that are derived from de Wit output experiments. In these binary competition matrices, the effect of species A on species B is assigned a one if species A grows better in mixture than in monoculture. A zero is assigned otherwise. Thus, for any given species pair, the two interaction coefficients specify four possible outcomes, corresponding to the four theoretical possibilities of the two-species Lotka-Volterra competition equations (species A wins, species B wins, stable coexistence, unstable coexistence). Shipley (1993) looked for the presence of "completely transitive" pathways in such matrices. In a completely transitive pathway, the species can be arranged in a strict hierarchy of competitive relationships, such that species A outcompetes species B, B outcompetes C, and A outcompetes C. If C could outcompete A, the path would be intransitive. The ecological significance of completely transitive pathways is that all species in such a pathway can be competitively excluded except for the single competitive dominant.

For his null model, Shipley (1993) randomly filled the competition matrix with ones and zeros, based on their frequency of occurrence in the original matrix. For a given frequency of "winning" interactions, the state of each coefficient was independent of the state of any other coefficient. The null model generated the expected number of pathways of a given length for an assemblage with randomly structured competitive hierarchies.

Shipley (1993) applied this test for transitive pathways to 10 published plant competition matrices that were based on de Wit plantings. The results were clear-cut: all but one matrix had significantly more transitive pathways than predicted by the null model. The finding that competitive interactions between species are often organized in linear hierarchies is very similar to Hallett's (1991) results for mammal assemblages, even though the null models and metrics used were rather different.

In summary, null model analyses of community matrices have generated consistent results for diverse assemblages of plants, mammals, lizards, and birds. Most of these matrices are more mathematically stable than predicted by chance. Compared to the universe of possible species interactions, those that are observed tend to be simple linear hierarchies involving only a small subset of species. Interestingly, these patterns are qualitatively in line with the original stability-complexity models of Gardner and Ashby (1970) and May (1972).

How these stability properties relate to the persistence of assemblages in nature is another matter entirely. For example, Rabinowitz et al. (1984) used de

Wit plantings to estimate the competitive abilities of sparse and common prairie grasses. Contrary to their expectations, the uncommon species were superior, not inferior, competitors. Thus, these grass species were rare in nature in spite of, not because of, their competitive abilities. At least in this assemblage, factors other than species interactions, and hence community stability, were responsible for relative abundance.

PERSISTENCE STABILITY AND THE CONCORDANCE OF SPECIES RANKS THROUGH TIME

Although mathematical stability has been difficult to address with field data, many empirical studies have explored the idea of community persistence (Pimm 1984b)—the tendency for species composition and rank abundances of species to remain constant through time. Empirical tests of community persistence have not relied on mathematical stability analyses, but they have been interpreted in a consistent theoretical framework. Assemblages for which species rank abundances remain constant through time have been described as equilibrial, deterministic, and controlled by strong biotic interactions, whereas assemblages in which rank abundances repeatedly change are nonequilibrial, stochastic, and not controlled by species interactions (Grossman 1982; Wiens 1984). In hindsight, these conclusions about underlying forces controlling community structure are premature. In particular, a pattern of rank concordances does not necessarily imply deterministic, biotic interactions (Yant et al. 1984; Ebeling et al. 1990). Early on, MacArthur (1955) pointed out that autecological factors independently stabilizing the abundance of each species can generate assemblage stability. However, the temporal pattern of abundances is important in that it can at least give insight into whether or not assemblages are at an equilibrium state.

Grossman (1982) popularized the analysis of species ranks in a study of California tidepool fishes. Tidepools were repeatedly defaunated and sampled over a 29-month period. Grossman (1982) found that despite repeated defaunation, the assemblage returned to a characteristic species composition and relative abundance (Figure 10.5). From this pattern, he concluded that the intertidal fish assemblage was both resilient and persistent. In contrast, 12 years of samples of stream fishes from a single site in Indiana showed no concordance of rank abundances through time (Figure 10.6), and Grossman et al. (1982) concluded that this assemblage was probably regulated by stochastic factors.

Perhaps because the nonequilibrium conclusion was unpopular, the second, but not the first, of Grossman's studies provoked a series of rebuttals. Critics

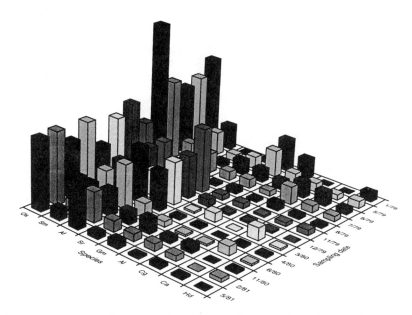

Figure 10.5. Relative abundance of resident coastal tidepool fishes. The height of each bar is proportional to the relative abundance of a species collected on a particular sampling date. By Kendall's *W,* the abundance rankings of the species were significantly concordant among censuses. Os = *Oligocottus snyderi;* Sm = *Scorpaenichthys marmoratus;* Af = *Apodichthys flavidus;* Sr = *Sebastes rastrelliger;* Gm = *Gibbsonia metzi;* Al = *Artedius lateralis;* Cg = *Clinocottus globiceps;* Ca = *Clinocottus analis;* Hd = *Hexagrammos decagrammos.* Data from Table 3 of Grossman (1982).

complained that guild designations (Herbold 1984) and choice of site, season, and sampling methods (Rahel et al. 1984; Yant et al. 1984) exaggerated the patterns of variability in this assemblage. The sampling issues raised by these critics are probably typical of any study that spans a 12-year period, and Grossman et al. (1985) responded effectively to many of the criticisms.

Important statistical issues were raised as well. Grossman (1982; Grossman et al. 1982) used Kendall's *W* as a statistical test of rank concordance. For this test, the null hypothesis is that different orderings of species rank abundances are equally probable from one year to the next. The alternative hypothesis is that ranks are unusually concordant among years. One problem with applying Kendall's *W* to assemblage data is that the test is sensitive to sample size (Rahel et al. 1984). In particular, if many rare species are included in the analysis, the test will often reveal concordance, even though there may be important shifts in rank abundance of the more common species. This is not necessarily an artifact. Indeed, one of the critical questions in studies of community stability is why

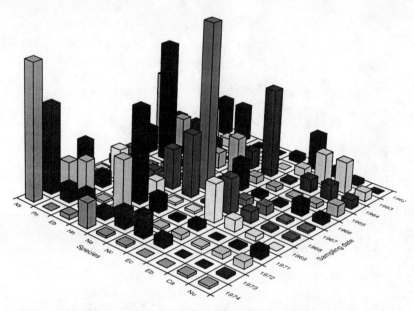

Figure 10.6. Relative abundance of common Indiana stream fishes. The height of each bar is proportional to the relative abundance of a species collected on a particular sampling date. By Kendall's *W*, the abundance rankings of the species were not significantly concordant among censuses. Ns = *Notropis spilopterus*; Pn = *Pimephales notatus;* Eb = *Etheostoma blennoides;* Hn = *Hybognathus nuchalis;* Na = *Notropis atherinoides;* Nc = *Notropis chrysocephalus;* Ec = *Etheostoma caeruleum;* Eb = *Ericymba buccata;* Ca = *Campostoma anomalum;* Nu = *Notropis umbratilus.* Data from Table 4 of Grossman et al. (1982).

rare species never become widespread and abundant. If assemblages are carefully defined a priori, and sample-size effects are examined, rare species need not bias the test.

A second difficulty with Kendall's *W* is that the test results are sensitive to the underlying species abundance distribution (Jumars 1980). For this reason, Jumars (1980) recommended testing the data against an appropriate sampling model that treats fluctuations in relative abundance as sampling error. The test is a simple chi-squared analysis of a species × time table, in which each entry is the number of individuals sampled of a particular species. The null hypothesis is that all the samples are drawn from the same species abundance distribution. The alternative hypothesis is that the samples come from different distributions, causing relative abundances to change through time. The test may be problematic because individuals are rarely sampled independently of one another in field studies. Pooling collections and treating the data as in-

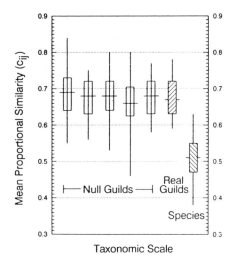

Figure 10.7. Proportional similarity between censuses of coral reef fishes. Similarity is higher when species are organized into guilds (right hatching) than when they are counted individually (left hatching), but this is a sampling effect found in random guild assignments. Horizontal lines are means, vertical lines are ranges, and vertical bars are standard errors. From Sale, P. F., and J. A. Guy. 1992. Persistence of community structure: what happens when you change taxonomic scale? *Coral Reefs* 11:147–154, Figure 1. Copyright © 1992 by Springer-Verlag GmbH & Co. KG.

dependent may greatly inflate the Type I error (Kramer and Schmidhammer 1992), making the test overly sensitive to minor fluctuations in abundance.

Other null models have been used to examine temporal changes in assemblage structure. For example, Sale and Douglas (1984) found that the species composition of Australian coral reef fish assemblages varied greatly through time, so that similarity indices between consecutive samples were usually low. In comparison with a null model, species associations changed substantially from census to census (Sale and Steel 1989). Sale and Guy (1992) explored the possibility that assemblage structure was obscured by a dilution effect, and postulated that species classified into ecological feeding guilds might reveal more temporal concordance in composition. Similarity indices at the guild level were indeed higher than for the total set of species. However, this appears to be entirely an artifact of sample size, because random assignment of species to pseudoguilds yielded comparable similarity indices (Figure 10.7).

Ebeling et al. (1990) built several null models that directly evaluated the behavior of Kendall's W. Their data consisted of annual estimates of abundance for a guild of five species of surfperches that inhabited rocky subtidal reefs off the California coast. Kendall's W indicated a high degree of concordance in rank abundances, with one species (*Embiotoca jacksoni*) retaining first rank in 12 different censuses. Random census data were constructed by generating artificial population tracks for each species. Each species abundance was allowed to change according to a proportion drawn uniformly from a −1.0 to 1.0 range, subject to constraints in four different null models.

Models 1 and 2, which retained autecological population limits for each species, typically generated large, statistically significant values of W, and there was a substantial probability (0.21 and 0.35, respectively) of always finding the same species in the first rank. Models 3 and 4, which permitted more violent fluctuations in species abundance, had substantially lower values of Kendall's W. The analyses of Ebeling et al. (1990) demonstrate that deterministic species interactions need not be invoked for assemblages in which species rank abundances are strongly concordant through time.

Finally, Evans (1988) took a multivariate approach to analyzing changes in community structure through time. Grasshopper assemblages in six tallgrass prairie sites were sampled by sweep net from 1982 to 1986. Evans (1988) used a detrended correspondence analysis to ordinate the relative abundances of species at each site. In this analysis, assemblage structure appeared as a set of six connected vectors when plotted on the first two axes of the ordination. Next, Evans (1988) adapted a null model by Kareiva and Shigesada (1983), which was originally used to describe insect movement as a random walk in two-dimensional space. Observed vector lengths and angular displacements were randomly sampled to construct a correlated random walk in two-dimensional space. The squared displacement from an initial position increased with time in this null model. In contrast, the observed vectors for the grasshopper assemblages were steady or slightly decreasing across years (Figure 10.8). The results suggest that changes in the frequencies of different species were less than expected by chance. However, the patterns are difficult to interpret, because the detrended correspondence analysis obscures the pattern of change for individual species and because the null model of random change in community structure is not based directly on changes in abundance of individual species.

In summary, a variety of statistical tests and null model procedures reveal a substantial amount of concordance in assemblage structure through time. Some of this concordance may simply reflect the lifespans of the component species (Connell and Sousa 1983), but most studies have been long enough for substantial population turnover to occur. Lawton and Gaston (1989) argued that most assemblages of organisms show this pattern; Eric R. Pianka (personal communication in Pimm 1984b) suggested that, with the exception of successional

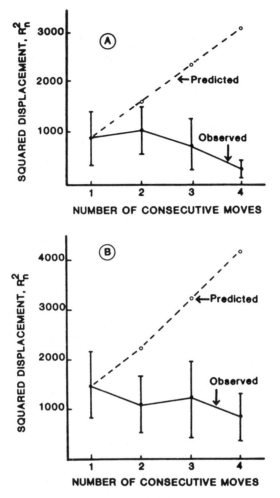

Figure 10.8. Temporal change in community structure of prairie grasshoppers compared with a null model of random change. The *x* axis is the number of consecutive "moves" or changes in ordination after 1 to 4 years. The *y* axis is the squared displacement vector of ordinated community structure. The null model of a random walk predicts increasing change in community structure, whereas the observed assemblages showed little change from their initial structure. Vertical lines indicate 95% confidence intervals. Dashed line is the predicted value from the null model of Kareiva and Shigesada (1983). Analyses are shown with (**A**) and without (**B**) *Phoetaliotes nebrascensis,* the numerical dominant in the assemblage. From Evans (1988), with permission.

systems, most assemblages of organisms will be stable during the lifetime of an ecologist. Yet, there is a growing literature suggesting that many assemblages may not be in an equilibrium state (Rotenberry and Wiens 1980; Sale and Douglas 1984; Boecklen and Price 1991).

In many communities, certain species are persistent but chronically rare, and it remains an important challenge to understand why this is so (Rabinowitz 1981). Larger-scale null models of species composition that incorporate regional source pools and colonization potential (Cornell and Lawton 1992) may be necessary to complement small-scale null models of population change for an understanding of temporal constancy of species assemblages.

PATTERNS OF FOOD WEB STRUCTURE

Null models have been frequently used to quantify and describe general food web patterns. These analyses have used a large database of published webs, initially compiled by Cohen (1978) and expanded by Briand (1983) and by Briand and Cohen (1987). This compendium of published webs is important because it forms the basis for the conventional wisdom of how food webs are organized in nature (Figure 10.9).

However, the compiled webs suffer from some serious, perhaps debilitating, distortions. The major problem with the compiled webs is that they often lump taxa into "trophic groups." This lumping may represent an attempt to depict only the important interactions in the food web, but it may also reflect artistic convenience (Paine 1988) and taxonomic biases against invertebrates and small-bodied organisms (Pimm 1982). Lumping in published food webs is not random and is almost always concentrated near the base of the food chain. This introduces a systematic bias into the webs that may distort basic food web patterns. For example, Cohen (1977) found that the ratio of the number of prey species to the number of predator species in webs was often 3:4. Such ratios arise from stable Lotka-Volterra food webs with apparent competition between prey species via shared enemies (Mithen and Lawton 1986; see Chapter 7 for tests of the related hypothesis that predator and prey *abundances* are relatively constant). But the ratio may simply represent differential lumping of prey categories (Pimm 1982), and is not predicted by other simple theories of community development (Glasser 1983).

For now, we accept the food web data "as is" and show how null models have been used to elucidate nonrandom patterns in the webs. We review null model tests of three food web patterns: trophic chain length, interval webs, and

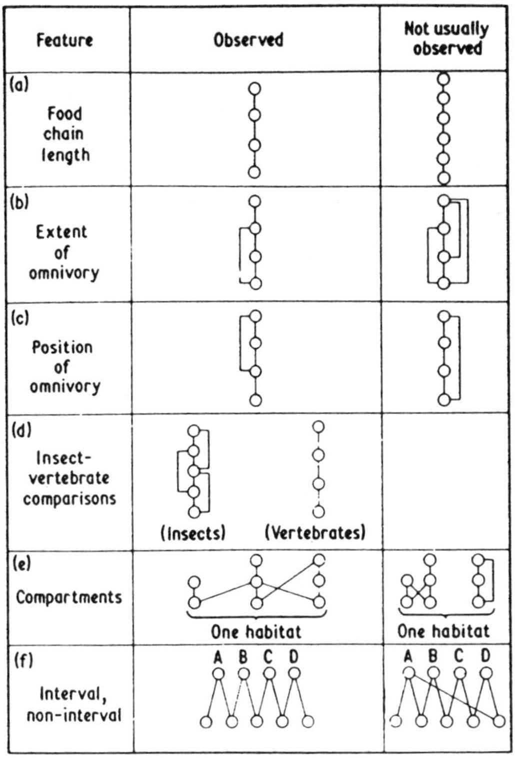

Figure 10.9. A catalog of features typically observed in published food webs. Features "not usually observed" often represent comparisons with null models. From Pimm (1982), with permission.

connectance. We conclude by summarizing recent controversies over the reality of these patterns and new directions in food web analysis.

Is There a Limit to the Number of Trophic Links in an Assemblage?

Considerations of the ecological pyramid of numbers (Elton 1927) and the inefficient transfer of energy from one trophic level to the next (Lindemann 1942) suggest that energetic constraints may limit the number of trophic levels in a web. Alternatively, food chain length may be limited by body size and design constraints on predators (Pimm 1982, 1984a). Optimal foraging principles also predict that species should forage low in the food web (Hastings and Conrad 1979), which would lead to short food chains. Finally, short food chains may be more stable than long ones and reflect dynamic constraints of the sort predicted by Gardner and Ashby (1970).

But a simpler (null) explanation is that there is no biological or mathematical significance to observed chain lengths and they simply follow the expected pattern for a set of randomly linked species. Before we can decide whether observed food chains—which typically have two or three links (Pimm et al. 1991)—are unusually short, they must be compared to an appropriate null model.

Pimm (1980a) constructed random food webs subject to some simple constraints. His webs retained predator and prey numbers, ensured that every predator consumed at least one prey species (and that each prey species had at least one predator), and did not allow for loops within the same trophic level. By retaining observed trophic levels, the null model may have incorporated some important structure it was trying to detect. This would cause the simulated webs to be more similar in appearance to the observed webs, and in that sense the test for food chain length was conservative.

For a set of 14 published webs, Pimm (1980a) found that observed chain lengths were typically shorter than expected. The patterns for any single web often could have arisen by chance, but the consistent result across the set of 14 webs was highly improbable. These tests also revealed that omnivory (feeding on more than one trophic level) was relatively uncommon and that when it did occur, it was usually between adjacent trophic levels.

These conclusions were limited to the data in hand; for example, observed levels of omnivory may be considerably higher in zooplankton food webs (Sprules and Bowerman 1988). Other sorts of data are needed to distinguish among the alternative mechanisms that have been proposed to account for short chain lengths (Pimm 1982), but these null model tests did suggest that chain lengths in published webs were unusually short.

Do Food Webs Exhibit Internal Structure?

Cohen (1978) noted an interesting property of predators at the same trophic level in a food web. If the predators are ordered on the basis of the prey species they consume, the overlaps in diet among the set of predators can sometimes be represented in a one-dimensional graph. These "interval food webs" correspond to a set of predators that partition prey species in a simple fashion. Cohen (1978) suggested that this nonrandom pattern indicated niche differentiation among the predators and that the major axis of ecological differentiation was one-dimensional.

Cohen (1978) tested for the presence of interval food webs with a set of six null models based on the randomization of the food web matrix. These models placed fixed or probabilistic constraints on either the row, column, or total sums of the food web matrix. Cohen's (1978) models were more "null" than Pimm's (1980a) because they allowed for loops and may even have included predators with no prey and prey with no predators. There were usually more observed interval food webs than expected by chance for all six of the models, perhaps providing support for simple models of niche overlap.

However, other null models of food webs do not give this same result. Yodzis (1982) tested for the presence of "cliques," a form of ecosystem compartmentalization that is similar to the interval graph. Each species pair in a clique has at least one prey species in common, and the dominant clique is one that contains no other clique. Cliques in a food web correspond roughly to trophic guilds, although they tend to contain more species than the typical guild.

Yodzis's (1981) null model for testing for cliques was more restrictive and complex than Cohen's (1978) models. Yodzis (1981) established the parameters n (the number of primary producer species), p (production per primary producer), and e (ecological efficiency of consumers). Beginning with the set of n primary producers, consumers were added sequentially to the community. Each consumer was assigned to a random set of producer species and removed a randomly chosen fraction of the remaining production, reminiscent of the mechanics of MacArthur's (1957) broken-stick model (see Chapter 3). This process was repeated for higher trophic levels until energetic constraints forbade the addition of more species. For each real web, constants were fitted so that the null web could plausibly be viewed as having been chosen at random from the universe of all possible webs with the parameters n, p, and e.

Compared to these null webs, real food webs had very few dominant cliques, even though other properties, such as predator/prey ratios and number of trophic links, were well fit by this model (Yodzis 1981). These constraints on the number of dominant cliques in turn seemed to account for the presence of interval graphs detected by Cohen (1978). Perhaps these elements of internal structure represent "small, functionally coevolved guilds or component communities," which Colwell (1979) suggested as the focus of study in community ecology. But neither Yodzis (1981) nor Cohen (1978) provided satisfying biological explanations for these units of organization that are inspired by graph theory.

What Is the Relationship Between Species Richness and Connectance?

Dynamical constraints (Gardner and Ashby 1970; Rejmánek and Starý 1979) suggest that connectance should decline with increasing species richness, per-

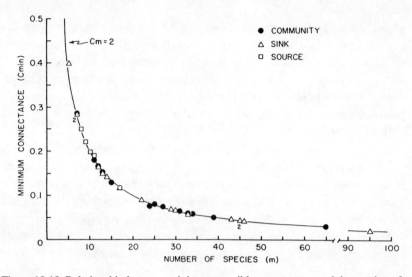

Figure 10.10. Relationship between minimum possible connectance and the number of species in a community. The curve represents the hyperbolic function $Cm = 2$. "Community webs" were defined as sets of organisms selected from a habitat without regard to their trophic relationships. "Sink webs" were constructed by selecting a set of predators and tracing the connections to their prey. "Source webs" were constructed by selecting a set of prey and tracing the connections to their predators. From Auerbach, M. J. Stability, probability, and the topology of food webs. In: *Ecological Communities: Conceptual Issues and the Evidence.* D. R. Strong, Jr., D. Simberloff, L. G. Abele, and A. B. Thistle (eds). Copyright © 1984 by Princeton University Press. Reprinted by permission of Princeton University Press.

haps in hyperbolic fashion if interaction strength is held constant (May 1972). The pattern is certainly common in published food webs (Rejmánek and Starý 1979; Pimm et al. 1991; but see Winemiller 1989). But connectance could also decrease if each species fed upon the same number of prey species, regardless of web size (Pimm 1980b), which seems biologically reasonable.

Auerbach (1984) noted that for a web of m species, a minimum connectance of $2/m$ is necessary to maintain at least one link for each species in the web; this constraint by itself can generate a hyperbolic relationship between species richness and connectance. A similar bound on maximum connectance arises if predator identities are maintained and looping is forbidden, as in Pimm's (1980a) null models. Published food webs nicely fit these constraining curves (Figure 10.10).

Kenny and Loehle (1991) calculated the expected connectance for a web with S species and k links. The only constraint on this expectation was that all

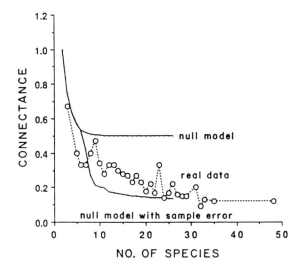

Figure 10.11. Relationship between connectance and species number for several aquatic ecosystems. The null model is the expected connectance for a randomly connected web of a given number of species. The null model with sampling error assumes that links in the observed web are sampled in proportion to their relative strength. From Kenny and Loehle (1991), with permission.

species had at least one link; loops were not disallowed. Connectance decreased with increasing S in this model, but the observed connectances in Briand and Cohen's (1987) compiled webs were too low to be fit by this model.

However, this comparison is valid only if the entire web is known. In reality, the published webs represent a small and probably nonrandom subset of the true web structure. Thus, a null model for connectance needs to incorporate not only the observed numbers of species and links, but also some element of sampling error. Such a model is difficult to formulate, because the links that are missing from an observed food web are not random. Missing food web links do not simply represent rare species, either, because most top predators are rare, but they are usually well represented in food webs.

Instead, Kenny and Loehle (1991) argued that the "missing links" in published food webs probably represent very small energy transfers, corresponding to prey items that rarely occur in a predator's diet. Kenny and Loehle (1991) explored the use of energy transfer in food web sampling by analyzing food webs for several large aquatic systems that had been compiled by Robert E. Ulanowicz specifically for the purpose of quantifying energy transfers. The plot of ranked link sizes (biomass or carbon transfer) was well fit by a geometric series, in which each link is some constant fraction of the size of link before it. This fraction ranged from 0.75 to 0.95 in the observed data sets. Randomly sampling from this distribution yielded an expected connectance for a web that has been constructed with sampling error. The connectance in these truncated webs provided a good match to the observed values (Figure 10.11). This null model effectively accounted for observed connectance by assuming only that the underlying linkage strengths followed a log series and that observed web links were randomly sampled in proportion to link strength. The quantitative linkages were important only in determining sampling biases, not in influencing web stability. These findings suggest that linkage strength is a key to understanding both the biological (Paine 1992) and the statistical (Ulanowicz and Wolff 1991) properties of food webs.

Are Food Webs Real?

In a special feature section of *Ecology,* Paine (1988) provocatively questioned the biological reality of published food webs. He argued that most webs have been so overly simplified or "sanitized" that it is premature to make any claims about general food web patterns in nature. He also emphasized that only a direct study of interaction strengths (Paine 1992) will reveal the forces that organize assemblages, and that qualitative depictions of interaction sign (+ or –) will not uncover critical linkages such as keystone species (Paine 1966).

Perhaps in response to his criticisms, several authors have recently published very detailed food webs and compared the patterns in those webs to the generalizations derived from previous web catalogs. The new webs are complex and do not conform to previous generalizations. They provide strong support for Paine's (1988) contention that published catalogs are inadequate and do not represent true web structure.

For example, Polis (1991) described a complex, species-rich food web for a desert community. This web included 174 species of vascular plants, 138 species of vertebrates, over 55 species of arachnids, and an estimated 2,000–3,000 species of other invertebrates and microorganisms. Even using a highly simplified subweb, Polis (1991) found an average of seven trophic links (Figure 10.12), compared to the "expected" two or three links in published webs. Although omnivory is claimed to be uncommon in food webs, 78% of the species in the desert web were omnivorous. Polis (1991) argued that lumping and deletion of biological species, inadequate dietary information, and a failure to recognize the presence of age structure and looping compromise the quality of most published webs.

Martinez (1991) found similar patterns for a well-resolved aquatic food web. For the 93 trophic taxa (most of which were resolved to the species or genus

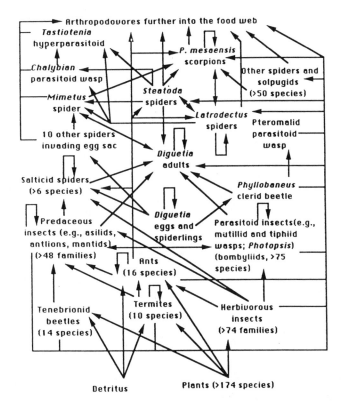

Figure 10.12. Trophic interactions of a few predaceous arthropods in a desert food web. This subweb represents a small fraction of all interactions. An arrow returning to a taxon indicates cannibalism. Reprinted by permission of the publisher from Polis, G. A. 1991. Complex trophic interactions in deserts: an empirical critique of food-web theory. *American Naturalist* 138:123–155. Copyright © 1991 by The University of Chicago.

level) of a Wisconsin lake, there were an average of more than 10 trophic links, with more links per species and more species at higher trophic levels than in other published webs. Other species-rich assemblages that show "atypical" trophic links and high levels of omnivory include estuarine (Hall and Raffaelli 1991) and tropical (Winemiller 1989) aquatic food webs. Even the celebrated hyperbola of connectance and species richness may not be valid (Martinez 1992). For at least one large food web (Winemiller 1989), connectance actually increased with increasing species richness (Figure 10.13).

Proponents of food web theory have acknowledged the limitations of published food webs (e.g., Pimm and Kitching 1988; Pimm et al. 1991; Schoenly

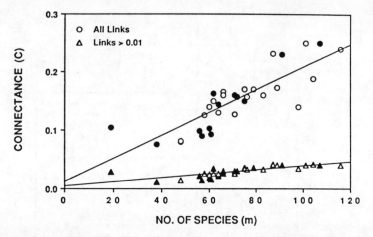

Figure 10.13. An increasing relationship between connectance and species richness for 34 food webs derived from four tropical fish study systems. Circles represent all links, and triangles represent strong links. Solid symbols are top-predator sink webs. Reprinted by permission of the publishers from Winemiller, K. O. 1989. Must connectance decrease with species richness? *American Naturalist* 134:960–968. Copyright © 1989 by The University of Chicago.

and Cohen 1991) but have suggested that the revealed patterns still tell us something important about how communities are assembled. One strategy to deal with poorly resolved food webs is to aggregate the data and then examine scale-invariant properties of the resulting webs (Sugihara et al. 1989; Havens 1992). Some food web properties do not change with aggregation, suggesting they are not sampling artifacts. However, because links are not randomly deleted from food webs initially, this aggregation does not remove biases that are inherent in simplified food webs (Kenny and Loehle 1991). On closer analysis, many of the web statistics do seem to be sensitive to aggregation (Martinez 1993a, b).

We think the arguments over scale-invariant properties of food webs are uninformative without comparison with a null model. Other constant metrics in community ecology, such as body size ratios of 1.3 (Chapter 6) and species-area slopes of 0.26 (Chapter 8), frequently appear but in no way imply a single, underlying cause. On the other hand, the fact that many web metrics are correlated with the number of species does not mean that the patterns are purely sampling phenomena. Only by comparison with a null model can we decide if a certain web metric is unusually large or small.

Along these lines, it will be especially interesting to compare food web properties of these new species-rich webs with null models. It might still be the case that the chain lengths in Polis's (1991) and Martinez's (1991) webs are unusually short, given the number of species they contain. Simplification of a food web is not necessarily a bad thing, particularly if the reduced web is the one that contains the strong linkages. But this aggregation can only be made when all links are thoroughly investigated and their strengths quantified. Perhaps when this is done, the resulting webs will appear like the ones in the current literature catalog, and we will have come full circle on the issue. But in the meantime, we agree with Paine (1988) that it is premature to say much about the underlying patterns of food web structure until we develop a large catalog of more detailed webs. It may be difficult to apply null models to such webs, however, because of constraints on computing time.

In summary, null models have had a long history in food web analysis and have revealed important nonrandom patterns. But, as Sale (1984) has pointed out, our vertebrate sensory systems predispose us to organize and simplify patterns in nature. It may turn out that the existing catalog of food webs is more a reflection of past perceptions of nature than an indicator of true structure.

RECOMMENDATIONS

In contrast to other areas of community ecology, null models have figured prominently in food web analysis, both in formulation of theoretical expectations and in testing existing food web patterns. Many food web patterns cannot be explained simply by the number of species or links in the collection. However, recent critical reviews suggest that the set of existing food web data is empirically flawed; null model tests are needed for new species-rich webs that more accurately reflect the links and interaction strengths in nature. When such data are available, the null models of Pimm (1980a) and Kenny and Loehle (1991) are appropriate for detecting pattern.

EPILOGUE

If your head is wax don't walk in the sun.
—Benjamin Franklin, *Poor Richard's Almanac*

In the preceding chapters, we discussed the history and application of null models in ecology. It should be clear to readers that we view null models as an integral part of the hypothetico-deductive method in science (Platt 1964, Connor and Simberloff 1986) and believe they have had a positive impact on community ecology. Nevertheless, null models have their limitations and can be subject to much abuse if certain aspects of quality control are neglected. Although it is more difficult to create than to criticize, our objective in this Epilogue is to point out some problems in the construction of null models that have been somewhat neglected in the literature.

CONSTRUCTION OF SOURCE POOLS

Although considerable attention has been focused on randomization algorithms in null models (see Chapter 7), the construction of species source pools and the underlying quality of the data have received less scrutiny. The species source pool for an island should include all species that have a *reasonable* probability of occurring on that island. Usually, the more isolated the island or archipelago, the fewer of its resident species are shared with other islands or mainland areas. If the fauna has undergone in situ speciation or differentiation, it may be even more difficult to designate an appropriate source pool. For reasons of convenience and tradition, source pools are often taken as the collection of all species in the archipelago (e.g., Strong et al. 1979), even when there is clearly the potential for colonization from adjacent mainland areas (e.g., Gotelli and Abele 1982). However, the source pool for two islands in an archipelago will rarely be identical, and source pool designation can have a strong effect on the outcome of null model tests (Graves and Gotelli 1983; Schoener 1988a).

A good example of variation in source pool construction can be found in a controversial series of analyses of the avifauna of the four Tres Marias Islands, which lie about 100 km off the Pacific coast of Mexico. The initial paper in the series was Grant's (1966) investigation of character displacement in ecologically similar species of Tres Marias birds. To determine whether bill sizes of island birds were unusual, Grant (1966:452) compared them with a pool of species from "an equivalent part of the mainland (same area and range of altitude, similar habitats, etc.)." He concluded that character displacement did occur among congeneric species on the islands.

In a study of species/genus (S/G) ratios of birds of the same islands, Simberloff (1970) included all species that occurred within 300 miles, excluding Baja California, in the source pool. A decade later, Strong et al. (1979:898) included species in the Tres Marias source pool "with habitat requirements and distributions such that they would likely inhabit the islands, and exclude species with obviously special habitat requirements that are not satisfied by the islands," that occurred in Nayarit and adjacent states. Grant and Abbott (1980) criticized Simberloff's (1970) source pool as being so large that nonrandom colonization might not have been detected had it occurred. Hendrickson (1981) went on to suggest a source pool of intermediate size, restricted to species from the nine avian families that occur on the islands that are resident at low elevations (900 m and below) in the states of Nayarit, Sinaloa, and Jalisco.

Simberloff (1984) followed these suggestions and reanalyzed the expected number of congeners on the islands using three mainland source pools, those of Grant (1966), Simberloff (1970), and Hendrickson (1981). He found that island generic compositions did not differ from random expectations regardless of the source pool used in calculations. Testing multiple source pools was an important innovation in null model analyses. Although the results did not differ in this case, Schoener (1988a) and, to a lesser extent, Graves and Gotelli (1983) both found that null model results were sensitive to source pool designation.

The Tres Marias source pools discussed above could be improved in several ways. The four islands parallel the coastline and span some 80 km. They vary considerably in elevation, area, and habitat (Nelson 1899). Yet, all the previous studies (Grant 1966: Simberloff 1970; Strong et al. 1979; Grant and Abbott 1980; Hendrickson 1981; Simberloff 1984) treated the four islands as a unit with identical source pools. If the distance between the source pool and the islands affects colonization probabilities (MacArthur and Wilson 1967), then source pools for widely separated islands are not identical. This is especially true for species-rich areas where many terminal range boundaries occur on the adjacent mainland.

In other words, species that occur within an arbitrary distance of one island [300 miles in Simberloff's (1970) analysis] may be outside that limit for another island in the same archipelago. This problem is magnified for large archipelagoes that are colonized from several mainland regions (e.g., the West Indies). Biogeographers continue to rely heavily on faunal lists from irregularly shaped geopolitical units. These data are easy to gather, but political states are rarely comparable on the basis of area and shape. Standardization of source pool areas can be achieved in several ways. We recommend that the source pool area for an island be delimited by a circle with a standardized radius (Graves and Gotelli 1983; see cover).

Habitat availability is of primary importance in determining what subset of the mainland avifauna could successfully colonize and persist on an island. The difference between the "total" source pool and the "habitat" pool can be substantial. The "total" pool consists of all mainland and island species within a geometrically standardized area, while the "habitat" pool (a subset of the total pool) includes only those species that breed in the spectrum of habitats present on the island.

We assume that source pool species that occur only in habitats not found on an island would not be expected to occur on it. This is not the same as saying that if a species does not occur on the island, one wouldn't expect it to. There are certain species that for all intents and purposes, have an infinitesimal probability of colonizing an island lacking its preferred habitat. For example, a habitat specialist of timberline coniferous forests of the Sierra Madre is unlikely to colonize the relatively low and dry Tres Marias Islands.

Both the total pool and the habitat pool are viewed from the frame of reference of the island, but the numerical difference between them for a habitat-depauperate island adjacent to a diverse mainland may be severalfold (Graves and Gotelli 1983). This technique allows one to standardize island-mainland comparisons for islands that differ greatly in habitat diversity. The determination of source pool status must be made on a case-by-case basis for each species and each island. As the type, area, and quality of habitats varies among islands, so does the potential source pool of colonizing species. Therefore, unless it can be demonstrated that the habitat characteristics of two islands are indistinguishable, their source pools must be independently derived. Although Grant (1966) and others acknowledged the role of habitat by restricting source pools to species from certain elevational zones, they still considered the source pools of all four islands to be identical.

What is the appropriate size of the Tres Marias source pool for null model tests of S/G ratios and size ratios? The radius of a circular source pool centered on the island should be large enough to incorporate a substantial enough area of the mainland to support the full range of habitats found on the focal island. For land-bridge islands within 100 km of the mainland, we have found that a source pool of radius 300 km is generally sufficient to achieve this objective (Graves and Gotelli 1983; Gotelli and Graves 1990).

For the Tres Marias avifauna, source pool radii of 400 or more kilometers include a larger set of potentially colonizing species, but also include species with little chance of colonizing a distant island because of small populations and restricted geographic ranges (Grant and Abbott 1980; Graves and Gotelli 1983). In any event, source pools cannot be adequately designated without detailed knowledge of the habitat characteristics of the island and mainland as well as the ecological requirements of source pool species. The effect of source pool size on null model results should be checked whenever possible (see Simberloff 1984). For instance, the inclusion of additional congeners or guild members from an enlarged source pool may change the results of a null model analysis from significant to nonsignificant, or vice versa.

Finally, we recommend that source pool methodology be discussed in detail in null model papers. If the entire species pool cannot be published in an appendix, then it should be submitted to a data bank for future reference. Situations such as the conflict over unpublished data for the Bismarck Archipelago (Connor and Simberloff 1979) and the Tres Marias Islands (Hendrickson 1981) should not be permitted by editorial boards of technical journals. In both of these cases, the cited authors were unable to obtain species lists from the authors of earlier publications (Diamond 1975, and Strong et al. 1979, respectively).

SPECIES TAXONOMY

Taxonomy has a considerable, but largely ignored, importance in null models. Even for relatively well-known groups of plants and animals, differences in taxonomy can affect the number of species in island biotas and source pools. For higher vertebrates, the recent surge toward usage of the "phylogenetic" species concept (Cracraft 1983), as opposed to the more widely recognized "biological" species concept (Mayr 1963), has nearly doubled the number of recognized "species" in certain avian genera (cf. Morony et. al. 1975; Sibley and Monroe 1990). The development of source pools for null models of island colonization has been most successful for vertebrate communities, principally birds; invertebrates and plants of islands and mainland areas are more poorly known. Cryptic or undescribed species may also be common in certain taxonomic groups, especially in tropical regions, thwarting source pool construction.

Null models are usually based on data compiled from papers, books, and technical reports, while fewer are based on raw unpublished data. We encourage ecologists to collaborate with systematists and to deposit voucher specimens in a recognized systematic collection in order to ensure quality control and repeatability, should a subsequent analysis be desired. At the very least, the taxonomic authority or reference for species lists should be stated in the methods section of studies using null models.

SEXUAL DIMORPHISM AND GEOGRAPHIC VARIATION

Sexual dimorphism in body mass is often ignored in null models of character displacement. For example, Schoener (1984), in a worldwide study of size differences among sympatric bird-eating hawks, averaged the size of males and females to produce a single value for each species. Size averaging was performed to facilitate modeling, but it hardly duplicated the distribution of body sizes present in communities of raptorial birds. The wings of females of some *Accipiter* hawk species are nearly a quarter longer than those of males (Brown and Amadon 1968). Thus, artificial female/male averages often represent a phenotype that does not occur in nature. A more biologically realistic approach is to treat sexually dimorphic species as two "morphospecies" in null models (e.g., Dayan, Simberloff et al. 1989).

Geographic variation in size, independent of sexual dimorphism, has also been neglected in null model studies. Populations of vertebrates often differ significantly among islands, reflecting genetic adaptations to local environments. Randomization algorithms should sample distinctive phenotypes that occur on islands within the source pool area (e.g., Losos 1990). In most cases, this task has been accomplished by choosing among mean values of morphological traits for island populations (see Strong et al. 1979; Case and Sidell 1983).

Accounting for geographic variation in size of mainland source pool species is more difficult. Among mainland bird species, whose populations are more or less continuously distributed, morphological variation is usually clinal (James 1982). "Average" phenotypes of morphological characters may differ significantly between source pool areas of distantly separated land-bridge islands. In some cases, significant patterns of geographic variation may occur *within* a circumscribed source pool. If morphological clines are steep, the "average" bill size for the source pool would most likely characterize only a fraction of the source pool populations. In other words, use of source pool averages for highly variable species is equivalent to reducing the size of the source pool.

If care is not taken, size averaging procedures can yield rather uninterpretable results. For instance, in calculating the sizes of geographically variable species of sympatric bird-eating hawks, Schoener (1984) first identified the two subspecies with the largest geographic ranges in Brown and Amadon (1968). He then averaged the mean wing length of males and females to produce a subspecies average for each of the two subspecies. Lastly, the subspecies averages were averaged to produce a single value for each species. Use of this measure of body size was further complicated by Brown and Amadon's (1968) original size data, which often consisted only of the range of wing measurements for each sex of each subspecies (no sample size or mean). Additionally, the number of subspecies (and the morphological variation among subspecies) of hawks varies greatly among species. The degree of sexual dimorphism also varies geographically, as does size within subspecies. Many of the sympatric bird-eating hawks occur in the tropics, where the size of geographic ranges is smallest and morphological variation from subspecies to subspecies is often pronounced. Yet, for several species with large latitudinal ranges, Schoener's (1984) species-specific average was calculated from the size of temperate zone subspecies.

As we explained earlier, the resulting "average" may bear little resemblance to the population in a particular raptor community. Schoener (1984) has acknowledged some of these criticisms, but they make it difficult to interpret the significance of his results (Wiens 1989). Similar criticisms have been directed toward other studies of character displacement (see Grant and Abbott 1980; Hendrickson 1981).

To combat "averaging" bias, we recommend that null ratios be computed by sampling from normal distributions of the morphological characters bracketed by the observed extremes for source pool populations. Sexual differences can be accommodated by sampling each sex separately. Utilizing a normal distribution of body sizes sampled from a known geographic locale preserves the geographic variation in body size that is inherent in mainland faunas.

DATA QUALITY

Large-scale biogeography is largely an armchair pursuit; the vast majority of studies are derived from data originally published for other purposes. An alarming number of studies are based on compilations and catalogs, without direct reference to original sources or specimens. Notwithstanding the emphasis placed on Monte Carlo and statistical methods in most recent discussions, data quality remains the most important component of null models. It is the data, after all, that are of primary interest, not the algorithm. In other words, a null model is only as good as the data it purports to evaluate. Unfortunately, there seem to be few quality control standards in the discipline.

We foresee an ominous trend in large-scale biogeography due to newly available electronic databases (e.g., US and Canadian Wildlife Service Breeding Bird Survey), compilations (e.g., Dunning 1993), checklists (e.g., Howard and Moore 1984; Sibley and Monroe 1990), and atlases (e.g., Root 1988c). Our concern lies not with the proffered convenience of new reference works, but with the fact that biologists who utilize these as their primary sources are at least twice removed from the raw data—some bird mass data in Dunning's (1993) handbook are thrice removed from the primary source! The methods, assumptions, and caveats expressed by the original authors, as well as an accounting of measurement and transcriptional error, are rarely presented in secondary data sources. Many users who cite compilations as their primary data never bother looking up the original sources.

We expect the naive use of biogeographic data by spreadsheet wizards to accelerate with the increasing availability of electronic data sets. We suggest, however, that data compilations should be used in the same fashion as a telephone directory, as a guide to the literature rather than a substitute for it. If ecologists lack personal experience with the species, habitats, and islands they wish to study, they should seek out expert collaborators for null model analyses! Poorly prepared and documented null models invite reanalysis and rebuttal. At least part of the contentious legacy of null model analysis in ecology is due to a cycle of weak publication and vitriolic rebuttal, *post hoc ergo propter hoc.*

This has been especially true in avian ecology. We believe that currently available data are probably insufficient to adequately test a number of famous biogeographic hypotheses, including the "taxon cycle" of West Indian birds (Ricklefs and Cox 1978), the existence of Pleistocene "refuges" for South American birds (Haffer 1974), and competitively driven extinctions of the Hawaiian avifauna (Moulton and Pimm 1983). We recommend that investigators routinely discuss and defend the sufficiency of their data for hypothesis testing.

HUMAN-CAUSED EXTINCTIONS ON ISLANDS

The classic works of island biogeography (e.g., MacArthur and Wilson 1967) were predicated on observations of "natural" communities—that is, islands with intact biotas. It has become abundantly clear in the past two decades that extant island biotas are not what they seem. Human-caused extinctions, commencing with the arrival of Polynesians and continuing through the present, have been reported on every large oceanic island in the Pacific intensively studied by paleontologists and archaeologists (e.g., Olson and James 1982; Steadman 1989). The discovery of numerous extinct subfossil vertebrates in cultural contexts in the West Indies, Mediterranean islands, and Madagascar suggests that this generalization can be extended to all islands reached by Stone Age humans (Martin and Klein 1984). Extinctions were caused by direct predation by humans, habitat destruction, and the introduction of other predators, such as rats, dogs, and pigs (Case et al. 1992).

The avifaunas of some isolated archipelagoes have suffered catastrophic declines of more than 50% in species number (e.g., the Hawaiian Islands and New Zealand). Prehistoric extinctions have caused puzzling distributional gaps in certain groups of birds (e.g., pigeons, parrots, flightless rails) that in light of paleontological research are seen as artificial (Steadman 1989). Most volant species of birds currently restricted to a single Pacific island had more extensive prehistoric distributions. Other species of animals and plants are likely to have been influenced by this wave of destruction as well.

Do these discoveries invalidate the empirical underpinnings of classical island biogeography? The answer, of course, depends upon the taxon and the island. However, enough paleontological evidence for birds, mammals, and reptiles has been gathered to cast doubt on some venerable biogeographic icons, such as species-area and immigration-extinction relationships for those taxonomic groups. Some contemporary studies (e.g., Juvik and Austring 1979) have been rendered obsolete by recent paleontological studies (James and Olson 1991; Olson and James 1991). The emerging paleontological evidence must be eventually reckoned with in island biogeographic and null model studies.

CETERIS PARIBUS

The *ceteris paribus* ("all other things being equal") clause of null models deserves strong scrutiny. Other things in island biogeography are never equal. The biotic characteristics of islands are seldom equal (habitat, species composition, etc.), human influence is rarely equal (e.g., extinctions, alteration of habitats), and physical factors are never equal (size, shape, elevation, rainfall, etc.). These differences in islands need to be incorporated into statistical tests for distribution patterns (Schoener and Adler 1991). For example, mutually exclusive distributions of island bird species ("checkerboards") are often interpreted as the result of interspecific competition (Diamond 1975). Of the several *ceteris paribus* assumptions in such an analysis, the two most important are that adequate amounts of the preferred habitats for each species occur on every island, and that historical constraints on dispersal or extinction have not caused the patterns. Yet, the implications of such assumptions are rarely discussed in detail.

QUESTIONS IN NULL MODEL STUDIES

We suggest that ecologists ask themselves the following questions before submitting the results of a null model study for publication:

1. *Were the species data (measurements, geographic distributions, habitat, etc.) of high quality and derived from personal field work, specimens, or original literature sources?*
2. *Were source pools constructed with a standardized methodology, taking into account the spatial distribution of habitats and resources?*
3. *Was the null model used appropriate for the question at hand, and was it thoroughly described in the methods so that others could use it?*
4. *Was the computer implementation of the null model checked for programming errors and was it tested with idealized data sets?*
5. *Were the* ceteris paribus *assumptions defended and discussed?*
6. *Will source pool and island species data be published or deposited in a databank for public access?*

Although some of these questions are unique to null model studies, most are appropriate for any biogeographic study that is conducted at large spatial scales and relies on nonexperimental data. If the answer to these questions is not an unqualified "yes," the author should reconsider whether the study is worthy of publication. We encourage authors, reviewers, and editors to maintain quality control by considering these requirements.

THE FUTURE

The lack of commercially available computer software has hindered the growth of null modeling in ecology. The null model approach to ecological problems has thus been the domain of computer-literate ecologists. Few ecologists are skilled enough to write complex algorithms, and even fewer computer programmers are knowledgeable in ecology. One needs to be accomplished in both disciplines in order to construct a useful null model. For this reason alone, we encourage collaborative efforts between computer-literate ecologists and data-oriented systematists.

Most biologists who currently use null models in ecology also write and understand the behavior of their own computer programs. This situation will change in the next decade as null model software tailored for ecological problems is developed and distributed. We see both benefits and disadvantages in this advancement. Wide public access to null model software will do for null models what the introduction of statistical software did for the rest of ecology—it will stimulate the routine application of null model analyses to nonexperimental ecological data and allow more kinds of biologists to use null models than have done so in the past. But it will also spawn a surfeit of studies in which the algorithms are inappropriately and indiscriminately applied to data. Be that as it may, the worm has turned. We hope the suggestions in this Epilogue and the recommendations at the end of each chapter will at least serve to increase the quality of future null model studies.

LITERATURE CITED

Abbott, I. 1977. Species richness, turnover, and equilibrium in insular floras near Perth, Western Australia. Australian Journal of Botany 25:193–208.

Abbott, I. 1983. The meaning of z in species/area regressions and the study of species turnover in island biogeography. Oikos 41:385–390.

Abbott, I., K. Abbott and P. R. Grant. 1977. Comparative ecology of Galápagos Ground Finches (*Geospiza* Gould): evaluation of the importance of floristic diversity and interspecific competition. Ecological Monographs 47:151–184.

Abele, L. G. 1974. Species diversity of decapod crustaceans in marine habitats. Ecology 55:156–161.

Abele, L. G. 1976. Comparative species richness in fluctuating and constant environments: coral-associated decapod crustaceans. Science 192:461–463.

Abele, L. G. 1984. Biogeography, colonization and experimental community structure of coral-associated crustaceans. pp. 123–137 in: *Ecological Communities: Conceptual Issues and the Evidence*. D. R. Strong, Jr., D. Simberloff, L. G. Abele and A. B. Thistle (eds). Princeton University Press, Princeton.

Abele, L. G. and W. K. Patton. 1976. The size of coral heads and the community biology of associated decapod crustaceans. Journal of Biogeography 3:35–47.

Abele, L. G. and K. Walters. 1979a. Marine benthic diversity: a critique and alternative explanation. Journal of Biogeography 6:115–126.

Abele, L. G. and K. Walters. 1979b. The stability-time hypothesis: reevaluation of the data. American Naturalist 114:559–568.

Abrams, P. 1975. Limiting similarity and the form of the competition coefficient. Theoretical Population Biology 8:356-375.

Abrams, P. A. 1981. Comparing randomly constructed and real communities: a comment. American Naturalist 118:776–782.

Abrams, P. A. 1986. Character displacement and niche shift analyzed using consumer-resource models of competition. Theoretical Population Biology 29:107–160.

Abramsky, Z., M. A. Bowers and M. Rosenzweig. 1986. Detecting interspecific competition in the field: testing the regression method. Oikos 47:199–204.

Absalao, R. S. 1991. Environmental discrimination among soft-bottom mollusc associations off Lagoa Dos Patos, South Brazil. Estuarine and Coastal Shelf Science 32:71–86.

Adams, J. E. and E. D. McCune. 1979. Application of the generalized jack-knife to Shannon's measure of information used as an index of diversity. pp. 117–131 in: *Ecological Diversity in Theory and Practice*. J. F. Grassle, G. P. Patil, W. Smith and C. Taillie (eds). International Cooperative Publishing House, Fairland, Maryland.

Alatalo, R. V. 1982. Bird species distributions in the Galápagos and other archipelagoes: competition or chance? Ecology 63:881–887.

Anderson, G. R. V., A. H. Ehrlich, P. R. Ehrlich, J. D. Roughgarden, B. C. Russell and F. H. Talbot. 1981. The community structure of coral reef fishes. American Naturalist 117:476–495.

Anderson, R. C. and S. Schelfhout. 1980. Phenological patterns among tallgrass prairie plants and their implications for pollinator competition. American Midland Naturalist 104:253–263.

Anderson, S. 1984. Areography of North American fishes, amphibians, and reptiles. American Museum Novitates 2 2802:1–16.

Anderson, S. 1985. The theory of range-size (rs) distributions. American Museum Novitates 2 2833:1–13.

Anderson, S. and L. F. Marcus. 1993. Effect of quadrat size on measurements of species density. Journal of Biogeography 20:421–428.

Andrewartha, H. G. and L. C. Birch. 1954. *The Distribution and Abundance of Animals*. University of Chicago Press, Chicago.

Antia, D. D. J. 1977. A comparison of diversity and trophic nuclei of live and dead molluscan faunas from the Essex Chenier Plain, England. Paleobiology 3:404–414.

Archie, J. W. 1989. A randomization test for phylogenetic information in systematic data. Systematic Zoology 38:239–252.

Arita, H. T. 1993. Tests for morphological competitive displacement: a reassessment of parameters. Ecology 74:627–630.

Armbruster, W. S. 1986. Reproductive interactions between sympatric *Dalechampia* species: are natural assemblages "random" or organized? Ecology 67:522–533.

Armbruster, W. S., M. E. Edwards and E. M. Debevec. 1994. Floral character displacement generates assemblage structure of western Australian triggerplants (*Stylidium*). Ecology 75:315–329.

Armstrong, R. A. and R. McGhee. 1980. Competitive exclusion. American Naturalist 115:151–170.

Aronson, R. B. and T. J. Givnish. 1983. Optimal central-place foragers: a comparison with null hypotheses. Ecology 64:395–399.

Arrhenius, O. 1921. Species and area. Journal of Ecology 9:95–99.

Ashmole, N. P. 1968. Body size, prey size, and ecological segregation in five sympatric tropical terns (Aves: Laridae). Systematic Zoology 17:292–304.

Ashton, P. S., T. J. Givnish and S. Appanah. 1988. Staggered flowering in the Dipterocarpaceae: new insights into floral induction and the evolution of mast fruiting in the aseasonal tropics. American Naturalist 132:44–66.

Atmar, W. and B. D. Patterson. 1993. On the measure of order and disorder in the distribution of species on archipelagos. Oecologia 96:373–382.

Auclaire, A. N. and F. G. Goff. 1971. Diversity relations of upland forests in the western Great Lakes area. American Naturalist 105:499–528.

Auerbach, M. J. 1979. Some real communities are unstable. Nature 279:821.

Auerbach, M. J. 1984. Stability, probability, and the topology of food webs. pp. 413–438 in: *Ecological Communities: Conceptual Issues and the Evidence*. D. R.

Strong Jr., D. Simberloff, L. G. Abele and A. B. Thistle (eds). Princeton University Press, Princeton.

Augsburger, C. K. 1980. Mass-flowering of a tropical shrub (*Hybanthus prunifolius*): influence on pollinator attraction and movement. Evolution 34:474–488.

Augsburger, C. K. 1981. Reproductive synchrony of a tropical shrub: experimental studies on the effects of pollinators and seed predators on *Hybanthus prunifolius* (Violaceae). Ecology 62:775–788.

Bagenal, T. B. 1951. A note on the papers of Elton and Williams on the generic relations of species in small ecological communities. Journal of Animal Ecology 20:242–245.

Barangé, M. and B. Campos. 1991. Models of species abundance: a critique of and an alternative to the dynamics model. Marine Ecology Progress Series 69:293–298.

Baroni-Urbani, C. and M. W. Buser. 1976. Similarity of binary data. Systematic Zoology 25:251–259.

Barton, D. E. and F. N. David. 1956. Some notes on ordered random intervals. Journal of the Royal Statistical Society B 18:79–94.

Barton, D. E. and F. N. David. 1959. The dispersion of a number of species. Journal of the Royal Statistical Society B 21:190–194.

Berger, J. A. 1990. Macrofauna recolonization of subtidal sediments. Experimental studies on defaunated sediment contaminated with crude oil in two Norwegian fjords with unequal eutrophication status. I. Community responses. Marine Ecology Progress Series 66:103–115.

Bertness, M. D. and S. D. Hacker. 1994. Physical stress and positive associations among marsh plants. American Naturalist 144:363–372.

Beukema, J. J. 1991. Changes in composition of bottom fauna of a tidal-flat area during a period of eutrophication. Marine Biology 111:293–301.

Beven, S., E. F. Connor and K. Beven. 1984. Avian biogeography in the Amazon basin and the biological model of diversification. Journal of Biogeography 11:383–399.

Biehl, C. C. and W. J. Matthews. 1984. Small fish community structure in Ozark streams: improvements in the statistical analysis of presence-absence data. American Midland Naturalist 11:371–382.

Bird, R. D. 1930. Biotic communities of the aspen parkland of central Canada. Ecology 11:356–442.

Blackburn, T. M., P. H. Harvey and M. D. Pagel. 1990. Species number, population density and body size relationships in natural communities. Journal of Animal Ecology 59:335–345.

Blake, J. G. and J. R. Karr. 1987. Breeding birds of isolated woodlots: area and habitat relationships. Ecology 68:1724–1734.

Blouin, M. S. and E. F. Connor. 1985. Is there a best shape for nature reserves? Biological Conservation 32:277–288.

Bock, C. E. and R. E. Ricklefs. 1983. Range size and local abundance of some North American songbirds: a positive correlation. American Naturalist 122:295–299.

Boecklen, W. J. 1986. Effects of habitat heterogeneity on the species-area relationships of forest birds. Journal of Biogeography 13:59–68.

Boecklen, W. J. and N. J. Gotelli. 1984. Island biogeographic theory and conservation practice: species-area or specious-area relationships? Biological Conservation 29:63–80.

Boecklen, W. J. and C. NeSmith. 1985. Hutchinsonian ratios and log-normal distributions. Evolution 39:695–698.

Boecklen, W. J. and J. Nocedal. 1991. Are species trajectories bounded or not? Journal of Biogeography 18:647–652.

Boecklen, W. J. and P. W. Price. 1991. Nonequilibrial community structure of sawflies on arroyo willow. Oecologia 85:483–491.

Boecklen, W. J. and D. Simberloff. 1986. Area-based extinction models in conservation. pp. 247–276 in: *Dynamics of Extinction.* D. K. Elliott (ed). John Wiley & Sons, New York.

Bolger, D. T., A. C. Alberts and M. E. Soulé. 1991. Occurrence patterns of bird species in habitat fragments: sampling, extinction, and nested species subsets. American Naturalist 137:155–166.

Bookstein, F. L. 1984. A statistical method for biological shape comparisons. Journal of Theoretical Biology 107:475–520.

Bossert, W. H. 1963. Simulation of character displacement. Ph. D. dissertation, Harvard University.

Bossert, W. H. 1968. Project TACT. Memorandum 85. Department of Applied Mathematics, Harvard University.

Boswell, M. T. and G. P. Patil. 1971. Chance mechanisms generating the logarithmic series distribution used in the analysis of number of species and individuals. pp. 99–130 in: *Statistical Ecology, Volume 3.* G. P. Patil, E. C. Pielou and W. E. Waters (eds). Pennsylvania State University Press, University Park.

Bowers, M. A. 1988. Relationships between local distribution and geographic range of desert heteromyid rodents. Oikos 53:303–308.

Bowers, M. A. and J. H. Brown. 1982. Body size and coexistence in desert rodents: chance or community structure? Ecology 63:391–400.

Bowman, R. I. 1961. Morphological differentiation and adaptation in the Galápagos finches. University of California Publications in Zoology 58:1–302.

Bradley, R. A. and D. W. Bradley. 1985. Do non-random patterns of species in niche space imply competition? Oikos 45:443–445.

Brady, R. H. 1979. Natural selection and the criteria by which a theory is judged. Systematic Zoology 28:600–621.

Brandl, R. and W. Topp. 1985. Size structure of *Pterostichus* spp. (Carabidae): aspects of competition. Oikos 44:234–238.

Briand, F. 1983. Environmental control of food web structure. Ecology 64:253–263.

Briand, F. and J. E. Cohen. 1987. Environmental correlates of food chain length. Science 238:956–960.

Brown, G. B. 1950. *Science: Its Method and Its Philosophy.* George Allen & Unwin, London.

Brown, J. H. 1971. Mammals on mountaintops: nonequilibrium insular biogeography. American Naturalist 105:467–478.

Brown, J. H. 1973. Species diversity of seed-eating desert rodents in sand dune habitats. Ecology 54:775–787.

Brown, J. H. 1975. Geographical ecology of desert rodents. pp. 314–341 in: *Ecology and Evolution of Communities.* M. L. Cody and J. M. Diamond (eds). Harvard University Press, Cambridge.

Brown, J. H. 1981. Two decades of homage to Santa Rosalia: towards a general theory of diversity. American Zoologist 21:877–888.

Brown, J. H. 1984. On the relationship between abundance and distribution of species. American Naturalist 124:255–279.

Brown, J. H. 1988. Species diversity. pp. 57–89 in: *Analytical Biogeography*. A. A. Myers and P. S. Giller (eds). Chapman and Hall, London.

Brown, J. H. and M. A. Bowers. 1985. Community organization in hummingbirds: relationships between morphology and ecology. Auk 102:251–269.

Brown, J. H. and E. J. Heske. 1990. Control of a desert-grassland transition by a keystone rodent guild. Science 250:1705–1707.

Brown, J. H. and A. Kodric-Brown. 1977. Turnover rates in insular biogeography: effect of immigration on extinction. Ecology 58:445–449.

Brown, J. H. and M. V. Lomolino. 1989. Independent discovery of the equilibrium theory of island biogeography. Ecology 70:1954–1957.

Brown, J. H. and B. A. Maurer. 1987. Evolution of species assemblages: effects of energetic constraints and species dynamics on the diversification of the North American avifauna. American Naturalist 130:1–17.

Brown, J. H. and B. A. Maurer. 1989. Macroecology: the division of food and space among species on continents. Science 243:1145–1150.

Brown, J. H. and J. C. Munger. 1985. Experimental manipulation of a desert rodent community: food addition and species removal. Ecology 66:1545–1563.

Brown, J. H. and P. F. Nicoletto. 1991. Spatial scaling of species composition: body masses of North American land mammals. American Naturalist 138:1478–1512.

Brown, J. H., O. J. Reichman and D. W. Davidson. 1979. Granivory in desert ecosystems. Annual Review of Ecology and Systematics 10:201–227.

Brown, J. W. and P. A. Opler. 1990. Patterns of butterfly species density in peninsular Florida. Journal of Biogeography 17:615–622.

Brown, L. H. and D. Amadon. 1968. *Eagles, Hawks, and Falcons of the World*. McGraw-Hill, New York.

Brown, W. L. and E. O. Wilson. 1956. Character displacement. Systematic Zoology 5:49–64.

Buckley, R. 1982. The habitat-unit model of island biogeography. Journal of Biogeography 9:339–344.

Bulmer, M. G. 1974. Density-dependent selection and character displacement. American Naturalist 108:45–58.

Bunge, J. and M. Fitzpatrick. 1993. Estimating the number of species: a review. Journal of the American Statistical Association 88:364–373.

Bush, A. O. and J. C. Holmes. 1983. Niche separation and the broken-stick model: use with multiple assemblages. American Naturalist 122:849–855.

Bush, M. B., P. A. Colinvaux, M. C. Wiemann, D. R. Piperno and K. -B. Liu. 1990. Late Pleistocene temperature depression and vegetation change in Ecuadorian Amazonia. Quaternary Research 14:330–345.

Butman, C. A. 1989. Sediment-trap experiments on the importance of hydrodynamical processes in distributing settling invertebrate larvae in near-bottom waters. Journal of Experimental Marine Biology and Ecology 134:37–88.

Calef, C. E. and N. J. Hancock. 1974. Wenlock and Ludlow marine communities in Wales and the Welsh Borderland. Paleontology 17:779–810.

Carlquist, S. J. 1974. *Island Biology.* Columbia University Press, New York.

Carothers, J. H. 1982. Effects of trophic morphology and behavior on foraging rates of three Hawaiian honeycreepers. Oecologia 55:157–159.

Carothers, J. H. 1986. Homage to Huxley: on the conceptual origin of minimum size ratios among competing species. American Naturalist 128:440–442.

Carothers, J. H. and F. M. Jaksić. 1984. Time as a niche difference: the role of interference competition. Oikos 42:403–406.

Carter, R. N. and S. D. Prince. 1981. Epidemic models used to explain biogeographical distribution limits. Nature 293:644–645.

Case, T. J. 1975. Species numbers, density compensation, and colonizing ability of lizards on islands in the Gulf of California. Ecology 56:3–18.

Case, T. J. 1983a Niche overlap and the assembly of island lizard communities. Oikos 41:427–433.

Case, T. J. 1983b. Sympatry and size similarity in *Cnemidophorus.* pp. 297–325 in: *Lizard Ecology. Study of a Model Organism.* R. B. Huey, E. R. Pianka and T. W. Schoener (eds). Harvard University Press, Cambridge.

Case, T. J., D. T. Bolger and A. D. Richman. 1992. Reptile extinctions: the last ten thousand years. pp. 91–125 in: *Conservation Biology.* P. L. Fielder and S. K. Jain (eds). Chapman and Hall, New York.

Case, T. J. and M. L. Cody. 1987. Testing theories of island biogeography. American Scientist 75:402–412.

Case, T. J. and J. M. Diamond (eds). 1986. *Community Ecology.* Harper & Row, New York.

Case, T. J., J. Faaborg and R. Sidell. 1983. The role of body size in the assembly of West Indian bird communities. Evolution 37:1062–1074.

Case, T. J., M. E. Gilpin and J. M. Diamond. 1979. Overexploitation, interference competition, and excess density compensation in insular faunas. American Naturalist 113:843–854.

Case, T. J. and R. Sidell. 1983. Pattern and chance in the structure of model and natural communities. Evolution 37:832–849.

Castro, G. 1989. Energy costs and avian distributions: limitations or chance?—a comment. Ecology 70:1181–1182.

Caswell, H. 1976. Community structure: a neutral model analysis. Ecological Monographs 46:327–354.

Caswell, H. 1983. Reply to a comment by Ugland and Gray. Ecology 64:605–606.

Caswell, H. 1988. Theory and models in ecology: a different perspective. Ecological Modelling 43:33–44.

Caughley, G., D. Grice, R. Barker and B. Brown. 1988. The edge of the range. Journal of Animal Ecology 57:771–785.

Chao, A. 1984. Non-parametric estimation of the number of classes in a population. Scandinavian Journal of Statistics 11:265–270.

Chapin, F. S. I., J. B. McGraw and G. R. Shaver. 1989. Competition causes regular spacing of alder in Alaska shrub tundra. Oecologia 79:412–416.

Chapman, A. R. O. 1973. A critique of prevailing attitudes towards the control of seaweed zonation on the sea shore. Botanica Marina 15:80–82.

Cheetham, A. H. and J. E. Hazel. 1969. Binary (presence-absence) similarity coefficients. Journal of Paleontology 43:1130–1136.

Cherry, L. M., S. M. Case, J. G. Kunkel, J. S. Wyles and A. C. Wilson. 1982. Body shape metrics and organismal evolution. Evolution 36:914–933.

Clark, C. W. and M. L. Rosenzweig. 1994. Extinction and colonization processes: parameter estimates from sporadic surveys. American Naturalist 143:583–596.

Clements, F. E. 1904. The development and structure of vegetation. Botanical Survey of Nebraska 7:5–175.

Cochran, W. G. 1950. The comparison of percentages in matched samples. Biometrika 37:256–266.

Cody, M. L. 1973. Character convergence. Annual Review of Ecology and Systematics 4:189–211.

Cody, M. L. 1974. *Competition and the Structure of Bird Communities.* Princeton University Press, Princeton.

Cody, M. L. and J. M. Diamond (eds). 1975. *Ecology and Evolution of Communities.* Harvard University Press, Cambridge.

Cohen, J. E. 1968. Alternate derivations of a species-abundance relation. American Naturalist 102:165–172.

Cohen, J. E. 1977. Ratio of prey to predators in community webs. Nature 270:165–167.

Cohen, J. E. 1978. *Food Webs and Niche Space.* Princeton University Press, Princeton.

Cole, B. J. 1980. Trophic structure of a grassland insect community. Nature 288:76–77.

Cole, B. J. 1981. Overlap, regularity, and flowering phenologies. American Naturalist 117:993–997.

Cole, B. J. 1983. Assembly of mangrove ant communities: patterns of geographical distribution. Journal of Animal Ecology 52:339–347.

Coleman, B. D. 1981. On random placement and species-area relations. Mathematical Biosciences 54:191–215.

Coleman, B. D., M. A. Mares, M. R. Willig and Y. -H. Hsieh. 1982. Randomness, area, and species richness. Ecology 63:1121–1133.

Collins, S. L. and S. M. Glenn. 1990. A hierarchical analysis of species' abundance patterns in grassland vegetation. American Naturalist 135:633–648.

Colman, J. 1933. The nature of the intertidal zonation of plants and animals. Marine Biological Association of the United Kingdom 18:435–476.

Colwell, R. K. 1979. Toward a unified approach to the study of species diversity. pp. 75–91 in: *Ecological Diversity in Theory and Practice.* J. F. Grassle, G. P. Patil, W. Smith and C. Taillie (eds). International Cooperative Publishing House, Fairland, Maryland.

Colwell, R. K. and J. A. Coddington. 1994. Estimating terrestrial biodiversity through extrapolation. Philosophical Transactions of the Royal Society of London B 345:101–118.

Colwell, R. K. and D. J. Futuyma. 1971. On the measurement of niche breadth and overlap. Ecology 52:567–576.

Colwell, R. K. and G. C. Hurtt. 1994. Nonbiological gradients in species richness and a spurious Rapoport effect. American Naturalist 144:570–595.

Colwell, R. K. and D. W. Winkler. 1984. A null model for null models in biogeography. pp. 344–359 in: *Ecological Communities: Conceptual Issues and the Evidence.* D. R. Strong, Jr., D. Simberloff, L. G. Abele and A. B. Thistle (eds). Princeton University Press, Princeton.

Connell, J. H. 1961. The influence of interspecific competition and other factors on the distribution of the barnacle *Chthamalus stellatus*. Ecology 42:710–723.

Connell, J. H. 1975. Some mechanisms producing structure in natural communities: a model and evidence from field experiments. pp. 460–490 in: *Ecology and Evolution of Communities*. M. L. Cody and J. M. Diamond (eds). Harvard University Press, Cambridge.

Connell, J. H. 1980. Diversity and the coevolution of competitors, or the ghost of competition past. Oikos 35:131–138.

Connell, J. H. and R. O. Slatyer. 1977. Mechanisms of succession in natural communities and their role in community stability and organization. American Naturalist 111:1119–1144.

Connell, J. H. and W. P. Sousa. 1983. On the evidence needed to judge ecological stability or persistence. American Naturalist 121:789–824.

Connolly, J., P. Wayne and R. Murray. 1990. Time course of plant-plant interactions in experimental mixtures of annuals—density, frequency and nutrient effects. Oecologia 82:513–526.

Connor, E. F. and E. D. McCoy. 1979. The statistics and biology of the species-area relationship. American Naturalist 113:791–833.

Connor, E. F., E. D. McCoy and B. J. Cosby. 1983. Model discrimination and expected slope values in species-area studies. American Naturalist 122:789–796.

Connor, E. F. and D. Simberloff. 1978. Species number and compositional similarity of the Galápagos flora and avifauna. Ecological Monographs 48:219–248.

Connor, E. F. and D. Simberloff. 1979. The assembly of species communities: chance or competition? Ecology 60:1132–1140.

Connor, E. F. and D. Simberloff. 1983. Interspecific competition and species co-occurrence patterns on islands: null models and the evaluation of evidence. Oikos 41:455–465.

Connor, E. F. and D. Simberloff. 1984. Neutral models of species' co-occurrence patterns. pp. 316–331 in: *Ecological Communities: Conceptual Issues and the Evidence*. D. R. Strong Jr., D. Simberloff, L. G. Abele and A. B. Thistle (eds). Princeton University Press, Princeton.

Connor, E. F. and D. Simberloff. 1986. Competition, scientific method, and null models in ecology. American Scientist 74:155–162.

Cook, R. E. 1969. Variation in species density of North American birds. Systematic Zoology 18:63–84.

Cornell, H. V. and J. H. Lawton. 1992. Species interactions, local and regional processes, and limits to the richness of ecological communities: a theoretical perspective. Journal of Animal Ecology 61:1–12.

Cracraft, J. 1983. Species concepts and speciation analysis. Current Ornithology 1:159–187.

Craighead, J. J. and F. C. Craighead. 1956. *Hawks, Owls and Wildlife*. Stackpole Company and Wildlife Management Institute, Harrisburg, Pennsylvania.

Crowder, L. B. 1980. Ecological convergence of community structure: a neutral model analysis. Ecology 61:194–198.

Crowell, K. L. 1973. Experimental zoogeography: introductions of mice to small islands. American Naturalist 107:534–558.

Crowell, K. L. 1983. Islands—insight or artifact?: population dynamics and habitat utilization in insular rodents. Oikos 41:442–454.

Crowell, K. L. and S. L. Pimm. 1976. Competition and niche shifts of mice introduced onto small islands. Oikos 27:251–258.

Crowley, P. H. 1992. Density dependence, boundedness, and attraction: detecting stability in stochastic systems. Oecologia 90:246–254.

Cutler, A. 1991. Nested faunas and extinction in fragmented habitats. Conservation Biology 5:496–505.

Dale, M. R. T. 1984. The contiguity of upslope and downslope boundaries of species in a zoned community. Oikos 42:92–96.

Dale, M. R. T. 1986. Overlap and spacing of species' ranges on an environmental gradient. Oikos 47:303–308.

Dale, M. R. T. 1988. The spacing and intermingling of species boundaries on an environmental gradient. Oikos 53:351–356.

Damuth, J. 1981. Population density and body size in mammals. Nature 290:699–700.

Damuth, J. 1987. Interspecific allometry of population density in mammals and other animals: the independence of body mass and population energy use. Biological Journal of the Linnean Society 31:193–246.

Darlington, P. J. 1957. *Zoogeography: The Geographical Distribution of Animals.* John Wiley & Sons, New York.

Darwin, C. 1859. *The Origin of Species by Means of Natural Selection.* Murray, London.

Dayan, T. and D. Simberloff 1994. Character displacement, sexual dimorphism, and morphological variation among British and Irish mustelids. Ecology 75:1063–1073.

Dayan, T., D. Simberloff, E. Tchernov and Y. Yom-Tov. 1989. Inter- and intraspecific character displacement in mustelids. Ecology 70:1526–1539.

Dayan, T., D. Simberloff, E. Tchernov and Y. Yom-Tov. 1990. Feline canines: community-wide character displacement among the small cats of Israel. American Naturalist 136:39–60.

Dayan, T., D. Simberloff, E. Tchernov and Y. Yom-Tov. 1992. Canine carnassials: character displacement in the wolves, jackals and foxes of Israel. Biological Journal of the Linnean Society 45:315–331.

Dayan, T., E. Tchernov, Y. Yom-Tov and D. Simberloff. 1989. Ecological character displacement in Saharo-Arabian *Vulpes:* outfoxing Bergmann's rule. Oikos 58:263–272.

Dean-Ross, D. 1990. Response of attached bacteria to zinc in artificial streams. Canadian Journal of Microbiology 36:561–566.

DeAngelis, D. L. 1975. Stability and connectance in food web models. Ecology 56:238–243.

De Vita, J. 1979. Niche separation and the broken-stick model. American Naturalist 114:171–178.

de Wit, C. T. 1960. On competition. Verslagen van Landbouwkundige Onderzoekingen 66:1–82.

den Boer, P. J. 1981. On the survival of populations in a heterogeneous and variable environment. Oecologia 50:39–53.

Diamond, J. M. 1969. Avifaunal equilibria and species turnover rates on the Channel Islands of California. Proceedings of the National Academy of Sciences USA 64:57–63.

322 ▪ *Literature Cited*

Diamond, J. M. 1975. Assembly of species communities. pp. 342–444 in: *Ecology and Evolution of Communities*. M. L. Cody and J. M. Diamond (eds). Harvard University Press, Cambridge.

Diamond, J. M. 1978. Niche shifts and the rediscovery of interspecific competition. American Scientist 66:322–330.

Diamond, J. M. 1983. Survival of bird populations stranded on land-bridge islands. National Geographic Society Research Reports 15:127–141.

Diamond, J. 1986. Overview: laboratory experiments, field experiments, and natural experiments. pp. 3–22 in: *Community Ecology*. T. J. Case and J. Diamond (eds). Harper & Row, New York.

Diamond, J. M. and M. E. Gilpin. 1980. Turnover noise: contribution to variance in species number and prediction from immigration and extinction curves. American Naturalist 115:884–889.

Diamond, J. M. and M. E. Gilpin. 1982. Examination of the "null" model of Connor and Simberloff for species co-occurrences on islands. Oecologia 52:64–74.

Diamond, J. M. and R. M. May. 1977. Species turnover rates on islands: dependence on census interval. Science 197:266–270.

Diamond, J. and S. Pimm. 1993. Survival times of bird populations: a reply. American Naturalist 142:1030–1035.

Diamond, J., S. L. Pimm, M. E. Gilpin and M. LeCroy. 1989. Rapid evolution of character displacement in myzomelid honeyeaters. American Naturalist 134:675–708.

Dickman, C. R. 1986. An experimental study of competition between two species of dasyurid marsupials. Ecological Monographs 56:221–241.

Dickman, M. 1968. Some indices of diversity. Ecology 49:1191–1193.

Dillon, R. T., Jr. 1981. Patterns in the morphology and distribution of gastropods in Oneida Lake, New York, detected using computer-generated null hypotheses. American Naturalist 118:83–101.

Dobson, A. P. and S. W. Pacala. 1992. The parasites of *Anolis* lizards in the northern Lesser Antilles. II. The structure of the parasite community. Oecologia 92:118–125.

Dobzhansky, T. 1950. Evolution in the tropics. American Scientist 38:209–221.

Donagho, W. 1965. Oahu bird survey. Elepaio 26:53–54.

Doty, M. S. 1946. Critical tide factors that are correlated with the vertical distribution of marine algae and other organisms along the Pacific Coast. Ecology 27:315–328.

Doty, M. S. and J. G. Archer. 1950. An experimental test of the tide factor hypothesis. American Journal of Botany 37:458–464.

Drake, J. A. 1990. Communities as assembled structures: do rules govern pattern? Trends in Ecology and Evolution 5:159–164.

Drake, J. A. 1991. Community-assembly mechanics and the structure of an experimental species ensemble. American Naturalist 137:1–26.

Dunbar, M. J. 1980. The blunting of Occam's razor, or to hell with parsimony. Canadian Journal of Zoology 58:123–128.

Dunn, C. P. and C. Loehle. 1988. Species-area parameter estimation: testing the null model of lack of relationship. Journal of Biogeography 15:721–728.

Dunning, J. B. 1993. *CRC Handbook of Avian Body Masses*. CRC Press, Boca Raton, Florida.

Dyar, H. G. 1890. The number of molts of lepidopterous larvae. Psyche 5:420–422.

Eadie, J. M., L. Broekhoven and P. Colgan. 1987. Size ratios and artifacts: Hutchinson's rule revisited. American Naturalist 129:1–17.

Ebeling, A. W., S. J. Holbrook and R. J. Schmitt. 1990. Temporally concordant structure of a fish assemblage: bound or determined? American Naturalist 135:63–73.

Edgington, E. S. 1987. *Randomization Tests.* Marcel Dekker, New York.

Eldridge, J. L. and D. H. Johnson. 1988. Size differences in migrant sandpiper flocks: ghosts in ephemeral guilds. Oecologia 77:433–444.

Elgar, M. A. and P. H. Harvey. 1987. Basal metabolic rates in mammals: allometry, phylogeny, and ecology. Functional Ecology 1:25–36.

Elton, C. S. 1927. *Animal Ecology.* Macmillan, New York.

Elton, C. 1946. Competition and the structure of ecological communities. Journal of Animal Ecology 15:54–68.

Elton, C. S. 1958. *The Ecology of Invasions by Animals and Plants.* Chapman & Hall, London.

Enders, F. 1976. Size, food-finding, and Dyar's constant. Environmental Entomology 5:1–10.

Endler, J. A. 1982. Problems in distinguishing historical from ecological factors in biogeography. American Zoologist 22:411–452.

Engstrom, R. T., R. L. Crawford and W. W. Baker. 1984. Breeding bird populations in relation to changing forest structure following fire exclusion: a 15-year study. Wilson Bulletin 96:437–450.

Engstrom, R. T. and F. C. James. 1981. Plot size as a factor in winter bird-population studies. Condor 83:34–41.

Erwin, T. L. 1981. Taxon pulses, vicariance, and dispersal: an evolutionary synthesis illustrated by carabid beetles. pp. 159–196 in: *Vicariance Biogeography: A Critique.* G. Nelson and D. E. Rosen (eds). Columbia University Press, New York.

Evans, E. W. 1988. Community dynamics of prairie grasshoppers subjected to periodic fire: trajectories or random walks in time? Oikos 52:283–292.

Evans, F. C. and W. W. Murdoch. 1968. Taxonomic composition, trophic structure and seasonal occurrence in a grassland insect community. Journal of Animal Ecology 37:259–273.

Ewens, W. J. 1972. The sampling theory of selectively neutral alleles. Theoretical Population Biology 3:87–112.

Faaborg, J. 1979. Qualitative patterns of avian extinction on Neotropical land-bridge islands: lessons for conservation. Journal of Applied Ecology 16:99–107.

Faeth, S. H. and E. F. Connor. 1979. Supersaturated and relaxing island faunas: a critique of the species-age relationship. Journal of Biogeography 6:311–316.

Fager, E. W. 1972. Diversity: a sampling study. American Naturalist 106:293–310.

Feinsinger, P., E. E. Spears and R. W. Poole. 1981. A simple measure of niche breadth. Ecology 62:27–32.

Feller, W. 1940. On the logistic law of growth and its empirical verifications in biology. Acta Biotheoretica 5:51–66.

Feller, W. 1968. *An Introduction to Probability Theory and Its Applications.* John Wiley & Sons, New York.

Felsenstein, J. 1985. Confidence limits on phylogenies: an approach using the bootstrap. Evolution 39:783–791.

Fenchel, T. 1975. Character displacement and coexistence in mud snails (Hydro-biidae). Oecologia 20:19–32.

Field, J. 1992. Guild structure in solitary spider-hunting wasps (Hymenoptera: Pompilidae) compared with null model predictions. Ecological Entomology 17:198–208.

Fienberg, S. E. 1980. *The Analysis of Cross-Classified Categorical Data*. MIT Press, Cambridge.

Findley, J. S. and M. T. Findley. 1985. A search for pattern in butterfly fish communities. American Naturalist 126:800–816.

Fischer, A. G. 1960. Latitudinal variations in organic diversity. Evolution 14:64–81.

Fisher, R. A., A. S. Corbet and C. B. Williams. 1943. The relation between the number of species and the number of individuals in a random sample of an animal population. Journal of Animal Ecology 12:42–58.

Flanagan, L. B. and W. Moser. 1985. Flowering phenology, floral display and reproductive success in dioecious *Aralia nudicaulis* L. (Araliaceae). Oecologia 68:23–28.

Fleming, T. H. 1985. Coexistence of five sympatric *Piper* (Piperaceae) species in a tropical dry forest. Ecology 66:688–700.

Fleming, T. H. and B. L. Partridge. 1984. On the analysis of phenological overlap. Oecologia 62:344–350.

Flessa, K. W. 1975. Area, continental drift and mammalian diversity. Paleobiology 1:189–194.

Foote, M. 1991. Morphological and taxonomic diversity in a clade's history: the blastoid record and stochastic simulations. Contributions, Ann Arbor Museum of Paleontology 28:101–140.

Fox, B. J. 1987. Species assembly and the evolution of community structure. Evolutionary Ecology 1:201–213.

Fox, B. J. 1989. Small-mammal community pattern in Australian heathland: a taxonomically based rule for species assembly. pp. 91–103 in: *Patterns in the Structure of Mammalian Communities*. D. W. Morris, Z. Abramsky, B. J. Fox and M. R. Willig (eds). Special Publication 28 of The Museum, Texas Tech University, Lubbock.

Fox, B. J. and J. H. Brown. 1993. Assembly rules for functional groups in North American desert rodent communities. Oikos 67:358–370.

Fox, B. J. and G. L. Kirkland, Jr. 1992. An assembly rule for functional groups applied to North American soricid communities. Journal of Mammalogy 73:491–503.

Fuentes, E. R. 1976. Ecological convergence of lizard communities in Chile and California. Ecology 57:3–17.

Fuentes, E. R. 1980. Convergence of community structure: neutral model vs. field data. Ecology 61:198–200.

Gardiner, F. P. and R. L. Haedrich. 1978. Zonation in the deep sea benthic megafauna. Oecologia 31:311–317.

Gardner, M. R. and W. R. Ashby. 1970. Connectance of large dynamic (cybernetic) systems: critical values for stability. Nature 228:784.

Gaston, K. J. 1990. Patterns in the geographical ranges of species. Biological Reviews 65:105–129.

Gaston, K. J. 1991. How large is a species' geographic range? Oikos 61:434–438.

Gaston, K. J. and J. H. Lawton. 1988a. Patterns in body size, population dynamics, and regional distribution of bracken herbivores. American Naturalist 132:662–680.

Gaston, K. J. and J. H. Lawton. 1988b. Patterns in the distribution and abundance of insect populations. Nature 331:709–712.

Gaston, K. J. and J. H. Lawton. 1989. Insect herbivores on bracken do not support the core-satellite hypothesis. American Naturalist 134:761–777.

Gaston, K. J. and J. H. Lawton. 1990. Effects of scale and habitat on the relationship between regional distribution and local abundance. Oikos 58:329–335.

Gatz, A. J., Jr. 1979. Community organization in fishes as indicated by morphological features. Ecology 60:711–718.

Gauch, H. G., Jr. 1982. *Multivariate Analysis in Community Ecology.* Cambridge University Press, Cambridge.

Gause, G. F. 1934. *The Struggle for Existence.* Williams & Wilkins, Baltimore.

Georgian, T. and J. B. Wallace. 1983. Seasonal production dynamics in a guild of periphyton-grazing insects in a southern Appalachian stream. Ecology 64:1236–1248.

Ghent, A. W. 1991. Insights into diversity and niche breadth analyses from exact small-sample tests of the equal abundance hypothesis. American Midland Naturalist 126:213–255.

Gilbert, F. S. 1980. The equilibrium theory of island biogeography: fact or fiction? Journal of Biogeography 7:209–235.

Gilpin, M. E. 1975. Stability of feasible predator-prey systems. Nature 254:137–139.

Gilpin, M. E., M. P. Carpenter and M. J. Pomerantz. 1986. The assembly of a laboratory community: multi-species competition in *Drosophila.* pp. 33–40 in: *Community Ecology.* T. J. Case and J. Diamond (eds). Harper & Row, New York.

Gilpin, M. E. and J. M. Diamond. 1981. Immigration and extinction probabilities for individual species: relation to incidence functions and species colonization curves. Proceedings of the National Academy of Sciences USA 78:392–396.

Gilpin, M. E. and J. M. Diamond. 1982. Factors contributing to non-randomness in species co-occurrences on islands. Oecologia 52:75–84.

Gilpin, M. E. and J. M. Diamond. 1984. Are species co-occurrences on islands non-random, and are null hypotheses useful in community ecology? pp. 297–315 in: *Ecological Communities: Conceptual Issues and the Evidence.* D. R. Strong, Jr., D. Simberloff, L. G. Abele and A. B. Thistle (eds). Princeton University Press, Princeton.

Gilpin, M. E. and J. M. Diamond. 1987. Comment on Wilson's null model. Oecologia 74:159–160.

Gilpin, M. E., J. M. Diamond, E. F. Connor and D. Simberloff. 1984. Rejoinders. pp. 332–343 in: *Ecological Communities: Conceptual Issues and the Evidence.* D. R. Strong, Jr., D. Simberloff, L. G. Abele and A. B. Thistle (eds). Princeton University Press, Princeton.

Glasser, J. W. 1983. Variation in niche breadth with trophic position: on the disparity between expected and observed species packing. American Naturalist 122:542–548.

Glasser, J. W. and H. J. Price. 1988. Evaluating expectations deduced from explicit hypotheses about mechanisms of competition. Oikos 51:57–70.

Gleason, H. A. 1926. The individualistic concept of the plant association. Bulletin of the Torrey Botanical Club 53:7–26.

Gleason, H. A. 1929. The significance of Raunkiaer's law of frequency. Ecology 10:406–408.

Gleeson, S. K. 1981. Character displacement in flowering phenologies. Oecologia 51:294–295.

Goh, B. S. and L. S. Jennings. 1977. Feasibility and stability in randomly assembled Lotka-Volterra models. Ecological Modelling 3:63–71.

Goldman, N. and P. J. D. Lambshead. 1989. Optimization of the Ewens-Caswell neutral model program for community diversity analysis. Marine Ecology Progress Series 50:255–262.

Good, I. J. 1953. The population frequencies of species and the estimation of population parameters. Biometrika 40:237–264.

Goodall, D. W. 1966. A new similarity index based on probability. Biometrics 22:882–907.

Goodall, D. W. 1974. A new method for the analysis of spatial pattern by random pairing of quadrats. Vegetatio 29:135–146.

Goodman, D. 1975. The theory of diversity-stability relationships in ecology. Quarterly Review of Biology 50:237–266.

Gotelli, N. J. 1991. Metapopulation models: the rescue effect, the propagule rain, and the core-satellite hypothesis. American Naturalist 138:768–776.

Gotelli, N. J. 1993. Ant lion zones: causes of high-density predator aggregations. Ecology 74:226–237.

Gotelli, N.J. In press. Ant community structure: effects of predatory ant lions. Ecology.

Gotelli, N. J. and L. G. Abele. 1982. Statistical distributions of West Indian land bird families. Journal of Biogeography 9:421–435.

Gotelli, N. J. and W. H. Bossert. 1991. Ecological character displacement in a variable environment. Theoretical Population Biology 39:49–62.

Gotelli, N. J. and G. R. Graves. 1990. Body size and the occurrence of avian species on land-bridge islands. Journal of Biogeography 17:315–325.

Gotelli, N. J. and W. G. Kelley. 1993. A general model of metapopulation dynamics. Oikos 68:36–44.

Gotelli, N. J., F. G. Lewis III and C. M. Young. 1987. Body-size differences in a colonizing amphipod-mollusc assemblage. Oecologia 72:104–108.

Gotelli, N. J. and D. Simberloff. 1987. The distribution and abundance of tallgrass prairie plants: a test of the core-satellite hypothesis. American Naturalist 130:18–35.

Gould, S. J. 1979. An allometric interpretation of species-area curves: the meaning of the coefficient. American Naturalist 114:335–343.

Gould, S. J. and R. C. Lewontin. 1979. The spandrels of San Marco and the Panglossian paradigm: a critique of the adaptationist programme. Proceedings of the Royal Society, London, B 205:581–598.

Gould, S. J., D. M. Raup, J. J. Sepkoski, Jr., T. J. M. Schopf and D. S. Simberloff. 1977. The shape of evolution: a comparison of real and random clades. Paleobiology 3:23–40.

Grace, J. B., J. Keough and G. R. Guntenspergen. 1992. Size bias in traditional analyses of substitutive competition experiments. Oecologia 90:429–434.

Grafen, A. 1984. Theoretical basis for the relationship between r^2 and random subsets of the community. Appendix to paper by Kennedy and Southwood. Journal of Animal Ecology 53:477–478.

Grant, P. R. 1966. Ecological compatibility of bird species on islands. American Naturalist 100:451–462.

Grant, P. R. 1972a. Convergent and divergent character displacement. Biological Journal of the Linnean Society 4:39–68.

Grant, P. R. 1972b. Interspecific competition among rodents. Annual Review of Ecology and Systematics 3:79–106.

Grant, P. R. and I. Abbott. 1980. Interspecific competition, island biogeography and null hypotheses. Evolution 34:332–341.

Grassle, J. F. and N. J. Maciolek. 1992. Deep-sea species richness: regional and local diversity estimates from quantitative bottom samples. American Naturalist 139:313–341.

Graves, G. R. 1985. Elevational correlates of speciation and intraspecific geographic variation in plumage in Andean forest birds. Auk 102:556–579.

Graves, G. R. and N. J. Gotelli. 1983. Neotropical land-bridge avifaunas: new approaches to null hypotheses in biogeography. Oikos 41:322–333.

Graves, G. R. and N. J. Gotelli. 1993. Assembly of avian mixed-species flocks in Amazonia. Proceedings of the National Academy of Sciences USA 90:1388–1391.

Green, R. H. 1971. A multivariate statistical approach to the Hutchinsonian niche: bivalve molluscs of central Canada. Ecology 52:543–556.

Greenslade, P. J. M. 1968a. The distribution of some insects of the Solomon Islands. Proceedings of the Linnean Society 179:189–196.

Greenslade, P. J. M. 1968b. Island patterns in the Solomon Islands bird fauna. Evolution 22:751–761.

Greenslade, P. J. M. 1969. Insect distribution patterns in the Solomon Islands. Philosophical Transactions of the Royal Society B 255:271–284.

Greig-Smith, P. 1964. *Quantitative Plant Ecology*. Butterworths, Washington.

Griffiths, D. 1986. Size-abundance relations in communities. American Naturalist 127:140–166.

Griffiths, R. A. 1987. Microhabitat and seasonal niche dynamics of smooth and palmate newts, *Triturus vulgaris* and *T. helveticus,* at a pond in mid-Wales. Journal of Animal Ecology 56:441–451.

Grosberg, R. K. 1982. Intertidal zonation of barnacles: the influence of planktonic zonation of larvae on vertical distribution of adults. Ecology 63:894–899.

Grossman, G. D. 1982. Dynamics and organization of a rocky intertidal fish assemblage: the persistence and resilience of taxocene structure. American Naturalist 119:611–637.

Grossman, G. D., M. C. Freeman, P. B. Moyle and J. O. Whittaker, Jr. 1985. Stochasticity and assemblage organization in an Indiana stream fish assemblage. American Naturalist 126:275–285.

Grossman, G. D., P. B. Moyle and J. O. Whittaker, Jr. 1982. Stochasticity in structural and functional characteristics of an Indiana stream fish assemblage: a test of community theory. American Naturalist 120:423–454.

Gyllenberg, M. and I. Hanski. 1992. Single-species metapopulation dynamics: a structured model. Theoretical Population Biology 42:35–61.

Haefner, J. W. 1980. On Gause's yeast experiments. Ecology 61:1551–1552.

Haefner, J. W. 1988a. Niche shifts in greater Antillean *Anolis* communities: effects of niche metric and biological resolution on null model tests. Oecologia 77:107–117.

Haefner, J. W. 1988b. Assembly rules for Greater Antillean *Anolis* lizards. Competition and random models compared. Oecologia 74:551–565.

Haefner, J. W., G. C. Poole, P. V. Dunn and R. T. Decker. 1991. Edge effects in computer models of spatial competition. Ecological Modelling 56:221–244.

Haffer, J. 1969. Speciation in Amazonian forest birds. Science 165:131–137.

Haffer, J. 1974. *Avian Speciation in Tropical South America, with a Systematic Survey of the Toucans (Ramphastidae) and Jacamars (Galbulidae)*. Nuttall Ornithological Club, Cambridge, Massachusetts.

Haffer, J. 1978. Distribution of Amazonian forest birds. Bonner Zool. Beitr. 29:38–78.

Haffer, J. 1982. General aspects of the refuge theory. pp. 6–26 in: *Biological Diversification in the Tropics*. G. Prance (ed). Columbia University Press, New York.

Haila, Y. 1983. Land birds on northern islands: a sampling metaphor for insular colonization. Oikos 41:334–351.

Haila, Y. and I. K. Hanski. 1993. Birds breeding on small British islands and extinction risks. American Naturalist 142:1025–1029.

Haila, Y., I. K. Hanski and S. Raivio. 1993. Turnover of breeding birds in small forest fragments: the "sampling" colonization hypothesis corroborated. Ecology 74:714–725.

Haila, Y. and O. Järvinen. 1981. The underexploited potential of bird censuses in insular ecology. Studies in Avian Biology 6:559–565.

Haila, Y. and O. Järvinen. 1983. Land bird communities on a Finnish island: species impoverishment and abundance patterns. Oikos 41:255–273.

Haila, Y., O. Järvinen and S. Kuusela. 1983. Colonization of islands by land birds: prevalence functions in a Finnish archipelago. Journal of Biogeography 10:499–531.

Haila, Y. and S. Kuusela. 1982. Efficiency of one-visit censuses of bird communities breeding on small islands. Ornis Scandinavica 13:17–24.

Hairston, N. G. 1964. Studies on the organization of animal communities. Journal of Animal Ecology 33:227–239.

Hairston, N. G. 1989. *Ecological Experiments: Purpose, Design, and Execution*. Cambridge University Press, Cambridge.

Hairston, N. G., F. E. Smith and L. B. Slobodkin. 1960. Community structure, population control, and competition. American Naturalist 94:421–425.

Hall, C. A. S. 1988. An assessment of several of the historically most influential theoretical models used in ecology and of the data provided in their support. Ecological Modelling 43:5–31.

Hall, S. J. and D. Raffaelli. 1991. Food-web patterns: lessons from a species-rich web. Journal of Animal Ecology 60:823–842.

Hallett, J. G. 1991. The structure and stability of small mammal faunas. Oecologia 88:383–393.

Hamill, D. N. and S. J. Wright. 1988. Interspecific interaction and similarity in species composition. American Naturalist 131:412–423.

Hamilton, T. H., R. H. Barth and G. L. Bush. 1963. Species abundance: natural regulation of insular variation. Science 142:1575–1577.

Hanski, I. 1978. Some comments on the measurement of niche metrics. Ecology 59:168–174.

Hanski, I. 1982a. Dynamics of regional distribution: the core and satellite species hypothesis. Oikos 38:210–221.

Hanski, I. 1982b. Structure in bumblebee communities. Annales Zoologici Fennici 19:319–326.

Hanski, I. 1983. Distributional ecology and abundance of dung and carrion feeding beetles (Scarabaeidae) in tropical rain forests in Sarawak, Borneo, Malaysia. Annales Zoologici Fennici 20:1–45.

Hanski, I. 1991. Reply to Nee, Gregory and May. Oikos 62:88–89.

Hanski, I. 1992. Inferences from ecological incidence functions. American Naturalist 139:657–662.

Hanski, I. and M. Gyllenberg. 1993. Two general metapopulation models and the core-satellite species hypothesis. American Naturalist 142:17–41.

Hanski, I., J. Kouki and A. Halkka. 1993. Three explanations of the positive relationship between distribution and abundance of species. pp. 108–116 in: *Community Diversity: Historical and Geographical Perspectives.* R. E. Ricklefs and D. Schluter (eds). University of Chicago Press, Chicago.

Hardin, G. 1960. The competitive exclusion principle. Science 131:1292–1297.

Harper, J. L. 1977. *Population Biology of Plants.* Academic Press, New York.

Harrison, S., D. D. Murphy and P. R. Ehrlich. 1988. Distribution of the bay checkerspot butterfly, *Euphydryas editha bayensis:* evidence for a metapopulation model. American Naturalist 132:360–382.

Harvey, P. H., R. K. Colwell, J. W. Silvertown and R. M. May. 1983. Null models in ecology. Annual Review of Ecology and Systematics 14:189–211.

Harvey, P. H. and H. C. J. Godfray. 1987. How species divide resources. American Naturalist 129:318–320.

Harvey, P. H. and M. D. Pagel. 1991. *The Comparative Method in Evolutionary Biology.* Oxford University Press, Oxford.

Harvey, P. H. and K. Ralls. 1985. Homage to the null weasel. pp. 155–171 in: *Essays in Honour of John Maynard Smith.* P. J. Greenwood, P. H. Harvey and M. Slatkin (eds). Cambridge University Press, Cambridge.

Hastings, A. 1987. Can competition be detected using species co-occurrence data? Ecology 68:117–123.

Hastings, H. H. and M. Conrad. 1979. Length and evolutionary stability of food chains. Nature 282:838–839.

Havens, K. 1992. Scale and structure in natural food webs. Science 257:1107–1109.

Hawkins, B. A. 1992. Parasitoid-host food webs and donor control. Oikos 65:159–162.

Heatwole, H. and R. Levins. 1972. Trophic structure stability and faunal change during recolonization. Ecology 53:531–534.

Heck, K. L., Jr., G. Van Belle and D. Simberloff. 1975. Explicit calculation of the rarefaction diversity measurement and the determination of sufficient sample size. Ecology 56:1459–1461.

Heinrich, B. 1976. Flowering phenologies: bog, woodland, and disturbed habitats. Ecology 57:890–899.

Hendrickson, J. A., Jr. 1981. Community-wide character displacement reexamined. Evolution 35:794–810.

Hendrickson, J. A., Jr. and P. R. Ehrlich. 1971. An expanded concept of "species diversity." Notulae Naturae of the Academy of Natural Sciences of Philadelphia 439:1–6.

Hengeveld, R. and J. Haeck. 1981. The distribution of abundance. II. Models and implications. Proceedings of the Koninklijke Nederlandse Akademie van Wetenschappen 84:257–284.

Hengeveld, R. and J. Haeck. 1982. The distribution of abundance. I. Measurements. Journal of Biogeography 9:303–316.

Hennig, W. 1966. *Phylogenetic Systematics.* University of Illinois Press, Urbana.

Henshaw, H. W. 1902. Complete list of the birds of the Hawaiian possessions, with notes on their habits. pp. 54–106 in: *All About Hawaii: The Recognized Book of Authentic Information on Hawaii, Combined With Thrum's Hawaiian Annual and Standard Guide.* Thrum, Honolulu.

Herbold, B. 1984. Structure of an Indiana stream fish assemblage: choosing an appropriate model. American Naturalist 124:561–572.

Heyer, W. R. 1974. Niche measurements of frog larvae from a seasonal tropical location in Thailand. Ecology 55:651–656.

Hill, M. O. 1973. Diversity and evenness: a unifying notation and its consequences. Ecology 54:427–432.

Hines, A. H. 1982. Coexistence in a kelp forest: size, population dynamics, and resource partitioning in a guild of spider crabs (Brachyura, Majidae). Ecological Monographs 52:179–198.

Hölldobler, B. 1986. Food robbing in ants, a form of interference competition. Oecologia 69:12–15.

Holt, R. D. 1984. Spatial heterogeneity, indirect interactions, and the coexistence of prey species. American Naturalist 124:377–406.

Hopf, F. A. and J. H. Brown. 1986. The bull's-eye method for testing randomness in ecological communities. Ecology 67:1139–1155.

Horn, H. S. and R. M. May. 1977. Limits to similarity among coexisting competitors. Nature 270:660–661.

Hotelling, H. 1933. Analysis of a complex of statistical variables into principal components. Journal of Educational Psychology 24:417–441.

Howard, R. A. and A. Moore. 1984. *A Complete Checklist of Birds of the World.* Macmillan, London.

Huey, R. B. and A. F. Bennett. 1987. Phylogenetic studies of coadaptation: preferred temperatures versus optimal performance temperatures of lizards. Evolution 41:1098–1115.

Huey, R. B. and E. R. Pianka. 1983. Temporal separation of activity and interspecific dietary overlap. pp. 281–290 in: *Lizard Ecology: Studies on a Model Organism.* R. B. Huey, T. W. Schoener and E. R. Pianka (eds). Harvard University Press, Cambridge.

Hughes, R. G. 1984. A model of the structure and dynamics of benthic marine invertebrate communities. Marine Ecology Progress Series 15:1–11.

Hughes, R. G. 1986. Theories and models of species abundance. American Naturalist 128:879–899.

Hurlbert, S. H. 1971. The nonconcept of species diversity: a critique and alternative parameters. Ecology 52:577–585.

Hurlbert, S. H. 1978. The measurement of niche overlap and some relatives. Ecology 59:67–77.

Hurlbert, S. H. 1990. Spatial distribution of the montane unicorn. Oikos 58:257–271.

Hutchinson, G. E. 1957. Concluding remarks. Cold Spring Harbor Symposia on Quantitative Biology. 22:415–427.

Hutchinson, G. E. 1959. Homage to Santa Rosalia or why are there so many kinds of animals? American Naturalist 93:145–159.

Huxley, J. 1942. *Evolution: The Modern Synthesis.* Harper, New York.

Inger, R. F. and R. K. Colwell. 1977. Organization of contiguous communities of amphibians and reptiles in Thailand. Ecological Monographs 47:229–253.

Innis, G. S. and J. W. Haefner. 1980. A neutral model of community organization. Journal of Theoretical Biology 87:529–558.

Inouye, R. S. and W. M. Schaffer. 1980. On the ecological meaning of ratio (de Wit) diagrams in plant ecology. Ecology 62:1679–1681.

Irwin, J. O. 1955. A unified derivation of some well-known frequency distributions of interest in biometry and statistics. Journal of the Royal Statistical Society A 118:389–404.

Jablonski, D. 1986. Background and mass extinctions: the alternation of macroevolutionary regimes. Science 231:129–133.

Jaccard, P. 1901. Étude comparative de la distribution florale dans une portion des Alpes et du Jura. Bulletin de la Societé Vaudoise de la science naturelle 37:547–579.

Jaccard, P. 1908. Nouvelles recherches sur la distribution florale. Bulletin de la Societé Vaudoise de la science naturelle 44:223–276.

Jackson, D. A., K. M. Somers and H. H. Harvey. 1989. Similarity coefficients: measures of co-occurrence and association or simply measures of occurrence? American Naturalist 133:436–453.

Jackson, D. A., K. M. Somers and H. H. Harvey. 1992. Null models and fish communities: evidence of nonrandom patterns. American Naturalist 139:930–951.

Jackson, J. B. C. 1981. Interspecific competition and species' distributions: the ghosts of theories and data past. American Zoologist 218:889–901.

Jaenike, J. 1978. Effect of island area on *Drosophila* population densities. Oecologia 36:327–332.

Jaksić, F. M. 1982. Inadequacy of activity time as a niche difference: the case of diurnal and nocturnal raptors. Oecologia 52:171–175.

Jaksić, F. M., H. W. Greene and J. L. Yáñez. 1981. The guild structure of a community of predatory vertebrates in central Chile. Oecologia 49:21–28.

Jaksić, F. M. and R. G. Medel. 1990. Objective recognition of guilds: testing for statistically significant species clusters. Oecologia 82:87–92.

James, F. C. 1982. The ecological morphology of birds: a review. Annales Zoologici Fennici 19:265–275.

James, F. C. and W. J. Boecklen. 1984. Interspecific morphological relationships and the densities of birds. pp. 458–477 in: *Ecological Communities: Conceptual Issues and the Evidence.* D. R. Strong, Jr., D. Simberloff, L. G. Abele and A. B. Thistle (eds). Princeton University Press, Princeton.

James, F. C. and C. E. McCulloch. 1985. Data analysis and the design of experiments in ornithology. pp. 1–63 in: *Current Ornithology.* R. F. Johnston (ed). Plenum Publishing Corporation, New York.

James, F. C. and C. E. McCulloch. 1990. Multivariate analysis in ecology and systematics: panacea or Pandora's box? Annual Review of Ecology and Systematics 21:129–166.

James, F. C. and S. Rathbun. 1981. Rarefaction, relative abundance, and diversity of avian communities. Auk 98:785–800.

James, F. C. and N. O. Wamer. 1982. Relationships between temperate forest bird communities and vegetation structure. Ecology 63:159–171.

James, H. F. and S. L. Olson. 1991. Descriptions of thirty-two new species of birds from the Hawaiian Islands. Part 2. Passeriformes. Ornithological Monographs 46.

Janzen, D. H. 1983. No park is an island: increase in interference from outside as park size decreases. Oikos 41:402–410.

Järvinen, O. 1979. Geographic gradients of stability in European land bird communities. Oecologia 38:51–69.

Järvinen, O. 1982. Species-to-genus ratios in biogeography: a historical note. Journal of Biogeography 9:363–370.

Järvinen, O. and L. Sammalisto. 1976. Regional trends in the avifauna of Finnish peatland bogs. Annales Zoologici Fennici 13:31–43.

Jeffries, M. J. and J. H. Lawton. 1984. Enemy free space and the structure of ecological communities. Biological Journal of the Linnean Society 23:269–286.

Joern, A. and L. R. Lawlor. 1981. Guild structure in grasshopper assemblages based on food and microhabitat resources. Oikos 37:93–104.

Johnson, M. P. 1974. Species number, endemism, and equilibrium in the Galápagos biota. AAAS Galápagos Symposium, San Francisco.

Johnson, M. P. and D. S. Simberloff. 1974. Environmental determinants of island species numbers in the British Isles. Journal of Biogeography 1:149–154.

Johnston, J. W. 1975. Ecological analysis of the Cayman Island avifauna. Bulletin of the Florida State Museum of Biological Science 19:235–300.

Jones, H. L. and J. M. Diamond. 1976. Short-time-base studies of turnover in breeding bird populations on the California Channel Islands. Condor 78:526–549.

Jones, M. J., L. A. Lace, M. V. Hounsome and K. Hamer. 1987. The butterflies and birds of Madeira and La Gomera: taxon cycles and human influence. Biological Journal of the Linnean Society 31:95–111.

Judas, M. 1988. The species-area relationship of European Lumbricidae (Annelida, Oligochaeta). Oecologia 76:579–587.

Juliano, S. A. and J. H. Lawton. 1990a. The relationship between competition and morphology. I. Morphological patterns among co-occurring dytiscid beetles. Journal of Animal Ecology 59:403–419.

Juliano, S. A. and J. H. Lawton. 1990b. The relationship between competition and morphology. II. Experiments on co-occurring dytiscid beetles. Journal of Animal Ecology 59:831–848.

Jumars, P. A. 1980. Rank correlation and concordance tests in community analyses, an inappropriate null hypothesis. Ecology 61:1553–1554.

Juvik, J. O. and A. P. Austring. 1979. The Hawaiian avifauna: biogeographic theory in evolutionary time. Journal of Biogeography 6:205–224.

Kareiva, P. and M. Anderson. 1988. Spatial aspects of species interactions: the wedding of models and experiments. pp. 38–54 in: *Community Ecology*. A. Hastings (ed). Springer-Verlag, Berlin.

Kareiva, P. M. and N. Shigesada. 1983. Analyzing insect movement as a correlated random walk. Oecologia 56:234–238.

Karr, J. R. 1982a. Avian extinction on Barro Colorado Island, Panama: a reassessment. American Naturalist 119:220–239.

Karr, J. R. 1982b. Population variability and extinction in the avifauna of a tropical land bridge island. Ecology 63:1975–1978.

Karr, J. R. and F. C. James. 1975. Ecomorphological configurations and convergent evolution. pp. 258–291 in: *Ecology and Evolution of Communities.* M. L. Cody and J. M. Diamond (eds). Harvard University Press, Cambridge.

Karr, J. R. and T. E. Martin. 1981. Random numbers and principal components: further searches for the unicorn. pp. 20–24 in: *The Use of Multivariate Statistics in Studies of Wildlife Habitat.* D. E. Capen (ed). USDA Forest Service General Technical RM–87.

Kelly, B. J., J. B. Wilson and A. F. Mark. 1989. Causes of the species-area relation: a study of islands in Lake Manapouri, New Zealand. Journal of Ecology 77:1021–1028.

Kempton, R. A. and L. R. Taylor. 1974. Log-series and log-normal parameters as diversity discriminants for the Lepidoptera. Journal of Animal Ecology 43:381–399.

Kennedy, C. E. J. and T. R. E. Southwood. 1984. The number of species of insects associated with British trees: a re-analysis. Journal of Animal Ecology 53:455–478.

Kenny, D. and C. Loehle. 1991. Are food webs randomly connected? Ecology 72:1794–1799.

Keough, M. J. and A. J. Butler. 1983. Temporal changes in species number in an assemblage of sessile marine invertebrates. Journal of Biogeography 10:317–330.

Kiltie, R. A. 1984. Size ratios among sympatric neotropical cats. Oecologia 61:411–416.

Kiltie, R. A. 1988. Interspecific size regularities in tropical felid assemblages. Oecologia 76:97–105.

King, C. M. and P. J. Moors. 1979. On co-existence, foraging strategy and the biogeography of weasels and stoats (*Mustela nivalis* and *M. erminea*) in Britain. Oecologia 39:129–150.

King, D. E. 1964. Relative abundance of species and MacArthur's model. Ecology 45:716–727.

Kjellsson, G. 1985. Seed fall and phenological overlap in a guild of ant-dispersed herbs. Oecologia 68:140–146.

Klotz, J. H. 1984. Diel differences in foraging in two ant species (Hymenoptera; Formicidae). Journal of the Kansas Entomological Society 57:111–118.

Kobayashi, S. 1982. The rarefaction diversity measurement and the spatial distribution of individuals. Japanese Journal of Ecology 32:255–258.

Kobayashi, S. 1983. Another calculation for the rarefaction diversity measurement for different spatial distributions. Japanese Journal of Ecology 33:101–102.

Kobayashi, S. 1991. Interspecific relations in forest floor coleopteran assemblages: niche overlap and guild structure. Researches on Population Ecology 33:345–360.

Koch, A. L. 1966. The logarithm in biology. 1. Mechanisms generating the log-normal distribution. Journal of Theoretical Biology 12:276–290.

Kochmer, J. P. and S. N. Handel. 1986. Constraints and competition in the evolution of flowering phenology. Ecological Monographs 56:303–325.

Kodric-Brown, A. and J. H. Brown. 1993. Highly structured fish communities in Australian desert springs. Ecology 74:1847–1855.

Kohn, A. J. 1959. The ecology of *Conus* in Hawaii. Ecological Monographs 29:49–90.

Kolasa, J. and E. Biesiadka. 1984. Diversity concept in ecology. Acta Biotheoretica 33:145–162.

Kolasa, J. and D. Strayer. 1988. Patterns of the abundance of species: a comparison of two hierarchical models. Oikos 53:235–241.

Kotliar, N. B. and J. A. Wiens. 1990. Multiple scales of patchiness and patch structure: a hierarchical framework for the study of heterogeneity. Oikos 59:253–260.

Kramer, M. and J. Schmidhammer. 1992. The chi-squared statistic in ethology: use and misuse. Animal Behaviour 44:833–841.

Kuhn, T. S. 1970. *The Structure of Scientific Revolutions*. University of Chicago Press, Chicago.

Lack, A. 1976. Competition for pollinators and evolution in *Centaurea*. New Phytologist 77:787–792.

Lack, D. L. 1947. *Darwin's Finches*. Cambridge University Press, Cambridge.

Lack, D. L. 1976. *Island Biology, Illustrated by the Land Birds of Jamaica*. University of California Press, Berkeley.

Lafferty, K. D., D. Sammond, and A. M. Kuris. 1994. Analysis of larval trematode communities. Ecology 75:2275–2285.

Lambshead, P. J. D. and A. J. Gooday. 1990. The impact of seasonally deposited phytodetritus on epifaunal and shallow infaunal benthic foraminiferal populations in the bathyl northeast Atlantic. The assemblage response. Deep-sea Research 37:1263–1284.

Lambshead, P. J. D., H. M. Platt and K. M. Shaw. 1983. The detection of differences among assemblages of marine benthic species based on an assessment of dominance and diversity. Journal of Natural History 17:859–874.

Lawlor, L. R. 1978. A comment on randomly constructed model ecosystems. American Naturalist 112:445–447.

Lawlor, L. R. 1979. Direct and indirect effects of n-species competition. Oecologia 43:355–364.

Lawlor, L. R. 1980a. Overlap, similarity, and competition coefficients. Ecology 61:245–251.

Lawlor, L. R. 1980b. Structure and stability in natural and randomly constructed competitive communities. American Naturalist 116:394–408.

Lawton, J. H. 1989. What is the relationship between population density and body size in animals? Oikos 55:429–434.

Lawton, J. H. 1990. Species richness and population dynamics of animal assemblages. Patterns in body size: abundance space. Philosophical Transactions of the Royal Society of London B 330:283–291.

Lawton, J. H. and K. J. Gaston. 1989. Temporal patterns in the herbivorous insects of bracken: a test of community predictability. Journal of Animal Ecology 58:1021–1034.

Lawton, J. H. and G. L. Woodroffe. 1991. Habitat and the distribution of water voles: why are there gaps in a species range? Journal of Animal Ecology 60:79–91.

Levin, D. A. 1971. The origin of reproductive isolating mechanisms in flowering plants. Taxon 20:91–113.

Levins, R. 1966. The strategy of model building in population biology. American Scientist 54:421–431.

Levins, R. 1968. *Evolution in Changing Environments*. Princeton University Press, Princeton.

Levins, R. 1969. Some demographic and genetic consequences of environmental heterogeneity for biological control. Bulletin of the Entomological Society of America 15:237–240.

Levins, R. 1970. Extinction. pp. 75–107 in: *Some Mathematical Questions in Biology. Lecture Notes on Mathematics in the Life Sciences.* M. Gerstenhaber (ed). American Mathematical Society, Providence, Rhode Island.

Levins, R. and R. Lewontin. 1980. Dialectics and reductionism in ecology. Synthese 43:47–78.

Lewin, R. 1983. Santa Rosalia was a goat. Science 221:636–639.

Liebherr, J. K. and A. E. Hajek. 1990. A cladistic test of the taxon cycle and taxon pulse hypotheses. Cladistics 6:39–59.

Lima, S. L. and L. M. Dill. 1990. Behavioral decisions made under the risk of predation: a review and prospectus. Canadian Journal of Zoology 68:619–640.

Lindemann, R. L. 1942. The trophic-dynamic aspect of ecology. Ecology 23:399–413.

Lindsey, A. H. 1982. Floral phenology patterns and breeding systems in *Thaspium* and *Zizia* (Apiaceae). Systematic Botany 7:1–12.

Lockwood, J. L., M. P. Moulton and S. K. Anderson. 1993. Morphological assortment and the assembly of communities of introduced passeriforms on oceanic islands: Tahiti versus Oahu. American Naturalist 141:398–408.

Loehle, C. 1987. Hypothesis testing in ecology: psychological aspects and the importance of theory maturation. Quarterly Review of Biology 62:397–409.

Loehle, C. 1990a. A guide to increased creativity in research—inspiration or perspiration? Bioscience 40:123–129.

Loehle, C. 1990b. Proper statistical treatment of species-area data. Oikos 57:143–145.

Lomolino, M. V. 1984. Mammalian island biogeography: effects of area, isolation and vagility. Oecologia 61: 376–382.

Lomolino, M. V. 1990. The target are hypothesis: the influence of island area on immigration rates of non-volant mammals. Oikos 57:297–300.

Lomolino, M. V. 1993. Matching of rodents of the Great Basin and Sonoran deserts on a species-by-species basis. Journal of Mammalogy 74:863–867.

Lomolino, M. V. in press. Determining causality of nested subsets: selective immigrations or selective extinctions? Journal of Biogeography.

Long, J. L. 1981. *Introduced Birds of the World.* Universe, New York.

Losos, J. B. 1990. A phylogenetic analysis of character displacement in Caribbean *Anolis* lizards. Evolution 44:558–569.

Losos, J. B., S. Naeem and R. K. Colwell. 1989. Hutchinsonian ratios and statistical power. Evolution 43:1820–1826.

Lotz, J. M. and W. F. Font. 1985. Structure of enteric helminth communities in two populations of *Eptesicus fuscus* (Chiroptera). Canadian Journal of Zoology 63:2969–2978.

Ludwig, J. A. and J. F. Reynolds. 1988. *Statistical Ecology: A Primer on Methods and Computing.* John Wiley & Sons, New York.

Lynch, J. D. 1989. The gauge of speciation: on the frequencies of modes of speciation. pp. 527–553 in: *Speciation and Its Consequences.* D. Otte and J. A. Endler (eds). Sinauer Associates, Sunderland, Massachusetts.

Lynch, J. F. and N. K. Johnson. 1974. Turnover and equilibria in insular avifaunas, with special reference to the California Channel Islands. Condor 78:370–384.

MacArthur, R. H. 1955. Fluctuations of animal populations and a measure of community stability. Ecology 36:533–536.

MacArthur, R. H. 1957. On the relative abundance of bird species. Proceedings of the National Academy of Sciences USA 43:293–295.

MacArthur, R. H. 1958. Population ecology of some warblers of northeastern coniferous forests. Ecology 39:599–619.

MacArthur, R. H. 1960. On the relative abundance of species. American Naturalist 45:25–36.

MacArthur, R. H. 1962. Growth and regulation of animal populations. Ecology 43:579.

MacArthur, R. 1966. Note on Mrs. Pielou's comments. Ecology 47:1074.

MacArthur, R. H. 1972. *Geographical Ecology.* Harper & Row, New York.

MacArthur, R. H., J. M. Diamond and J. R. Karr. 1972. Density compensation in island faunas. Ecology 53:330–342.

MacArthur, R. H. and R. Levins. 1967. The limiting similarity, convergence, and divergence of coexisting species. American Naturalist 101:377–385.

MacArthur, R. H. and J. W. MacArthur. 1961. On bird species diversity. Ecology 42:594–598.

MacArthur, R. H. and E. O. Wilson. 1963. An equilibrium theory of insular zoogeography. Evolution 17:373–387.

MacArthur, R. H. and E. O. Wilson. 1967. *The Theory of Island Biogeography.* Princeton University Press, Princeton.

MacNally, R. C. and J. M. Doolan. 1986. Patterns of morphology and behaviour in a cicada guild: a neutral model analysis. Australian Journal of Ecology 11:279–294.

Magurran, A. E. 1988. *Ecological Diversity and Its Measurement.* Princeton University Press, Princeton.

Maillefer, A. 1929. Le coefficient générique de P. Jacard et sa signification. Mémoires de la Société Vaudoise des Sciences Naturelles 3:113–183.

Maiorana, V. C. 1978. An explanation of ecological and developmental constants. Nature 273:375–377.

Malanson, G. P. 1982. The assembly of hanging gardens: effects of age, area, and location. American Naturalist 119:145–150.

Manly, B. F. J. 1991. *Randomization and Monte Carlo Methods in Biology.* Chapman and Hall, London.

Margalef, R. 1958. Information theory in ecology. Gen. Syste. 3:36–71.

Margalef, R. 1968. *Perspectives in Ecological Theory.* University of Chicago Press, Chicago.

Martin, P. S. and R. G. Klein. 1984. *Quaternary Extinctions.* University of Arizona Press, Tucson.

Martin, T. E. 1981. Species-area slopes and coefficients: a caution on their interpretation. American Naturalist 118:823–837.

Martin, T. E. 1988. Habitat and area effects on forest bird assemblages: is nest predation an influence? Ecology 69:74–84.

Martinez, N. D. 1991. Artifacts or attributes? Effects of resolution on the Little Rock Lake food web. Ecological Monographs 61:367–392.

Martinez, N. D. 1992. Constant connectance in community food webs. American Naturalist 140:1208–1218.

Martinez, N. D. 1993a. Effect of scale on food web structure. Science 260:242–243.

Martinez, N. D. 1993b. Effects of resolution on food web structure. Oikos 66:403–412.

Matthews, W. J. 1982. Small fish community structure in Ozark streams: structured assembly patterns or random abundance of species? American Midland Naturalist 107:42–54.

May, R. M. 1972. Will a large complex system be stable? Nature 238:413–414.

May, R. M. 1973. *Stability and Complexity in Model Ecosystems.* Princeton University Press, Princeton.

May, R. M. 1974. Ecosystem patterns in randomly fluctuating environments. Progress in Theoretical Ecology 3:1–50.

May, R. M. 1975a. Patterns of species abundance and diversity. pp. 81–120 in: *Ecology and Evolution of Communities.* M. L. Cody and J. M. Diamond (eds). Harvard University Press, Cambridge.

May, R. M. 1975b. Some notes on estimating the competition matrix, α. Ecology 56:737–741.

May, R. M. 1978. The evolution of ecological systems. Scientific American 239:160–175.

May, R. M. and R. H. MacArthur. 1972. Niche overlap as a function of environmental variability. Proceedings of the National Academy of Sciences USA 69:1109–1113.

May, R. M. and J. Seger. 1986. Ideas in ecology. American Scientist 74:256–267.

Mayr, E. 1963. *Animal Species and Evolution.* Harvard University Press, Cambridge.

McCoy, E. D. 1982. The application of island-biogeographic theory to forest tracts: problems in the determination of turnover rates. Biological Conservation 22:217–227.

McCoy, E. D. 1990. The distribution of insects along elevational gradients. Oikos 58:313–322.

McCoy, E. D. and E. F. Connor. 1976. Environmental determinants of island species number in the British Isles: a reconsideration. Journal of Biogeography 3:381–382.

McCoy, E. D. and K. L. Heck, Jr. 1987. Some observations on the use of taxonomic similarity in large-scale biogeography. Journal of Biogeography 14:79–87.

McCulloch, C. E. 1985. Variance tests for species association. Ecology 66:1676–1681.

McFarlane, D. A. 1989. Patterns of species co-occurrence in the Antillean bat fauna. Mammalia 53:59–66.

McFarlane, D. A. 1991. The species-genus relationship in Antillean bat communities. Mammalia 55:363–370.

McGuinness, K. A. 1984a. Equations and explanations in the study of species-area curves. Biological Reviews 59:423–440.

McGuinness, K. A. 1984b. Species-area relations of communities on intertidal boulders: testing the null hypothesis. Journal of Biogeography 11:439–456.

McGuinness, K. A. 1988. Explaining patterns in abundances of organisms on boulders: the failure of 'natural experiments.' Marine Ecology Progress Series 48:199–204.

McIntosh, R. P. 1962. Raunkiaer's "law of frequency." Ecology 43:533–535.

McIntosh, R. P. 1980. The background and some current problems of theoretical ecology. Synthese 43:195–255.

M'Closkey, R. T. 1978. Niche separation and assembly in four species of Sonoran desert rodents. American Naturalist 112:683–694.

McNaughton, S. J. 1977. Diversity and stability of ecological communities: a comment on the risk of empiricism in ecology. American Naturalist 111:515–525.

Means, D. B. and D. Simberloff. 1987. The peninsula effect: habitat-correlated species decline in Florida's herpetofauna. Journal of Biogeography 14:551–568.

Mehlhop, P. and J. F. Lynch. 1986. Bird/habitat relationships along a successional gradient in the Maryland coastal plain. The American Midland Naturalist 116:225–239.

Mertz, D. B. and D. E. McCauley. 1980. The domain of laboratory ecology. Synthese 43:95–110.

Miles, D. B., R. E. Ricklefs and J. Travis. 1987. Concordance of ecomorphological relationships in three assemblages of passerine birds. American Naturalist 129:347–364.

Miller, R. I. and R. G. Wiegert. 1989. Documenting completeness, species-area relations, and the species-abundance distribution of a regional flora. Ecology 70:16–22.

Milligan, B. G. 1985. Evolutionary divergence and character displacement in two phenotypically-variable, competing species. Evolution 39:1207–1222.

Milne, B. T. 1992. Spatial aggregation and neutral models in fractal landscapes. American Naturalist 139:32–57.

Mithen, S. J. and J. H. Lawton. 1986. Food-web models that generate constant predator-prey ratios. Oecologia 69:542–550.

Moreau, R. E. 1948. Ecological isolation in a rich tropical avifauna. Journal of Animal Ecology 17:113–126.

Moreau, R. E. 1966. *The Bird Faunas of Africa and its Islands.* Academic Press, New York.

Morony, J. J., Jr., W. J. Bock and J. Farrand, Jr. 1975. *Reference List of the Birds of the World.* American Museum of Natural History, New York.

Morse, D. R., N. E. Stork and J. H. Lawton. 1988. Species number, species abundance and body length relationships of arboreal beetles in Bornean lowland rain forest trees. Ecological Entomology 13:25–37.

Mosimann, J. E. and F. C. James. 1979. New statistical methods for allometry with application to Florida red-winged blackbirds. Evolution 33:444–459.

Moskat, C. and T. Szekely. 1989. Habitat distribution of breeding birds in relation to forest succession. Folia Zoologica 38:363–376.

Mosquin, T. 1971. Competition for pollinators as a stimulus for the evolution of flowering time. Oikos 22:398–402.

Motomura, I. 1932. On the statistical treatment of communities. Zoological Magazine, Tokyo 44:379–383.

Moulton, M. P. 1985. Morphological similarity and coexistence of congeners: an experimental test with introduced Hawaiian birds. Oikos 44:301–305.

Moulton, M. P. 1993. The all-or-none pattern in introduced Hawaiian passeriformes: the role of competition sustained. American Naturalist 141:105–119.

Moulton, M. P. and J. L. Lockwood. 1992. Morphological dispersion of introduced Hawaiian finches: evidence for competition and a Narcissus effect. Evolutionary Ecology 6:45–55.

Moulton, M. P. and S. L. Pimm. 1983. The introduced Hawaiian avifauna: biogeographic evidence for competition. American Naturalist 121:669–690.

Moulton, M. P. and S. L. Pimm. 1986. The extent of competition in shaping an introduced avifauna. pp. 80–97 in: *Community Ecology.* T. J. Case and J. Diamond (eds). Harper & Row, New York.

Moulton, M. P. and S. L. Pimm. 1987. Morphological assortment in introduced Hawaiian passerines. Evolutionary Ecology 1:113–124.

Munger, J. C. and J. H. Brown. 1981. Competition in desert rodents: an experiment with semipermeable exclosures. Science 211:510–512.

Munroe, E. G. 1948. The geographical distribution of butterflies in the West Indies. Dissertation, Cornell University.

Murray, K. G., P. Feinsinger, W. H. Busby, Y. B. Linhart, J. H. Beach and S. Kinsman. 1987. Evaluation of character displacement among plants in two tropical pollination guilds. Ecology 68:1283–1293.

Mushinsky, H. R. and J. J. Hebrard. 1977a. Food partitioning by five species of water snakes in Louisiana. Herpetologica 33:162–166.

Mushinsky, H. R. and J. J. Hebrard. 1977b. The use of time by sympatric water snakes. Canadian Journal of Zoology 55:1545–1550.

Naeem, S. and B. A. Hawkins. 1994. Minimal community structure: how parasitoids divide resources. Ecology 75:79–85.

Nee, S., R. D. Gregory and R. M. May. 1991. Core and satellite species: theory and artefacts. Oikos 62:83–87.

Nelson, B. W., C. A. C. Ferreira, M. F. d. Silva and M. L. Kawasaki. 1990. Endemism centres, refugia and botanical collection density in Brazilian Amazonia. Nature 345:714–716.

Nelson, E. W. 1899. Birds of the Tres Marias Islands. North American Fauna 14:7–62.

Niemelä, J., Y. Haila, E. Halme, T. Lahti, T. Pajunen and P. Punttila. 1988. The distribution of carabid beetles in fragments of old coniferous taiga and adjacent managed forest. Annales Zoologici Fennici 25:107–119.

Niemi, G. J. 1985. Patterns of morphological evolution in bird genera of New World and Old World peatlands. Ecology 66:1215–1228.

Nilsson, S. G. and I. N. Nilsson. 1983. Are estimated species turnover rates on islands largely sampling errors? American Naturalist 121:595–597.

Nitecki, M. H. and A. Hoffman (eds). 1987. *Neutral Models in Biology.* Oxford University Press, Oxford.

Novotný, V. 1991. Effect of habitat persistence on the relationship between geographic distribution and local abundance. Oikos 61:431–433.

Nudds, T. D., K. F. Abraham, C. D. Ankney and P. D. Tebbel. 1981. Are size gaps in dabbling- and wading-bird arrays real? American Naturalist 118:549–553.

Oksanen, L., S. D. Fretwell and O. Järvinen. 1979. Interspecific aggression and the limiting similarity of close competitors: the problem of size gaps in some community arrays. American Naturalist 114:117–129.

Olson, D. M. 1994. The distribution of leaf litter invertebrates along a Neotropical altitudinal gradient. Journal of Tropical Ecology 10:129–150.

Olson, S. L. and H. F. James. 1982. Fossil birds from the Hawaiian Islands: evidence for wholesale extinction by man before Western contact. Science 217:633–635.

Olson, S. L. and H. F. James. 1991. Descriptions of thirty-two new species of birds from the Hawaiian Islands. Part I. Non-Passeriformes. Ornithological Monographs 45.

Orr, R. T. 1960. An analysis of recent land mammals. Systematic Zoology 9:171–178.

Osman, R. W. 1977. The establishment and development of a marine epifaunal community. Ecological Monographs 47:37–63.

Osman, R. W. and R. B. Whitlatch. 1978. Patterns of species diversity: fact or artifact? Paleobiology 4:41–54.

Pagel, M. D., P. H. Harvey and H. C. J. Godfray. 1991. Species-abundance, biomass, and resource-use distributions. American Naturalist 138:836–850.

Pagel, M. D., R. M. May and A. R. Collie. 1991. Ecological aspects of the geographical distribution and diversity of mammalian species. American Naturalist 137:791–815.

Paine, R. T. 1966. Food web complexity and species diversity. American Naturalist 100:65–75.

Paine, R. T. 1977. Controlled manipulations in the marine intertidal zone, and their contributions to ecological theory. pp. 245–270 in: *The Changing Scenes in Natural Sciences, 1776–1976*. Special Publication 12 of the Academy of Natural Sciences, Philadelphia.

Paine, R. T. 1988. Food webs: road maps of interactions or grist for theoretical development? Ecology 69:1648–1654.

Paine, R. T. 1992. Food-web analysis through measurement of per capita interaction strength. Nature 355:73–75.

Paine, R. T. and S. A. Levin. 1981. Intertidal landscapes: disturbance and the dynamics of pattern. Ecological Monographs 51:145–178.

Palmer, M. W. 1987. Variability in species richness within Minnesota oldfields: a use of the variance test. Vegetatio 70:61–64.

Palmer, M. W. 1990. The estimation of species richness by extrapolation. Ecology 71:1195–1198.

Palmgren, A. 1925. Die Artenzahl als pflanzengeographischer Charakter sowie der Zufall und die sekuläre Landhebung als pflanzengeographische Faktoren. Ein pflanzengeographischer Entwurf, basiert auf Material aus dem åländischen Schärenarchipel. Acta Botanica Fennica 1:1–143.

Parrish, J. A. D. and F. A. Bazzaz. 1979. Difference in pollination niche relationships in early and late successional plant communities. Ecology 60:597–610.

Patrick, R. 1968. The structure of diatom communities in similar ecological conditions. American Naturalist 102:173–183.

Patterson, B. D. 1987. The principle of nested subsets and its implications for biological conservation. Conservation Biology 1:323–334.

Patterson, B. D. 1990. On the temporal development of nested subset patterns of species composition. Oikos 59:330–342.

Patterson, B. D. and W. Atmar. 1986. Nested subsets and the structure of insular mammalian faunas and archipelagos. Biological Journal of the Linnean Society 28:65–82.

Patterson, B. D. and J. H. Brown. 1991. Regionally nested patterns of species composition in granivorous rodent assemblages. Journal of Biogeography 18:395–402.

Pearson, D. L. 1986. Community structure and species co-occurrence: a basis for developing broader generalizations. Oikos 46:419–423.

Pearson, D. L. and S. A. Juliano. 1991. Mandible length ratios as a mechanism for co-occurrence: evidence from a world-wide comparison of tiger beetle assemblages (Cicindelidae). Oikos 61:223–233.

Peet, R. K. 1974. The measurement of species diversity. Annual Review of Ecology and Systematics 5:285–307.

Peet, R. K. 1975. Relative diversity indices. Ecology 56:496–498.

Peltonen, A. and I. Hanski. 1991. Patterns of island occupancy explained by colonization and extinction rates of shrews. Ecology 72:1698–1708.

Peters, R. H. 1976. Tautology in evolution and ecology. American Naturalist 110:1–12.

Peters, R. H. 1991. *A Critique for Ecology.* Cambridge University Press, Cambridge.

Peters, R. H. and K. Wasenberg. 1983. The effect of body size on animal abundance. Oecologia 60:89–96.

Petraitis, P. S. 1979. Likelihood measures of niche breadth and overlap. Ecology 60:703–710.

Pianka, E. R. 1966. Latitudinal gradients in species diversity: a review of concepts. American Naturalist 100:33–34.

Pianka, E. R. 1967. Lizard species diversity. Ecology 48:333–351.

Pianka, E. R. 1972. *r* and *K* selection or *b* and *d* selection? American Naturalist 106:581–588.

Pianka, E. R. 1973. The structure of lizard communities. Annual Review of Ecology and Systematics 4:53–74.

Pianka, E. R. 1974. Niche overlap and diffuse competition. Proceedings of the National Academy of Sciences, USA 71:2141–2145.

Pianka, E. R. 1980. Guild structure in desert lizards. Oikos 35:194–201.

Pianka, E. R. 1986. *Ecology and Natural History of Desert Lizards.* Princeton University Press, Princeton.

Pianka, E. R. 1994. *Evolutionary Ecology.* 5th edition. HarperCollins, New York.

Pianka, E. R., R. B. Huey and L. R. Lawlor. 1979. Niche segregation in desert lizards. pp. 67–115 in: *Analysis of Ecological Systems.* D. J. Horn, R. Mitchell and G. R. Stairs (eds). Ohio State University Press, Columbus.

Pielou, D. P. and E. C. Pielou. 1968. Association among species of infrequent occurrence: the insect and spider fauna of *Polyporus betulinus* (Bulliard) Fries. Journal of Theoretical Biology 21:202–216.

Pielou, E. C. 1972a. 2^k contingency tables in ecology. Journal of Theoretical Biology 34:337–352.

Pielou, E. C. 1972b. Niche width and niche overlap: a method for measuring them. Ecology 53:687–692.

Pielou, E. C. 1974. *Population and Community Ecology: Principles and Methods.* Gordon and Breach Science Publishers, New York.

Pielou, E. C. 1975. *Ecological Diversity.* John Wiley & Sons, New York.

Pielou, E. C. 1977. The latitudinal spans of seaweed species and their patterns of overlap. Journal of Biogeography 4:299–311.

Pielou, E. C. 1978. Latitudinal overlap of seaweed species: evidence for quasi-sympatric speciation. Journal of Biogeography 5:227–238.

Pielou, E. C. 1979a. *Biogeography.* John Wiley & Sons, New York.

Pielou, E. C. 1979b. On A. J. Underwood's model for a random pattern. Oecologia 44:143–144.

Pielou, E. C. 1981a. The usefulness of ecological models: a stock-taking. Quarterly Review of Biology 56:17–31.

Pielou, E. C. 1981b. The broken-stick model: a common misunderstanding. American Naturalist 117:609–610.

Pielou, E. C. and A. N. Arnason. 1966. Correction to one of MacArthur's species-abundance formulas. Science 51:592.

Pielou, E. C. and R. D. Routledge. 1976. Salt marsh vegetation: latitudinal gradients in the zonation patterns. Oecologia 24:311–321.

Pimm, S. L. 1980a. The properties of food webs. Ecology 61 219–225.

Pimm, S. L. 1980b. Bounds on food web connectance. Nature 285:511.

Pimm, S. L. 1982. *Food Webs*. Chapman and Hall, London.

Pimm, S. L. 1983. Appendix: Monte Carlo analyses in ecology. pp. 290–296 in: *Lizard Ecology: Studies on a Model Organism*. R. B. Huey, T. W. Schoener and E. R. Pianka (eds). Harvard University Press, Cambridge.

Pimm, S. L. 1984a. Food chains and return times. pp. 396–412 in: *Ecological Communities: Conceptual Issues and the Evidence*. D. R. Strong, Jr., D. Simberloff, L. G. Abele and A. B. Thistle (eds). Princeton University Press, Princeton.

Pimm, S. L. 1984b. The complexity and stability of ecosystems. Nature 307:321–326.

Pimm, S. L. 1991. *The Balance of Nature? Ecological Issues in the Conservation of Species and Communities*. University of Chicago Press, Chicago.

Pimm, S. L. and R. L. Kitching. 1988. Food web patterns: trivial flaws or the basis of an active research program? Ecology 69:1669–1672.

Pimm, S. L., H. L. Jones and J. Diamond. 1988. On the risk of extinction. American Naturalist 132:757–785.

Pimm, S. L., J. H. Lawton and J. E. Cohen. 1991. Food web patterns and their consequences. Nature 350: 669–674.

Platt, H. M. and P. J. D. Lambshead. 1985. Neutral model analysis of patterns of marine benthic species diversity. Marine Ecology Progress Series 24:75–82.

Platt, J. R. 1964. Strong inference. Science 146:347–353.

Pleasants, J. M. 1980. Competition for bumblebee pollinators in Rocky Mountain plant communities. Ecology 61:1446–1459.

Pleasants, J. M. 1990. Null-model tests for competitive displacement: the fallacy of not focusing on the whole community. Ecology 71:1078–1084.

Pleasants, J. M. 1994. A comparison of test statistics used to detect competitive displacement in body size. Ecology 75:847–850.

Polis, G. A. 1984. Age structure component of niche width and intraspecific resource partitioning: can age groups function as ecological species? American Naturalist 123:541–564.

Polis, G. A. 1991. Complex trophic interactions in deserts: an empirical critique of food-web theory. American Naturalist 138:123–155.

Polis, G. A., C. A. Myers and R. D. Holt. 1989. The ecology and evolution of intraguild predation: potential competitors that eat each other. Annual Review of Ecology and Systematics 20:297–330.

Pólya, G. 1930. Eine Wahrscheinlichkeitsaufgabe in der Pflanzensoziologie. Vierteljahrsschrift der Naturforschenden Gesellschaft in Zürich 75:211–219.

Poole, R. W. and B. J. Rathcke. 1979. Regularity, randomness, and aggregation in flowering phenologies. Science 203:470–471.

Popper, K. R. 1959. *The Logic of Scientific Discovery*. Basic Books, New York.

Popper, K. R. 1965. Normal science and its dangers. pp. 51–58 in: *Criticism and the Growth of Knowledge*. I. Lakatos and A. Musgrave (eds). Cambridge University Press, Cambridge.

Popper, K. R. 1972. *Objective Knowledge: An Evolutionary Approach*. Clarendon Press, Oxford.

Porter, W. P., J. W. Mitchell, W. A. Beckman and C. B. DeWitt. 1973. Behavioural implications of mechanistic ecology: thermal and behavioural modeling of desert ectotherms and their microenvironment. Oecologia 13:1–54.

Power, D. M. 1975. Similarity among avifaunas of the Galápagos Islands. Ecology 56:616–626.

Prance, G. T. 1973. Phytogeographic support for the theory of Pleistocene forest refuges in the Amazon basin, based on evidence from distribution patterns in Caryocaraceae, Chrysobalanaceae, Dichaptelaceae, and Lechythidacea. Acta Amazonica 3:5–26.

Pregill, G. K. and S. L. Olson. 1981. Zoogoegraphy of West Indian vertebrates in relation to Pleistocene climatic cycles. Annual Review of Ecology and Systematics 12:75–98.

Preston, F. W. 1948. The commonness and rarity of species. Ecology 29:254–283.

Preston, F. W. 1960. Time and space and the variation of species. Ecology 41:612–627.

Preston, F. W. 1962. The canonical distribution of commonness and rarity, parts 1 and 2. Ecology 43:185–215,410–432.

Preston, F. W. 1981. Pseudo-lognormal distributions. Ecology 62:355–364.

Pulliam, H. R. 1975. Coexistence of sparrows:a test of community theory. Science 184:474–476.

Pulliam, H. R. 1983. Ecological community theory and the coexistence of sparrows. Ecology 64:45–52.

Quinn, J. F. and A. E. Dunham. 1983. On hypothesis testing in ecology and evolution. American Naturalist 122:602–617.

Quinn, S. L., J. B. Wilson and A. F. Mark. 1987. The island biogeography of Lake Manapouri, New Zealand. Journal of Biogeography 14:569–581.

Rabinowitz, D. 1978. Early growth of mangrove seedlings in Panama, and an hypothesis concerning the relationship of dispersal and zonation. Journal of Biogeography 5:113–133.

Rabinowitz, D. 1981. Seven forms of rarity. pp. 205–217 in: *The Biological Aspects of Rare Plant Conservation*. H. Synge (ed). John Wiley & Sons, New York.

Rabinowitz, D., S. Cairns and T. Dillon. 1986. Seven forms of rarity and their frequency in the flora of the British Isles. pp. 182–204 in: *Conservation Biology: The Science of Scarcity and Diversity*. M. E. Soulé (ed). Sinauer Associates, Sunderland, Massachusetts.

Rabinowitz, D., J. K. Rapp and P. M. Dixon. 1984. Competitive abilities of sparse grass species: means of persistence or cause of abundance? Ecology 65:1144–1154.

Rabinowitz, D., J. K. Rapp, V. L. Sork, B. J. Rathcke, G. A. Reese and J. C. Weaver. 1981. Phenological properties of wind and insect pollinated prairie plants. Ecology 62:49–56.

Rahel, F. J., J. D. Lyons and P. A. Cochran. 1984. Stochastic or deterministic regulation of assemblage structure? It may depend on how the assemblage is defined. American Naturalist 124:583–589.

Rainer, S. 1981. Temporal patterns in the structure of macrobenthic communities of an Australian estuary. Estuarine and Coastal Shelf Science 13:597–620.

Ranta, E. 1982. Species structure of North European bumblebee communities. Oikos 38:202–209.

Ranta, E. 1986. Competition and community structure: a null model analysis of the hummingbird assemblage on the slope of Volcan de Colima Mexico. Ornis Fennici 63:79–83.

Rapoport, E. H. 1982. *Areography: Geographical Strategies of Species.* Pergamon Press, Oxford.

Räsänen, M. E., J. S. Salo and R. J. Kalliola. 1987. Fluvial perturbance in the western Amazon basin: regulation by long-term sub-Andean tectonics. Science 238:1398–1401.

Rathcke, B. J. 1976. Competition and coexistence within a guild of herbivorous insects. Ecology 57:76–87.

Rathcke, B. J. 1984. Patterns of flowering phenologies: testability and causal inference using a random model. pp. 383–396 in: *Ecological Communities: Conceptual Issues and the Evidence.* D. R. Strong, Jr., D. Simberloff, L. G. Abele and A. B. Thistle (eds). Princeton University Press, Princeton.

Rathcke, B. 1988a. Flowering phenologies in a shrub community: competition and constraints. Journal of Ecology 76:975–994.

Rathcke, B. 1988b. Interactions for pollination among coflowering shrubs. Ecology 69:446–457.

Rathcke, B. and E. P. Lacey. 1985. Phenological patterns of terrestrial plants. Annual Review of Ecology and Systematics 16:179–214.

Raunkiaer, C. 1934. *The Life Forms of Plants and Statistical Plant Geography.* Clarendon Press, Oxford.

Raup, D. M. 1972. Taxonomic diversity during the phanerozoic. Science 177:1065–1071.

Raup, D. M. 1975. Taxonomic diversity estimation using rarefaction. Paleobiology 1:333–342.

Raup, D. M. 1979. Size of the Permo-Triassic bottleneck and its evolutionary implications. Science 206:217–218.

Raup, D. M., S. J. Gould, T. J. M. Schopf and D. S. Simberloff. 1973. Stochastic models of phylogeny and the evolution of diversity. Journal of Geology 81:525–542.

Reddingius, J. 1983. On species sharing islands: comment on an article by S. J. Wright and C. C. Biehl. American Naturalist 122:830–832.

Rejmánek, M. and P. Starý. 1979. Connectance in real biotic communities and critical values for stability in model ecosystems. Nature 280:311–313.

Rey, J. R. 1981. Ecological biogeography of arthropods on *Spartina* islands in northwest Florida. Ecological Monographs 5:237–265.

Rice, J. and R. J. Belland. 1982. A simulation study of moss floras using Jaccard's coefficient of similarity. Journal of Biogeography 9:411–419.

Ricklefs, R. E. 1970. Stage of taxon cycle and distribution of birds on Jamaica, Greater Antilles. Evolution 24:475–477.

Ricklefs, R. E. 1972. Dominance and the niche in bird communities. American Naturalist 106:538–545.

Ricklefs, R. E., D. Cochran and E. R. Pianka. 1981. A morphological analysis of the structure of communities of lizards in desert habitats. Ecology 62:1474–1483.

Ricklefs, R. E. and G. W. Cox. 1972. Taxon cycles in the West Indian avifauna. American Naturalist 106:195–219.

Ricklefs, R. E. and G. W. Cox. 1978. Stage of taxon cycle, habitat distribution, and population density in the avifauna of the West Indies. American Naturalist 112:875–895.

Ricklefs, R. E. and M. Lau. 1980. Bias and dispersion of overlap indices: results of some Monte Carlo Simulations. Ecology 61:1019–1024.

Ricklefs, R. E. and J. Travis. 1980. A morphological approach to the study of avian community organization. Auk 97:321–338.

Riechert, S. E. and C. R. Tracy. 1975. Thermal balance and prey availability: bases for a model relating web-site characteristics to spider reproductive success. Ecology 56:265–284.

Roach, D. A. 1986. Timing of seed production and dispersal in *Geranium carolinianum:* effects on fitness. Ecology 67:572–576.

Roberts, A. 1974. The stability of a feasible random ecosystem. Nature 251:607–608.

Roberts, A. and L. Stone. 1990. Island-sharing by archipelago species. Oecologia 83:560–567.

Robertson, C. 1895. The philosophy of flower seasons, and the phaenological relations of the entomophilous flora and the anthophilous insect fauna. American Naturalist 29:97–117.

Robson, D. S. 1972. Appendix: Statistical tests of significance. Journal of Theoretical Biology 34:350–352.

Rohde, K., M. Heap and D. Heap. 1993. Rapoport's rule does not apply to marine teleosts and cannot explain latitudinal gradients in species richness. American Naturalist 142:1–16.

Root, R. B. 1967. The niche exploitation pattern of the blue-gray gnatcatcher. Ecological Monographs 37:95–124.

Root, T. 1988a. Environmental factors associated with avian distributional boundaries. Journal of Biogeography 15:489–505.

Root, T. 1988b. Energy constraints on avian distributions and abundances. Ecology 69:330–339.

Root, T. 1988c. *Atlas of Wintering North American Birds.* University of Chicago Press, Chicago.

Root, T. 1989. Energy constraints on avian distributions: a reply to Castro. Ecology 70:1183–1185.

Rosenzweig, M. L. and Z. Abramsky. 1985. Detecting density-dependent habitat selection. American Naturalist 126:405–417.

Rosenzweig, M. L., Z. Abramsky and S. Brand. 1984. Estimating species interactions in heterogeneous environments. Oikos 43:329–340.

Rotenberry, J. T. and J. A. Wiens. 1980. Temporal variation in habitat structure and shrubsteppe bird dynamics. Oecologia 47:1–9.

Roth, V. L. 1981. Constancy in the size ratios of sympatric species. American Naturalist 118:394–404.

Roughgarden, J. 1974. Species packing and the competition function with illustrations from coral reef fish. Theoretical Population Biology 5:1–24.

Roughgarden, J. 1983. Competition and theory in community ecology. American Naturalist 122:583–601.

Roughgarden, J., S. Gaines and H. Possingham. 1988. Recruitment dynamics in complex life cycles. Science 241:1460–1466.

Rummel, J. D. and J. Roughgarden. 1983. Some differences between invasion-structured and coevolution-structured competitive communities: a preliminary theoretical analysis. Oikos 41:477–486.

Russell, M. P. and D. R. Lindberg. 1988. Real and random patterns associated with molluscan spatial and temporal distributions. Paleobiology 14:322–330.

Rydin, H. and S.-O. Borgegård. 1988. Plant species richness on islands over a century of primary succession: Lake Hjälmaren. Ecology 69:916–927.

Ryti, R. T. 1984. Perennials on rock islands: testing for patterns of colonization and competition. Oecologia 64:184–190.

Ryti, R. T. and T. J. Case. 1986. Overdispersion of ant colonies: a test of hypotheses. Oecologia 69:446–453.

Ryti, R. T. and M. E. Gilpin. 1987. The comparative analysis of species occurrence patterns on archipelagos. Oecologia 73:282–287.

Sabath, M. D. and J. M. Jones. 1973. Measurement of niche breadth and overlap: the Colwell-Futuyma method. Ecology 54:1143–1147.

Sale, P. F. 1974. Overlap in resource use, and interspecific competition. Oecologia 17:245–256.

Sale, P. F. 1979. Recruitment, loss and coexistence in a guild of territorial coral reef fishes. Oecologia 42:159–177.

Sale, P. F. 1982. Stock-recruitment relationships and regional coexistence in a lottery competitive system: a simulation study. American Naturalist 120:139–159.

Sale, P. F. 1984. The structure of communities of fish on coral reefs and the merit of a hypothesis-testing, manipulative approach to ecology. pp. 478–490 in: *Ecological Communities: Conceptual Issues and the Evidence.* D. R. Strong, Jr., D. Simberloff, L. G. Abele and A. B. Thistle (eds). Princeton University Press, Princeton.

Sale, P. F. and W. A. Douglas. 1984. Temporal variability in the community structure of fish on coral patch reefs and the relation of community structure to reef structure. Ecology 65:409–422.

Sale, P. F. and J. A. Guy. 1992. Persistence of community structure: what happens when you change taxonomic scale? Coral Reefs 11:147–154.

Sale, P. F. and W. J. Steel. 1989. Temporal variability in patterns of association among fish species on coral patch reefs. Marine Ecology Progress Series 51:35–47.

Sale, P. F. and D. McB. Williams. 1982. Community structure of coral reef fishes: are the patterns more than those expected by chance? American Naturalist 120:121–127.

Salo, J. 1987. Pleistocene forest refuges in the Amazon: evaluation of the biostratigraphical, lithostratigraphical and geomorphological data. Annales Zoologici Fennici 24:203–211.

Salo, J., R. Kalliola, I. Häkkinen, Y. Mäkinen, P. Niemelä, M. Puhakka and P. D. Coley. 1986. River dynamics and the diversity of Amazon lowland forest. Nature 322:254–258.

Salt, G. W. 1983. Roles: their limits and responsibilities in ecological and evolutionary research. American Naturalist 122:697–705.

Sanders, H. L. 1968. Marine benthic diversity: a comparative study. American Naturalist 102:243–282.

Sanders, H. L. and R. R. Hessler. 1969. Ecology of the deep-sea benthos. Science 163:1419–1424.

Schall, J. J. 1993. Community ecology of *Cnemidophorus* lizards in southwestern Texas: a test of the weed hypothesis. pp. 319–343 in: *Biology of Whiptail Lizards (Genus Cnemidophorus).* J. W. Wright and L. J. Vitt (eds). Oklahoma Museum of Natural History, Norman.

Scheibe, J. S. 1987. Climate, competition, and the structure of temperate zone lizard communities. Ecology 68:1424–1436.

Schemske, D. W. 1981. Floral convergence and pollinator sharing in two bee-pollinated tropical herbs. Ecology 62:946–954.

Scheuring, I. 1991. The fractal nature of vegetation and the species-area relation. Theoretical Population Biology 39:170–177.

Schluter, D. 1982. Distributions of Galápagos ground finches along an altitudinal gradient: the importance of food supply. Ecology 63:1504–1507.

Schluter, D. 1984. A variance test for detecting species associations, with some example applications. Ecology 65:998–1005.

Schluter, D. 1986a. Character displacement between distantly related taxa? Finches and bees in the Galápagos. American Naturalist 127:95–102.

Schluter, D. 1986b. Tests for similarity and convergence of finch communities. Ecology 67:1073–1085.

Schluter, D. 1990. Species-for-species matching. American Naturalist 136:560–568.

Schluter, D. and P. R. Grant. 1984. Determinants of morphological patterns in communities of Darwin's finches. American Naturalist 123:175–196.

Schluter, D. and J. D. McPhail. 1992. Ecological character displacement and speciation in sticklebacks. American Naturalist 140:85–108.

Schluter, D., T. D. Price and P. R. Grant. 1985. Ecological character displacement in Darwin's finches. Science 227:1056–1059.

Schluter, D. and R. E. Ricklefs. 1993. Convergence and the regional component of species diversity. pp. 230–240 in: *Species Diversity in Ecological Communities: Historical and Geographical Perspectives*. R. E. Ricklefs and D. Schluter (eds). University of Chicago Press, Chicago.

Schmitt, R. J. and S. J. Holbrook. 1986. Seasonally fluctuating resources and temporal variability of interspecific competition. Oecologia 69:1–11.

Schoener, A. and T. W. Schoener. 1981. The dynamics of the species-area relation in marine fouling systems. I. Biological correlates of changes in species-area slope. American Naturalist 118:339–360.

Schoener, T. W. 1965. The evolution of bill size differences among sympatric congeneric species of birds. Evolution 19:189–213.

Schoener, T. W. 1974a. Resource partitioning in ecological communities. Science 185:27–39.

Schoener, T. W. 1974b. Some methods for calculating competition coefficients from resource-utilization spectra. American Naturalist 108:332–340.

Schoener, T. W. 1974c. The compression hypothesis and temporal resource partitioning. Proceedings of the National Academy of Sciences USA 71:4169–4172.

Schoener, T. W. 1974d. Competition and the form of habitat shift. Theoretical Population Biology 6:265–307.

Schoener, T. W. 1976a. Alternatives to Lotka-Volterra competition: models of intermediate complexity. Theoretical Population Biology 10:309–333.

Schoener, T. W. 1976b. The species-area relation within archipelagos: models and evidence from island land birds. pp. 1–17. Proceedings of the 16th International Ornithological Congress, Canberra, Australia.

Schoener, T. W. 1982. The controversy over interspecific competition. American Scientist 70:586–595.

Schoener, T. W. 1983. Field experiments on interspecific competition. American Naturalist 122:240–285.

Schoener, T. W. 1984. Size differences among sympatric, bird-eating hawks: a worldwide survey. pp. 254–279 in: *Ecological Communities: Conceptual Issues and the Evidence*. D. R. Strong, Jr., D. Simberloff, L. G. Abele and A. B. Thistle (eds). Princeton University Press, Princeton.

Schoener, T. W. 1986a. Resource partitioning. pp. 91–125 in: *Community Ecology*. J. Kikkawa (ed). Blackwell, Oxford.

Schoener, T. W. 1986b. Overview: kinds of ecological communities—ecology becomes pluralistic. pp. 467–479 in: *Community Ecology*. T. J. Case and J. Diamond (eds). Harper & Row, New York.

Schoener, T. W. 1988a. Testing for non-randomness in sizes and habitats of West Indian lizards: choice of species pool affects conclusions from null models. Evolutionary Ecology 2:1–26.

Schoener, T. W. 1988b. On testing the MacArthur-Wilson model with data on rates. American Naturalist 131:847–864.

Schoener, T. W. and G. H. Adler. 1991. Greater resolution of distributional complementarities by controlling for habitat affinities: a study with Bahamian lizards and birds. American Naturalist 137:669–692.

Schoener, T. W. and A. Schoener. 1971a. Structural habitats of West Indian *Anolis* lizards. I. Lowland Jamaica. Breviora 368:1–53.

Schoener, T. W. and A. Schoener. 1971b. Structural habitats of West Indian *Anolis* lizards. II Puerto Rican uplands. Breviora 375:1–39.

Schoener, T. W. and A. Schoener. 1983. Distribution of vertebrates on some very small islands. I. Occurrence sequences of individual species. Journal of Animal Ecology 52:209–235.

Schoener, T. W. and C. A. Toft. 1983. Spider populations: extraordinarily high densities on islands without top predators. Science 219:1353–1355.

Schoenly, K. and J. E. Cohen. 1991. Temporal variation in food web structure: 16 empirical cases. Ecological Monographs 61:267–298.

Selvin, H. C. and A. Stewart. 1966. Data-dredging procedures in survey analysis. American Statistician 20:20–23.

Shelford, V. E. 1913. Animal communities in temperate America as illustrated in the Chicago region: a study in animal ecology. Geographic Society of Chicago Bulletin 5.

Shelly, T. E. and S. W. Christensen. 1982. Testing for competition: a critique of De Vita's use of the broken-stick model. American Naturalist 119:435–437.

Shine, R. 1989. Ecological causes for the evolution of sexual dimorphism: a review of the evidence. Quarterly Review of Biology 64:419–461.

Shipley, B. 1993. A null model for competitive hierarchies in competition matrices. Ecology 74:1693–1699.

Shrader-Frechette, K. S. and E. D. McCoy. 1992. Statistics, costs and rationality in ecological inference. Trends in Ecology and Evolution 7:96–99.

Shreeve, T. G. and C. F. Mason. 1980. The number of butterfly species in woodlands. Oecologia 45:414–418.

Shubert, L. E. 1984. *Algae as Ecological Indicators*. Academic Press, London.

Sibley, C. G. and B. L. Monroe, Jr. 1990. *Distribution and Taxonomy of Birds of the World*. Yale University Press, New Haven.

Siegel, A. F. and R. Z. German. 1982. Rarefaction and taxonomic diversity. Biometrics 38:235–241.

Siegfried, W. R. 1976. Segregation in feeding behavior of four diving ducks in southern Manitoba. Canadian Journal of Zoology 54:730–736.

Silvertown, J. W. 1983. The distribution of plants in limestone pavement: tests of species interaction and niche separation against null hypotheses. Journal of Ecology 71:819–828.

Silvertown, J. and J. B. Wilson. 1994. Community structure in a desert perennial community. Ecology 75:409–417.

Simberloff, D. S. 1969. Experimental zoogeography of islands: a model for insular colonization. Ecology 50:296–314.

Simberloff, D. 1970. Taxonomic diversity of island biotas. Evolution 24:23–47.

Simberloff, D. 1972. Properties of the rarefaction diversity measurement. American Naturalist 106:414–418.

Simberloff, D. 1976a. Species turnover and equilibrium island biogeography. Science 194:572–578.

Simberloff, D. 1976b. Trophic structure determination and equilibrium in an arthropod community. Ecology 57:395–398.

Simberloff, D. 1978a. Using island biogeographic distributions to determine if colonization is stochastic. American Naturalist 112:713–726.

Simberloff, D. 1978b. Use of rarefaction and related methods in ecology. pp. 150–165 in: *Biological Data in Water Pollution Assessment: Quantitative and Statistical Analyses*. K. L. Dickson, J. Cairns, Jr., and R. J. Livingston (eds). American Society for Testing and Materials, Philadelphia.

Simberloff, D. 1979a. Rarefaction as a distribution-free method of expressing and estimating diversity. pp. 159–170 in: *Ecological Diversity in Theory and Practice*. J. F. Grassle and G. P. Patil (eds). International Cooperative Publishing House, Fairland, Maryland.

Simberloff, D. 1979b. Constraints on community structure during colonization. pp. 415–424 in: *Environmental Biomonitoring, Assessment, Prediction, and Management—Certain Case Studies and Related Quantitative Issues*. J. Cairns Jr., G. P. Patil and W. E. Waters (eds). International Cooperative Publishing House, Fairland, Maryland.

Simberloff, D. 1980a. A succession of paradigms in ecology: essentialism to materialism and probabilism. Synthese 43:3–39.

Simberloff, D. 1980b. Reply. Synthese 43:79–93.

Simberloff, D. 1982. The status of competition theory in ecology. Annales Zoologici Fennici 19:241–253.

Simberloff, D. 1983a. Competition theory, hypothesis-testing, and other community ecological buzzwords. American Naturalist 122:626–635.

Simberloff, D. 1983b. Sizes of coexisting species. pp. 404–430 in: *Coevolution*. D. J. Futuyma and M. Slatkin (eds). Sinauer Associates, Sunderland, Massachusetts.

Simberloff, D. 1983c. When is an island community in equilibrium? Science 220:1275–1277.

Simberloff, D. 1984. Properties of coexisting bird species in two archipelagoes. pp. 234–253 in: *Ecological Communities: Conceptual Issues and the Evidence.* D. R. Strong, Jr., D. Simberloff, L. G. Abele and A. B. Thistle (eds). Princeton University Press, Princeton.

Simberloff, D. 1986. Are we on the verge of a mass extinction in tropical rain forests? pp. 165–180 in: *Dynamics of Extinction.* D. K. Elliott (ed.). John Wiley & Sons, New York.

Simberloff, D. and W. Boecklen. 1981. Santa Rosalia reconsidered: size ratios and competition. Evolution 35:1206–1228.

Simberloff, D. and W. Boecklen. 1991. Patterns of extinction in the introduced Hawaiian avifauna: a reexamination of the role of competition. American Naturalist 138:300–327.

Simberloff, D. and E. F. Connor. 1979. Q-mode and R-mode analyses of biogeographic distributions: null hypotheses based on random colonization. pp. 123–138 in: *Contemporary Quantitative Ecology and Related Ecometrics.* G. P. Patil and M. L. Rosenzweig (eds). International Cooperative Publishing House, Fairland, Maryland.

Simberloff, D. and E. F. Connor. 1981. Missing species combinations. American Naturalist 118:215–239.

Simberloff, D. and E. F. Connor. 1984. Inferring competition from biogeographic data: a reply to Wright and Biehl. American Naturalist 124:429–436.

Simberloff, D. and T. Dayan. 1991. The guild concept and the structure of ecological communities. Annual Review of Ecology and Systematics 22:115–143.

Simberloff, D. and N. Gotelli. 1984. Effects of insularisation on plant species richness in the prairie-forest ecotone. Biological Conservation 29:27–46.

Simberloff, D. and B. Levin. 1985. Predictable sequences of species loss with decreasing island area—land birds in two archipelagoes. New Zealand Journal of Ecology 8:11–20.

Simberloff, D. and J. -L. Martin. 1991. Nestedness of insular avifaunas: simple summary statistics masking complex species patterns. Ornis Fennica 68:178–192.

Simberloff, D. S. and E. O. Wilson. 1969. Experimental zoogeography of islands: the colonization of empty islands. Ecology 50:278–289.

Simpson, B. B. 1974. Glacial migrations of plants: island biogeographical evidence. Science 185:698–700.

Simpson, B. B. and J. Haffer. 1978. Speciation patterns in the Amazonian forest biota. Annual Review of Ecology and Systematics 9:497–518.

Simpson, E. H. 1949. Measurement of diversity. Nature 163:688.

Simpson, G. G. 1960. Notes on the measurement of faunal resemblance. American Journal of Science 258:300–311.

Simpson, G. G. 1964. Species density of North American recent mammals. Systematic Zoology 13:57–73.

Sinclair, D. F., J. E. Mosimann and D. A. Meeter. 1985a. Tests for character displacement. Biometrics 41:835–846.

Sinclair, D. F., J. E. Mosimann and D. A. Meeter. 1985b. Tests for deletion. Biometrics 41:847–857.

Slatkin, M. 1980. Ecological character displacement. Ecology 61:163–177.

Slatkin, M. 1984. Ecological causes of sexual dimorphism. Evolution 38:622–630.

Smart, J. S. 1976. Statistical tests of the broken-stick model of species-abundance relations. Journal of Theoretical Biology 59:127–139.

Smith, C. H. 1983. A system of world mammal faunal regions I. Logical and statistical derivation of the regions. Journal of Biogeography 10:455–466.

Smith, E. P., P. M. Stewart, and J. Cairns, Jr. 1985. Similarities between rarefaction methods. Hydrobiologia 120:167–169.

Smith, W. and F. Grassle. 1977. Sampling properties of a family of diversity measures. Biometrics 33:283–292.

Sneath, P. H. A. and R. R. Sokal. 1973. *Numerical Taxonomy*. W. H. Freeman, San Francisco.

Snow, B. K. and D. W. Snow. 1972. Feeding niches of hummingbirds in a Trinidad valley. Journal of Animal Ecology 41:471–485.

Soulé, M. A. and B. A. Wilcox (eds). 1980. *Conservation Biology: An Evolutionary-Ecological Perspective*. Sinauer Associates, Sunderland, Massachusetts.

Sousa, W. P. 1979. Disturbance in marine intertidal boulder fields: the nonequilibrium maintenance of species diversity. Ecology 60:1225–1239.

Sousa, W. P. 1984. The role of disturbance in natural communities. Annual Review of Ecology and Systematics 15:353–391.

Southwood, T. R. E. 1980. Ecology—a mixture of pattern and probabilism. Synthese 43:111–122.

Sprules, W. G. and J. E. Bowerman. 1988. Omnivory and food chain length in zoo-plankton food webs. Ecology 69:418–426.

Steadman, D. W. 1989. Extinction of birds in Eastern Polynesia: a review of the record, and comparisons with other island groups. Journal of Archaeological Science 16:177–205.

Stevens, G. C. 1986. Dissection of the species-area relationship among wood-boring insects and their host plants. American Naturalist 128:35–46.

Stevens, G. C. 1989. The latitudinal gradient in geographical range: how so many species coexist in the tropics. American Naturalist 133:240–256.

Stiles, F. G. 1977. Coadapted competitors: the flowering seasons of hummingbird-pollinated plants in a tropical forest. Science 198:1177–1178.

Stiles, F. G. 1979. Reply. Science 203:471.

Stone, L. and A. Roberts. 1990. The checkerboard score and species distributions. Oecologia 85:74–79.

Stone, L. and A. Roberts. 1992. Competitive exclusion, or species aggregation? An aid in deciding. Oecologia 91:419–424.

Strauss, R. E. 1982. Statistical significance of species clusters in association analysis. Ecology 63:634–639.

Strong, D. R., Jr. 1980. Null hypotheses in ecology. Synthese 43:271–285.

Strong, D. R., Jr. 1983. Natural variability and the manifold mechanisms of ecological communities. American Naturalist 122:636–660.

Strong, D. R., Jr. and D. A. Levin. 1975. Species richness of the parasitic fungi of British trees. Proceedings of the National Academy of Sciences USA 72:2116–2119.

Strong, D. R., Jr. and J. R. Rey. 1982. Testing for MacArthur-Wilson equilibrium with the arthropods of the miniature *Spartina* archipelago at Oyster Bay, Florida. American Zoologist 22:355–360.

Strong, D. R., Jr. and D. S. Simberloff. 1981. Straining at gnats and swallowing ratios: character displacement. Evolution 35:810–812.

Strong, D. R., Jr., D. Simberloff, L. G. Abele and A. B. Thistle (eds). 1984. *Ecological Communities: Conceptual Issues and the Evidence*. Princeton University Press, Princeton.

Strong, D. R., Jr., L. A. Szyska and D. Simberloff. 1979. Tests of community-wide character displacement against null hypotheses. Evolution 33:897–913.

Sugihara, G. 1980. Minimal community structure: an explanation of species abundance patterns. American Naturalist 116:770–787.

Sugihara, G. 1981. $S = CA^z$, $z = 1/4$: a reply to Connor and McCoy. American Naturalist 117:790–793.

Sugihara, G. 1986. Shuffled sticks: on calculating nonrandom niche overlaps. American Naturalist 127:554–560.

Sugihara, G. 1989. How *do* species divide resources? American Naturalist 133:458–463.

Sugihara, G., K. Schoenly and A. Trombla. 1989. Scale invariance in food web properties. Science 245:48–52.

Tagatz, M. E., G. R. Plaia, C. H. Deans and E. M. Lores. 1983. Toxicity of creosote-contaminated sediment to field- and laboratory-colonized estuarine benthic communities. Environmental Toxicology and Chemistry 2:441–450.

Taper, M. L. and T. J. Case. 1992. Models of character displacement and the theoretical robustness of taxon cycles. Evolution 46:317–333.

Taylor, B. 1991. Investigating species incidence over habitat fragments of different areas—a look at error estimation. Biological Journal of the Linnean Society 42:177–191.

Taylor, C. M. and N. J. Gotelli. 1994. The macroecology of *Cyprinella:* correlates of phylogeny, body size and geographic range. American Naturalist 144:549–569.

Taylor, R. J. and P. J. Regal. 1978. The peninsular effect on species diversity and the biogeography of Baja California. American Naturalist 112:583–593.

Taylor, W. D. 1979. Sampling data on the bactivorous ciliates of a small pond compared to neutral models of community structure. Ecology 60:876–883.

Terborgh, J. 1971. Distribution on environmental gradients: theory and a preliminary interpretation of distributional patterns in the avifauna of the Cordillera Vilcabamba, Peru. Ecology 52:23–40.

Terborgh, J. 1973a. Chance, habitat and dispersal in the distribution of birds in the West Indies. Evolution 27:338–349.

Terborgh, J. 1973b. On the notion of favorableness in plant ecology. American Naturalist 107:481–501.

Terborgh, J. 1977. Bird species diversity on an Andean elevational gradient. Ecology 58:1007–1019.

Terborgh, J. 1981. Discussion. pp. 64–66 in: *Vicariance Biogeography: A Critique*. G. Nelson and D. E. Rosen (eds). Columbia University Press, New York.

Terborgh, J. and B. Winter. 1978. Some causes of extinction. pp. 119–133 in: *Conservation Biology: An Evolutionary-Ecological Perspective*. M. E. Soulé and B. A. Wilcox (eds). Sinauer Associates, Sunderland, Massachusetts.

Thomson, J. D. 1978. Effects of stand composition on insect visitation in two-species mixtures of *Hieracium*. American Midland Naturalist 100:431–440.

Thomson, J. D. 1982. Patterns of visitation by animal pollinators. Oikos 39:241–250.

Thomson, J. D., B. J. Andrews and R. C. Plowright. 1981. The effect of a foreign pollen on ovule fertilization in *Diervilla lonicera* (Caprifoliacaea). New Phytologist 90:777–783.

Thomson, J. D. and K. A. Rusterholz. 1982. Overlap summary indices and the detection of community structure. Ecology 63:274–277.

Tipper, J. C. 1979. Rarefaction and rarefiction—the use and abuse of a method in paleoecology. Paleobiology 5:423–434.

Toft, C. A. and T. W. Schoener. 1983. Abundance and diversity of orb spiders on 106 Bahamian islands: biogeography at an intermediate trophic level. Oikos 41:411–426.

Toft, C. A. and P. J. Shea. 1983. Detecting community-wide patterns: estimating power strengthens statistical inference. American Naturalist 122:618–625.

Tokeshi, M. 1986. Resource utilization, overlap and temporal community dynamics: a null model analysis of an epiphytic chironomid community. Journal of Animal Ecology 55:491–506.

Tokeshi, M. 1990. Niche apportionment or random assortment: species abundance patterns revisited. Journal of Animal Ecology 59:1129–1146.

Tomascik, T. and F. Sander. 1987. Effects of eutrophication on reef building corals. II. Structure of scleractinian coral communities on fringing reefs, Barbados, West Indies. Marine Biology 94:53–75.

Tonkyn, D. W. and B. J. Cole. 1986. The statistical analysis of size ratios. American Naturalist 128:66–81.

Tracy, C. R. and K. A. Christian. 1986. Ecological relations among space, time, and thermal niche axes. Ecology 67:609–615.

Tracy, C. R. and T. L. George. 1992. On the determinants of extinction. American Naturalist 139:102–122.

Tracy, C. R. and T. L. George. 1993. Extinction probabilities for British island birds: a reply. American Naturalist 142:1036–1037.

Travis, J. and R. E. Ricklefs. 1983. A morphological comparison of island and mainland assemblages of Neotropical birds. Oikos 41:434–441.

Turelli, M. 1978a. A reexamination of stability in randomly varying versus deterministic environments with comments on the stochastic theory of limiting similarity. Theoretical Population Biology 13:244–267.

Turelli, M. 1978b. Does environmental variability limit niche overlap? Proceedings of the National Academy of Sciences USA 75:5085–5089.

Ueckert, D. N. and R. M. Hansen. 1972. Dietary overlap of grasshoppers on sandhill rangeland in northeastern Colorado. Oecologia 8:276–295.

Ugland, K. I. and J. S. Gray. 1982a. Reanalysis of Caswell's neutral models. Ecology 64:603–605.

Ugland, K. I. and J. S. Gray. 1982b. Lognormal distributions and the concept of community equilibrium. Oikos 39:171–178.

Ulanowicz, R. E. and W. F. Wolff. 1991. Ecosystem flow networks: loaded dice? Mathematical Biosciences 103:45–68.

Underwood, A. J. 1978a. The detection of non-random patterns of distribution of species along a gradient. Oecologia 36:317–326.

Underwood, A. J. 1978b. A refutation of critical tidal levels as determinants of the structure of intertidal communities on British shores. Journal of Experimental Marine Biology and Ecology 33:261–276.

Underwood, A. J. 1985. Physical factors and biological interactions: the necessity and nature of ecological experiments. pp. 372–390 in: *The Ecology of Rocky Coasts.* P. G. Moore and R. Seed (eds). Hodder and Stoughton, London.

Underwood, A. J. 1986. The analysis of competition by field experiments. pp. 240–268 in: *Community Ecology: Pattern and Process.* J. Kikkawa and D. J. Anderson (eds). Blackwell Scientific Publications, Melbourne.

Valentine, J. W., T. C. Foin and D. Peart. 1978. A provincial model of Phanerozoic marine diversity. Paleobiology 4:55–66.

Van Valen, L. 1973. Body size and numbers of plants and animals. Evolution 27:27–35.

Vandermeer, J. H. 1972. Niche theory. Annual Review of Ecology and Systematics 3:107–132.

Vannote, R. L. and B. W. Sweeney. 1980. Geographic analysis of thermal equilibria: a conceptual model for evaluating the effect of natural and modified thermal regimes on aquatic insect communities. American Naturalist 115:667–695.

Vanzolini, P. E. and E. E. Williams. 1973. South American anoles: the geographic differentiation and evolution of the *Anolis chrysolepis* group (Sauria, Iguanidae). Arg. Zool. J. São Paulo 19:1–240.

Vuilleumier, F. and D. Simberloff. 1980. Ecology versus history as determinants of patchy and insular distribution in high Andean birds. Evolutionary Biology 12:235–379.

Warwick, R. M. 1984. Species size distributions in marine benthic communities. Oecologia 61:32–41.

Warwick, R. M. and J. M. Gee. 1984. Community structure of estuarine meiobenthos. Marine Ecology Progress Series 18:97–112.

Waser, N. M. 1983. Competition for pollination and floral character differences among sympatric plant species: a review of the evidence. pp. 277–293 in: *Handbook of Experimental Pollination Biology.* C. E. Jones and R. J. Little (eds). Van Nostrand Reinhold Company, New York.

Washington, H. G. 1984. Diversity, biotic and similarity indices. Water Research 18:653–694.

Watkins, A. J. and J. B. Wilson. 1992. Fine-scale community structure of lawns. Journal of Ecology 80:15–24.

Werner, E. and J. Gilliam. 1984. The ontogenetic niche and species interactions in size-structured populations. Annual Review of Ecology and Systematics 15:393–425.

Westman, W. E. 1983. Island biogeography: studies on the xeric shrublands of the inner Channel Islands, California. Journal of Biogeography 10:97–118.

Wethey, D. S. 1983. Geographic limits and local zonation: the barnacles *Semibalanus (Balanus)* and *Chthamulus* in New England. Biological Bulletin 165:330–341.

Wethey, D. S. 1985. Catastrophe, extinction, and species diversity: a rocky intertidal example. Ecology 66:445–456.

Wheelright, N. T. 1985. Competition for dispersers, and the timing of flowering and fruiting in a guild of tropical trees. Oikos 44:465–477.

Whitcomb, B. L., R. F. Whitcomb and D. Bystrak. 1977. Island biogeography and 'habitat islands' of eastern forest. III. Long-term turnover and effects of selective logging on the avifauna of forest fragments. American Birds 31:17–23.

Whittaker, R. H. 1967. Gradient analysis of vegetation. Biological Reviews 49:207–264.

Whittaker, R. H. 1972. Evolution and measurement of species diversity. Taxon 21:213–251.

Whittam, T. S. and D. Siegel-Causey. 1981a. Species interactions and community structure in Alaskan seabird colonies. Ecology 62:1515–1524.

Whittam, T. S. and D. Siegel-Causey. 1981b. Species incidence functions and Alaskan seabird colonies. Journal of Biogeography 8:421–425.

Wiens, J. A. 1977. On competition and variable environments. American Scientist 65:590–598.

Wiens, J. A. 1980. Concluding comments: are bird communities real? Acta XVII Congressus Internationalis Ornithologici 1088–1089.

Wiens, J. A. 1981. Single-sample surveys of communities: are the revealed patterns real? American Naturalist 117:90–98.

Wiens, J. A. 1982. On size ratios and sequences in ecological communities: are there no rules? Annales Zoologici Fennici 19:297–308.

Wiens, J. A. 1984. On understanding a non-equilibrium world: myth and reality in community patterns and processes. pp. 439–457 in: *Ecological Communities: Conceptual Issues and the Evidence..* D. R. Strong, Jr., D. Simberloff, L. G. Abele and A. B. Thistle (eds). Princeton University Press, Princeton.

Wiens, J. A. 1989. *The Ecology of Bird Communities. Volume 1. Foundations And Patterns.* Cambridge University Press, Cambridge.

Wiens, J. A. 1991a. Ecomorphological comparisons of the shrub-desert avifaunas of Australia and North America. Oikos 60:55–63.

Wiens, J. A. 1991b. Ecological similarity of shrub-desert avifaunas of Australia and North America. Ecology 72:479–495.

Wiens, J. A., J. F. Addicott, T. J. Case and J. Diamond. 1986. Overview: the importance of spatial and temporal scale in ecological investigations. pp. 145–153 in: *Community Ecology.* T. J. Case and J. Diamond (eds). Harper & Row, New York.

Wiens, J. A. and J. T. Rotenberry. 1980. Patterns of morphology and ecology in grassland and shrubsteppe bird populations. Ecological Monographs 50:287–308.

Wiens, J. A. and J. T. Rotenberry. 1981a. Morphological size ratios and competition in ecological communities. American Naturalist 117:592–599.

Wiens, J. A. and J. T. Rotenberry. 1981b. Habitat associations and community structure of birds in shrubsteppe environments. Ecological Monographs 51:21–41.

Wiens, J. A., J. T. Rotenberry and B. V. Horne. 1987. Habitat occupancy patterns of North American shrubsteppe birds: the effects of spatial scale. Oikos 48:132–147.

Wilbur, H. M. 1988. Interactions between growing predators and growing prey. pp. 157–172 in: *Size-Structured Populations.* B. Ebenman and L. Persson (eds). Springer-Verlag, Berlin.

Wilbur, H. M. and J. Travis. 1984. An experimental approach to understanding pattern in natural communities. pp. 113–122 in: *Ecological Communities: Conceptual Issues and the Evidence.* D. R. Strong, Jr., D. Simberloff, L. G. Abele and A. B. Thistle (eds). Princeton University Press, Princeton.

Wiley, E. O. 1981. *Phylogenetics. The Theory and Practice of Phylogenetic Systematics.* John Wiley & Sons, New York.

Williams, C. B. 1943. Area and the number of species. Nature 152:264–267.

Williams, C. B. 1947a. The generic relations of species in small ecological communities. Journal of Animal Ecology 16:11–18.

Williams, C. B. 1947b. The logarithmic series and its application to biological problems. Journal of Ecology 34:253–272.

Williams, C. B. 1950. The application of the logarithmic series to the frequency of occurrence of plant species in quadrats. Journal of Ecology 38:107–138.

Williams, C. B. 1951. Intra-generic competition as illustrated by Moreau's records of East African bird communities. Journal of Animal Ecology 20:246–253.

Williams, C. B. 1964. *Patterns in the Balance of Nature.* Academic Press, New York.

Williams, E. E. 1972. The origin of faunas. Evolution of lizard congeners in a complex island fauna: a trial analysis. Evolutionary Biology 6:47–89.

Williams, E. E. 1983. Ecomorphs, faunas, island size, and diverse end points in island radiations of *Anolis.* pp. 326–370 in: *Lizard Ecology: Studies on a Model Organism.* R. B. Huey, E. R. Pianka and T. W. Schoener (eds). Harvard University Press, Cambridge.

Williams, M. R. 1995. Critical values of a statistic to detect competitive displacement. Ecology 76:646–647.

Williamson, M. 1981. *Island Populations.* Oxford University Press, Oxford.

Williamson, M. 1989. The MacArthur and Wilson theory today: true but trivial. Journal of Biogeography 16:3–4.

Williamson, M. H. 1973. Species diversity in ecological communities. pp. 325–335 in: *The Mathematical Theory of the Dynamics of Biological Populations.* M. S. Bartlett and R. W. Hiorns (eds). Academic Press, London.

Willis, E. O. 1974. Populations and local extinctions of birds on Barro Colorado Island, Panama. Ecological Monographs 44:153–169.

Wilson, D. S. 1975. The adequacy of body size as a niche difference. American Naturalist 109:769–784.

Wilson, E. O. 1959. Adaptive shift and dispersal in a tropical ant fauna. Evolution 13:122–144.

Wilson, E. O. 1961. The nature of the taxon cycle in the Melanesian ant fauna. American Naturalist 45:169–193.

Wilson, E. O. and D. S. Simberloff. 1969. Experimental zoogeography of islands: defaunation and monitoring techniques. Ecology 50:267–295.

Wilson, E. O. and E. O. Willis. 1975. Applied biogeography. pp. 522–534 in: *Ecology and Evolution of Communities.* M. L. Cody and J. M. Diamond (eds). Harvard University Press, Cambridge.

Wilson, J. B. 1987. Methods for detecting non-randomness in species co-occurrences: a contribution. Oecologia 73: 579–582.

Wilson, J. B. 1988. Community structure in the flora of islands in Lake Manapouri, New Zealand. Journal of Ecology 76:1030–1042.

Wilson, J. B. 1989. A null model of guild proportionality, applied to stratification of a New Zealand temperate rain forest. Oecologia 80:263–267.

Wilson, J. B. 1991a. Does vegetation science exist? Journal of Vegetation Science 2:289–290.

Wilson, J. B. 1991b. Methods for fitting dominance/diversity curves. Journal of Vegetation Science 2:35–46.

Wilson, J. B. 1993. Would we recognise a broken-stick community if we found one? Oikos 67:181–183.

Wilson, J. B. 1995. Null models for assembly rules: the Jack Horner effect is more insidious than the Narcissus effect. Oikos 72:139–144.

Wilson, J. B., H. Gitay and A. D. Q. Agnew. 1987. Does niche limitation exist? Functional Ecology 1:391–397.

Wilson, J. B., R. E. James, J. E. Newman and T. E. Myers. 1992. Rock pool algae: species composition determined by chance? Oecologia 91:150–152.

Wilson, J. B. and M. T. Sykes. 1988. Some tests for niche limitation by examination of species diversity in the Dunedin area, New Zealand. New Zealand Journal of Botany 26:237–244.

Winemiller, K. O. 1989. Must connectance decrease with species richness? American Naturalist 134:960–968.

Winemiller, K. O. and E. R. Pianka. 1990. Organization in natural assemblages of desert lizards and tropical fishes. Ecological Monographs 60:27–55.

Wolda, H. 1978. Fluctuations in abundance of tropical insects. American Naturalist 112:1017–1045.

Wolda, H. 1981. Similarity indices, sample size, and diversity. Oecologia 50:296–302.

Woolhouse, M. E. J. 1988. Population dynamics models: a plea for plurality. Perspectives in Biology and Medicine 31:510–523.

Wright, D. H. 1983. Species-energy theory: an extension of species-area theory. Oikos 41:496–506.

Wright, D. H. 1991. Correlations between incidence and abundance are expected by chance. Journal of Biogeography 18:463–466.

Wright, D. H. and J. H. Reeves. 1992. On the meaning and measurement of nestedness of species assemblages. Oecologia 92: 416–428.

Wright, S. J. 1980. Density compensation in island avifaunas. Oecologia 45:385–389.

Wright, S. J. 1981. Intra-archipelago vertebrate distributions: the slope of the species-area relation. American Naturalist 118:726–748.

Wright, S. J. and C. C. Biehl. 1982. Island biogeographic distributions: testing for random, regular, and aggregated patterns of species occurrence. American Naturalist 119:345–357.

Yant, P. R., J. R. Karr and P. L. Angermeier. 1984. Stochasticity in stream fish communities: an alternative interpretation. American Naturalist 124:573–582.

Yodzis, P. 1981. The structure of assembled communities. Journal of Theoretical Biology 92:103–117.

Yodzis, P. 1982. The compartmentation of real and assembled ecosystems. American Naturalist 120:551–570.

INDEX

362   ▪   *Index*